Bees
of Surrey

Bees
of Surrey

DAVID W. BALDOCK

with a key to genera by
GRAHAM A. COLLINS

SURREY WILDLIFE TRUST

Front cover photograph: *Andrena florea* on white bryony,
by Jeremy Early

ISBN 978-0-9556188-1-9

British Library Cataloguing-in-Publication Data.
A catalogue record for this book is available
from the British Library.

First published 2008
by Surrey Wildlife Trust
School Lane, Pirbright, Woking, Surrey GU24 0JN.

Produced by Flipside, Cranleigh.

FOREWORD

Surrey, with its entomologically rich mosaic of varied habitats, its climatically warm location in south-east England and the presence of large numbers of scarce and very rare bees, has attracted numerous hymenopterists for more than a century. These have been especially drawn to the extensive heathlands, but other habitats, such as the chalk of the North Downs and the large tracts of deciduous woodland, have also been incentives for visits. Some of these enthusiasts have lived in the county but many have visited it from elsewhere. As a result of their activities, numerous notes and lists of aculeates recorded from Surrey have been published in the entomological press, especially in journals such as the *Entomologist's Monthly Magazine.* However, despite the number of these communications, they have never been brought together. No book has previously been devoted entirely to Surrey bees or, for that matter, bees and wasps. Indeed, such books dealing exclusively with the aculeate fauna of any county are few and far between. This book is the result of many years of painstaking study by its author of the bees reported from the county.

The sheer number of bee species reported from Surrey makes the county one of the richest in Britain, perhaps the richest. It is, alas, a sad fact that many of the species are declining nationally and the British Hymenoptera Aculeata as a whole remains one of the most threatened groups of British insects, mainly as a result of habitat destruction. In the long term, climatic change is likely to present even greater changes in their fortunes. Thus this book provides a timely picture of the present situation affecting bees in the county and as a benchmark for survey work in the years ahead.

However, it is no mere list of bees. It will be seen that its format much resembles one of the plethora of recent avifaunas. The introductory sections are particularly valuable, dealing as they do with such topics as the topography of the county and the history of bee recording in Surrey, including that band of successive bee enthusiasts who have always been associated with the county during at least the last century and a half. David is one of the latest to take up the reins. I have known him for several years, both on his numerous visits to the Natural History Museum, London (where I was employed as the curator of bees prior to my retirement in 2007), and as a companion when exploring sites in Surrey for their bees. I remain impressed with his knowledge of bees generally and his single-mindedness in putting this latest survey together.

GEORGE R. ELSE

To my grandson

SAM

CONTENTS

"Men that undertake only one district

are much more likely to advance natural

knowledge than those that grasp at more

than they can possibly be acquainted with:

every kingdom, every province, should

have its own monographer."

GILBERT WHITE

PREFACE

Surrey can justifiably claim to have more species of bees, wasps and ants than any other county in Britain. No fewer than 490 species, out of the total British List of about 600, have been recorded within its boundaries during the last 160 years. The total number of bees on the British List is about 250, of which almost 90% have been recorded in Surrey. This is due partly to geography and geology; south-east England is one of the hottest and driest areas in the country and the western Weald is one of the finest locations for aculeates in the British Isles because of its varied geology of sands, gravels, chalk and clay. These produce the habitats most favoured by bees and wasps: dry acid grassland, chalk grassland, clay woodland and, above all, extensive areas of dry sandy heathland, possibly the most prolific habitat for bees and wasps in the country. Being entirely land-locked, Surrey lacks the only other important habitats for bees, the coastal sand dunes and soft rock cliffs.

Surrey's pre-eminence is also due to the number of recorders in the county, both past and present, whose work is described in detail later and who have ensured that Surrey is now perhaps the best-recorded county in Britain. It has been my privilege to play a part in that progression. By 1996 I had finished recording butterflies, dragonflies and larger moths for the Surrey Wildlife Atlas Project and had almost completed *Grasshoppers and Crickets of Surrey*. I started to look around for another group of insects that needed to be recorded and mapped, and decided on the bees, wasps and ants – otherwise known as aculeates.

At that time I was entirely ignorant about bees and wasps, knowing only that there was the honey bee, a few bumblebees and the common wasp, but I had heard that the heaths were excellent places for them. When I announced to a friend, who subsequently became one of the recorders, what I intended to do, he said "You must be mad", although I seem to remember he used rather stronger language. He pointed out that there were about 500 species of bees and wasps in Britain, and half of these, the bees, had no identification keys. However, I was not deterred and mentioned my intention to another friend, Graham Collins, who gave me a piece of constructive advice which I took and have thanked him for ever since. He suggested that I should open a database immediately and enter all the records from the very start, otherwise I would never cope with the huge numbers of records that would accumulate.

Next, I visited Mike Edwards in Midhurst as I knew he had been studying bees and wasps for about 30 years. He was as enthusiastic as ever and encouraged me to start immediately, and thereupon gave me a pair of specimens of virtually every aculeate known in Britain. When I asked him which of these I was likely to find in Surrey, he replied "Almost all of them". How right he has proved to be! He also gave me a copy of an early draft of the identification key to the British bees prepared by George Else, who at that time was working at the Natural History Museum, London, on bees and wasps; this invaluable key took me some time to understand but without it I could not have managed. Over the next two years I tried Mike's patience to the utmost by taking him my catches of bees and watching him identify them and learning from him the characters to look for on each species. Without his help and guidance I would probably have given up after a year.

In my ignorance I had decided to start on the bumblebees because there were only a few species, they were large, attractive and well coloured, they were common and there was a well-illustrated key with which to identify them. But it was late summer when I got going and at that time most of the workers were old and faded, and there were also males flying around. I became totally confused and could hardly identify any of them and I decided it would be better to look at another order of invertebrates. However, Mike never ceased to encourage me and after two years I had broken through the barrier. In short, I was hooked for life on these fascinating insects whose often striking beauty and varied life habits, such as cleptoparasitism, along with their considerable importance ecologically, made them the most interesting order I have studied. But even after ten years I still have much to learn about bees, not only about how and where to find them and how to identify them, but mostly about why they are doing what they are doing.

The well-known collector and recorder Kenneth Guichard also encouraged me to write this book whenever I visited him in London to benefit from his expertise in identifying the numerous bees and wasps I had collected abroad. Because of my interest in the Surrey bees he revisited Horsell Common, after a lapse of 25 years, and added a few more species to the site list, even though this was shortly before his death. Donald Baker also gave me great encouragement when I visited him on many occasions at his home in Ewell, giving me details of all the rarities which he had collected in Surrey and showing me most of these specimens in his vast collection. Shortly before his death he even described to me the exact place where he had found, 40 years earlier, the only specimen of the very rare *Andrena niveata* known from Surrey, thus enabling me to refind it on the last remaining cabbage plant in that site.

Originally, it had been intended that bees, ants and wasps would all be included in one book, which would take about 20 years to complete, but after a short while it became clear that each group would need its own atlas. John Pontin, one of Britain's experts on ants, was persuaded to write *Ants of Surrey* which was published in 2005. By 2007 the distribution maps for bees and wasps were about as complete as they were ever likely to be and almost all the intended photographs had been gathered; it was decided that *Bees of Surrey* should be published first because there was almost no modern literature on these insects. This is the eleventh in the series of county atlases covering various wildlife groups in Surrey, and it is hoped that *Wasps of Surrey* will be joining the series in the next year or two.

One vexed, but inescapable, problem concerns the use of English names for insects. Because the vast majority of bees are indistinguishable in the field, not only to the general public but also to most experts, they have never been given popular, common or English names except by Edward Step, 1932. There are however three species which have had English names for more than 200 years. The first is *Apis mellifera*, the Honey Bee (sometimes also known as the Honeybee, or occasionally as the honeybee); and even that has another name, the Hive Bee, used by Gilbert White and Edward Saunders, or sometimes yet a third name, the Honey or Hive Bee (or perhaps it should be the Hive or Honey Bee, or even the hive or honey bee). Even the one popular bee name has endless variations. The other two species with English names, which were known to Gilbert White in 1788 or earlier, are distinctive solitary bees. The first is *Eucera longicornis*, known as the Long-horned Bee on account of the unique, very long antennae of the males, but this bee is now very scarce and unlikely to be seen by the casual observer; the second is *Anthidium manicatum*, known as the Wool-carder Bee on account of its behaviour of shaving hairs off plants for the construction of its nest. This name is not used much these days and care must be taken not to confuse it with the Common Carder-bee, a relatively new name for a species of bumblebee. English names will mean nothing to anyone outside Britain, especially such cumbersome names as Hairy-footed Flower Bee for *Anthophora plumipes*. Surely to avoid this confusion it is far better to use the scientific, Latin, binomial name; the first, or generic name, is always written with the first letter in capitals, and the second, or specific, name without capitals. This scientific name ensures that it will be known by all hymenopterists throughout the world. For this reason I have avoided the use of English names in this book.

Flower names are different. English names have been in common usage for very many years and are known and used by layman and expert alike. English names are therefore used throughout in this book, but a list of their scientific names is given in Appendix 4.

Technical language has been avoided so far as possible in order to make the book more readable for non-experts, but special terms for parts of a bee's body and its behaviour are unavoidable, such as propodeum, tarsus and monolectic. However, a glossary of such terms is given in Appendix 3.

It was decided not to include a full checklist of all bee species, partly because this is extremely long but also because it is easily obtainable by any interested reader by joining the Bees, Wasps and Ants Recording Society (BWARS) and receiving the Members' Handbook with the checklist in it. However, there is a short checklist to the different genera of bees on page 115.

Surrey has an enormous number of important sites for bees and wasps and it was thought that many of these should be listed and some of them given a brief description, with a note of the rarer species to be found at each site. The grid reference for each of the sites described is also given, but the gazetteer of sites in Appendix 1 gives grid references for all sites mentioned in the book.

I hope that the information in this book will be of use, not only to bee experts, both professional and amateur, in Surrey, but also to those in other counties of Britain, and will encourage those who want to know more about bees but have no other sources. The distribution maps should act as a benchmark for all future workers on Surrey's bees, and provide a useful comparison when, hopefully, another survey is carried out in 2100.

ACKNOWLEDGEMENTS AND
LIST OF RECORDERS

The preparation and publication of this volume has been a team effort from beginning to end, as it has been with the previous volumes. The four core recorders, Graham Collins, Roger Hawkins, Andrew Halstead and Jonty Denton, who sent me a steady flow of records each year, are the same four who have contributed so many records to other volumes. It would be hard to find not only such dedicated contributors, but also such a versatile team of naturalists, mostly amateur, who can turn their attention to different orders of insects every few years. Roger Morris had surveyed Mitcham Common intensively in 1984 and also recorded bees all over Surrey when collecting data for his book *Hoverflies of Surrey,* but when he moved from Surrey in 1995 he sent me his 5,000 aculeate records. Mike Edwards, who gave me enormous help when I started, also visited Surrey every year when carrying out professional surveys in the county, and amassed a large number of records.

Graham not only wrote the generic key but also prepared the maps, gave me enormous help with computer problems over the last ten years, read through the first draft and also checked some of my more difficult identifications; without his help I doubt whether this book would have ever seen the light of day. Roger Hawkins has once more had the unenviable task of proof-reading, a job which he has carried out with finesse yet again. George Else helped me with historical records whilst he was still at the Natural History Museum, London, and with more general help and encouragement since he retired, including reading through the draft of this book for which he has kindly written the Foreword. All of this has, I am afraid, distracted him from finishing his own book on British bees, which is still eagerly awaited by all bee enthusiasts. Michael Archer has kindly allowed me to use his profiles to the subfamilies and genera, which he prepared for the BWARS Members Handbook.

But what really makes this book so appealing are the beautiful plates. I hope that these will cause the reader to realise how attractive bees are on close inspection and to spend more time in future on observing them. The quality of these plates is due to the three photographers, Graham Collins, Jeremy Early and David Element, who have spent innumerable hours in the field to catch just the right moment for that all-important shot; bees are not the easiest of insects to photograph. My worry is that the text does not do justice to the photographs.

Clare Windsor has produced this book with her usual blend of skill combined with cool efficiency in making sure that everything is done to a strict timetable. Alistair Kirk, of Surrey Wildlife Trust, has ensured the continuity of the atlas series with his enthusiasm for the project and had no hesitation in agreeing to have 48 plates in the book when he had seen the quality of the photographs.

Heather B. Hawker, MBE and a Deputy Lieutenant of Surrey, who is a Council Member of Surrey Wildlife Trust, has made a generous donation towards the cost of publication of this book. Heather is a liveryman of the Worshipful Company of Wax Chandlers, one of the City Guilds. The Company, which was granted a Royal Charter in 1484, was established in 1358 in order to regulate the trade in bees-wax and to ensure the quality of the bees-wax used for candles so that they burnt true and smokeless; hence its motto 'Truth is Light'. Nowadays it administers charitable funds, mainly directed towards education and bee-keeping, as well as towards encouraging innovation in the modern wax industry.

The Wildlife Trust also gratefully acknowledges the generous financial support given by Surrey County Council, on behalf of the Surrey Biodiversity Partnership, towards the cost of producing this book.

All the maps in this book were prepared using the DMap programme written by Dr Alan Morton of Imperial College at Silwood Park.

I have dedicated this book to my grandson Sam in recognition of his help in typing parts of this volume and enlightening me in the world of computer technology. I also thank my wife Manon for her patient tolerance of my obsession with bees.

LIST OF RECORDERS

The following people have contributed records, from one to many thousands, and where records are given in the text the recorders are normally indicated by their initials. Recorders are listed in alphabetical order of their initials to enable easy identification.

AES	A.E.Stubbs	JPB	J.P.Brock	PJH	P.J.Hodge
AJDM	A.J.D.Morris	JPE	J.P.Early	PRH	P.R.Harvey
AJH	A.J.Halstead	JRD	J.R.Dobson	RAJ	R.A.Jones
AJP	A.J.Pontin	JSD	J.S.Denton	RDH	R.D.Hawkins
ASD	A.S.Davidson	KMG	K.M.Guichard	RKAM	R.K.A.Morris
CWP	C.W.Plant	KNAA	K.N.A.Alexander	RMF	R.M.Fry
DAC	D.A.Coleman	ME	M.Edwards	RWJU	R.W.J.Uffen
DBB	D.B.Baker	MEA	M.E.Archer	SFI	S.F.Imber
DE	D.Element	MNS	M.N.Smith	SGD	S.G.Dodd
DWB	D.W.Baldock	MSP	M.S.Parsons	SJF	S.J.Falk
GAC	G.A.Collins	OWR	O.W.Richards	SPMR	S.P.M.Roberts
GBC	G.B.Collins	PFY	P.F.Yeo	SRM	S.R.Miles
GRE	G.R.Else	PJC	P.J.Chandler	VVP	V.V.Proklov

SURREY – THE SURVEY AREA

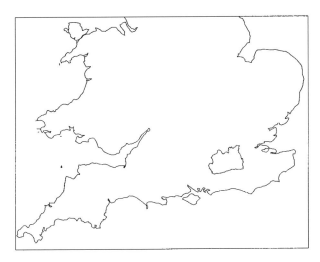

Surrey in relation to southern England

As with all the previous atlases in this series, the Surrey of this survey is the traditional county rather than the modern one. It dates from the proposal of H.C. Watson in 1852 to divide Britain into units of approximately equal size for the purpose of botanical recording.

Watson chose the county as his basic unit, but divided large counties into smaller units which he named vice-counties. Surrey was small enough to be kept as a single vice-county, whereas neighbouring Sussex, Hampshire and Kent are all divided into two halves, each of which are similar in size to Surrey.

The Surrey of this survey, known as the Watsonian vice-county 17, includes the following districts that are no longer part of the modern county of Surrey: the London Boroughs of Wandsworth, Lambeth and Southwark that were transferred to the London County Council in 1889; the London Boroughs of Richmond, Kingston, Merton, Sutton and Croydon that formed part of Greater London in 1965; and Gatwick Airport, transferred to West Sussex in 1974.

The only significant part of modern Surrey outside our survey area is the borough of Spelthorne, including Staines, Ashford and Sunbury, which is north of the Thames and was transferred from Middlesex (VC21) in 1965. The parish of Dockenfield to the south of Farnham is also part of modern Surrey although in the vice-county of North Hampshire (VC12). The construction of the A331 resulted in a slight diversion of the channel of the Blackwater which forms the county boundary near Lakeside Park, Ash.

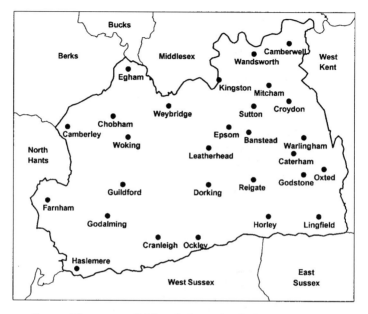

Surrey (Vice-county 17) in relation to bordering vice-counties

In the north-east the boundary of the vice-county follows approximately that separating the London Boroughs of Croydon and Southwark from Bromley and Lewisham, but also includes the former urban district of Penge and half the grounds of the Crystal Palace which are part of modern Bromley. The vice-county boundary differs slightly from the modern boundary between the boroughs of Southwark and Lewisham and can be followed by studying old maps. One problem area with the vice-county boundaries is the position of the islands in the River Thames (known as Aits or Ayts), some of which lie closer to the Surrey than the Middlesex bank, yet at present are nearly all considered part of VC21.

GEOLOGY, CLIMATE AND DISTRIBUTION

Bees, being a group of mainly warmth-loving insects, are on the edge of their range in the cool, damp and rather sunless climate of Britain which explains why there are only about 260 species here out of a world total of probably 30,000, although only 16,000 have so far been described (Michener, 2000). The distribution of these species within Britain and Surrey is dependent mainly on the climate, but also on geology and how this affects the habitat.

Surrey, in the extreme south-eastern corner of Britain, has a warmer and drier climate than most other counties and it is mainly for this reason that most of the British species are found here; the few species that are missing from Surrey are those which occur mainly on or near the coast, where the climate is even milder, or are northern species, found only in Scotland or north of a line between the Wash and the Severn.

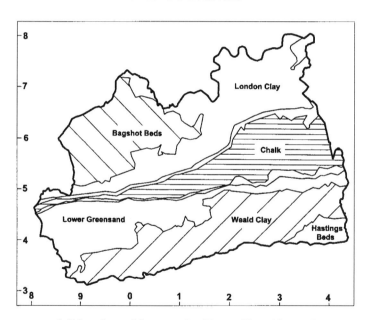

Solid geology of Surrey, after **'Butterflies of Surrey'**

Ground-nesting bees prefer to nest in well-drained soils, such as sand and chalk, but the undoubted influence of geology on distribution is not in terms of actual soil types but in the way the topography, and thus the microclimate and habitat, are affected. Surrey is fortunate in having a varied geology, which has produced many hilly features with warm, south-facing slopes as well as many large areas of poor sandy soils which have prevented any large-scale agriculture. Because of this the county still has a high proportion of semi-natural habitat, a feature which is preferred by most species of bees.

The basic solid geology of the county is fairly simple and is shown above. A ridge of Chalk with a steep south-facing escarpment runs from west to east across the whole county, with a parallel ridge of Lower Greensand running to the south of it. In the west, on either side of these features, are large areas of sand; in the north the damper Bagshot Sands overlying clay and in the south the drier Lower Greensand expands into a wide area of country reaching the county boundary at Haslemere. In the east there are large areas of clay on either side of the chalk and sand ridges; in the north the acid London Clay and in the south the heavy but less acid Weald Clay. The best account of the geology of Surrey is by Stevens in Lousley (1976).

These varied soils produce equally varied habitat. Much of the North Downs is covered by thin chalk soils which are too dry for anything but grassland; the south-facing escarpment still has many areas of downland turf although this is rapidly disappearing due to lack of grazing. The hot, dry, sandy soils of the west support a rich heathland habitat but much of this has disappeared under buildings and encroaching pine and birch woodland, again due to lack of grazing. Much of the wet, heavy clay is still predominantly covered in oak woodland because it makes poor agricultural soil.

WHAT IS A BEE?

Bees are closely related to wasps; both of them, together with ants, form the group called Hymenoptera Aculeata because all the species are equipped, in the females, with stinging apparatus. Bees evolved from wasps probably about 40 million years ago, or possibly even earlier, at some stage after pollen-bearing flowers had arisen in the early Cretaceous. Wasps appear in the fossil record as early as about 140 million years ago but the first fossil bee, in amber, may be 80 million years old and most bees in Baltic amber are only about 35 million years old.

The main difference between bees and wasps is that bees feed their young on a pollen/nectar mixture whilst most wasps feed them on invertebrate prey. Bees, except the cuckoo bees and a few other species, are much more hairy than wasps; wasps appear to be shiny and hairless but under a microscope they can be seen to have short simple hairs whereas bees have much longer, and often dense, plumose hairs and also have specially adapted plumose hairs on their hindlegs or under their abdomen for collecting pollen. But in other respects bees and wasps are very similar in appearance. The females of both have stings; wasps use their stings for paralysing their prey as well as for defence but the bees use them only in defence. Both have a characteristic constricted waist; wasps generally have a more pronounced 'wasp-waist' as they need to be able to twist their body around to sting their prey. Both have a propodeum, the back of the thorax which is actually part of the abdomen, and both have two pairs of membranous wings connected by a row of hooks on the front of the hindwing. Both have similar antennae with 12 (females) to 13 (males) segments, similar eyes with large compound eyes on the side of the head and three small ocelli on the top, and similar mandibles of varying shape to suit their requirements; these mandibles are used by wasps for cutting up prey as well as for nest construction while bees use them only for nest construction. Both construct similar nests and cells in the soil or in old beetle holes or other crevices and both sip nectar for energy, using similar but varied mouth-parts and tongues. The great majority of bees and wasps are solitary but a few species of both are social; there are many species of cuckoo bees and cuckoo wasps.

The drawings overleaf show the main parts of a bee and of the head but these are dealt with in rather more detail in the key to the genera.

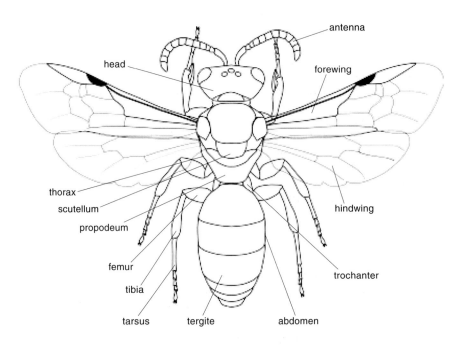

The main parts of a bee

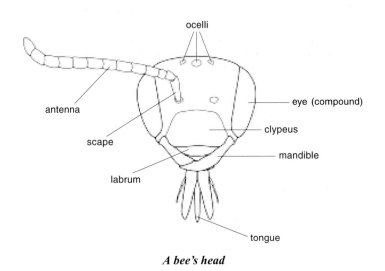

A bee's head

HISTORY OF ACULEATE RECORDING IN SURREY

Few of those who study aculeate Hymenoptera (members of the superfamilies Chrysidoidea, Apoidea and Vespoidea within the sub-order Apocrita, all possessing the capacity to sting) have ever focused solely on one group among bees, wasps and ants to the exclusion of the others, so the history of recording properly tends to involve all three. Surrey probably has more historical records than any other county not just because it has many prime sites for aculeates but because Edward Saunders, who wrote the classic book *The Hymenoptera Aculeata of the British Islands*, published in 1896, lived in Woking for most of his life and attracted a circle of other distinguished hymenopterists to the area.

The prime sites include Horsell and Chobham Commons, Byfleet, Weybridge and Oxshott Heath, all within easy walking distance of railway stations. This meant that many eminent hymenopterists, such as F. Smith, O.W. Richards and I.H.H. Yarrow, frequently visited the county from London. But it also meant that other good sites, such as the heathlands of the south-west, the Weald Clay woodlands around Chiddingfold and much of the North Downs, all of which were difficult to get to by train, were almost entirely neglected by the earlier collectors, other than O.H. Latter who lived at Godalming.

The earliest known collector was **James F. Stephens**, who recorded three species from Ripley in about 1830.

Another early collector was **Frederick Smith**, who joined the staff of the British Museum in 1850 and was Senior Assistant in the Zoological Department of the Museum till his death in 1879. He was the author of, amongst many works, three 'Catalogues' of the British Hymenoptera in the 1850s. He collected mainly in the Weybridge area, close to the station (80 records of his are included in the total records for Surrey), and from there collected an extraordinary assortment of rarities: including *Halictus maculatus, Ceropales variegata* in 1844, *Lestica clypeata* in 1848 and 1853, *Megachile lapponica* in 1847, probably *Hylaeus punctulatissimus* in 1850, *Lasioglossum sexnotatum* in 1858, *Ceratina cyanea* in 1876 and *Megachile ericetorum* in 1884. Some of these species have never been recorded in Britain since then. He also collected *Argogorytes fargei* at Wandsworth and Battersea in 1837 and *Eumenes coarctatus* at Addington Woods in 1859. He is said to have augmented his meagre earnings at the Museum by collecting and identifying bees and wasps at the weekends for other collectors. His main collection is at Oxford University Museum although part of it is at the Natural History Museum, London (NHML).

Another early collector, well known for his large Indian collections, was **G.A.J. Rothney** who collected a few specimens at Croydon and Shirley in 1870, including *Formica sanguinea, Osmia pilicornis* and *Ceratina cyanea*, none of which are found there today. Another was **Dr E. Capron** (14 records mentioned by Saunders in his book and in the *Victoria County History*) who collected around Shere in about 1870 and who recorded *Crabro scutellatus* new to Britain in 1878 near Guildford (possibly Whitmoor Common).

As indicated above, Surrey's most famous hymenopterist is **Edward Saunders**. He was born at Wandsworth in 1848 and moved to Reigate in 1857. There his father, W.W. Saunders, a well-known entomologist, had a large collection of insects including Shuckard's fine collection of British Hymenoptera and it was there that Saunders started his lifelong interest in the aculeates. He married in 1872 and moved back to Wandsworth, then to Bromley and finally in 1887 to St Anne's, Mount Hermon Road, Woking where he remained with his family of six children until his death in 1910. He worked at Lloyds in the City all his life and therefore needed to live near a railway station. No doubt he chose St Anne's as a residence not only because it was a five-minute walk from the station but also because it was close to Horsell and Chobham Commons, both well-known collecting localities that he had visited frequently in previous years. Horsell Common, with its famous sandpit, was a much more open and extensive heathland in those days and, being only a ten-minute walk from his house, was no doubt the locality referred to on his many specimen labels marked "Woking". His large collection of aculeates is in the NHML but his diaries and letters are in the Hope Collection, Oxford University Museum. His early work *Synopsis of British Hymenoptera* was published in parts from 1880 to 1884 and refers to many Surrey records, especially from Chobham. *The Hymenoptera Aculeata of the British Islands* contains many more Surrey records, especially from Woking, and in 1902 his chapter on Hymenoptera Aculeata was published in *A Victoria County History of Surrey* (VCH), which gives a complete list of all the aculeates known to him from Surrey. He notes that "the aculeates are exceedingly well represented in Surrey, 312 species being recorded out of the 384 which have hitherto occurred in Britain". This list included ants but not the Chrysidoidea, although his friend and neighbour F.D. Morice appended a chapter on the Chrysididae, or jewel wasps, with a list of 16 Surrey species out of about 20 then known in Britain. By 1902 therefore, the total number of species recorded from Surrey stood at 328. His list includes 169 bees, which compares with the present total of 222. In addition, Saunders published about 70 articles and notes in the *Entomologist's Monthly Magazine* (EMM) between 1876 (when he announced his capture at Chobham Common of *Odynerus reniformis* as new to Britain) and his death in 1910. Many of these are accounts of his collecting trips to Chobham and Woking and include the first British records for *Priocnemis parvula*, *Arachnospila wesmaeli* and *A. minutula*, all from West End Common in 1880.

The Rev. Francis D. Morice was another eminent hymenopterist, who, on retirement as a schoolmaster at Rugby School in 1894, bought the house next to his friend Saunders in Mount Hermon Road, Woking, and died there in 1926. Both are buried in neighbouring graves in Brookwood Cemetery, only about two miles from their homes, and a fitting place for two such famous hymenopterists, surrounded as it is by such rarities as *Andrena marginata*, *Nomada argentata* and *Ceratina cyanea*. Morice (170 records) was a specialist in Chrysididae and wrote the chapter on this family in the Surrey volume of the VCH. He also wrote 12 articles in the EMM between 1897 and 1913, mainly on his captures of rarities in Surrey, such as *Odynerus reniformis* and *Heriades truncorum* and his discovery of *Hedychridium coriaceum* as new to Britain from Ottershaw in 1897. Morice's main collection is at Oxford University Museum. His main interest, though, was in sawflies.

During the early heyday of hymenopterist collectors, from about 1880 to 1914, Saunders and Morice attracted a large circle of collectors to the west Surrey heaths, many of whom published their accounts in the EMM, and as a result a mass of records was produced. All the collectors of the time, not only from Surrey but from all over Britain, would bring or send their specimens for identification or confirmation to Morice or Saunders.

One very prolific collector in Saunders time was **Charles H. Mortimer** (217 records) who lived most of his life at Holmwood till his death in 1932, although he lived at Byfleet from 1920 to 1923. Between 1895 and 1921 he contributed many short articles to the EMM about collecting in Surrey, including his account of finding both sexes of the extremely rare bee *Dufourea halictula* (previously only recorded once in Britain) at Byfleet in June 1913, with notes on its habits, and his second British record of *Homonotus sanguinolentus* at Holmwood in 1907. He recorded *Ectemnius rubicola* as new to Britain in 1890 at Downside, Cobham, *Andrena niveata* in 1913 at Byfleet and *Psenulus schencki* in 1922 at Holmwood. He also recorded such rarities as *Ceropales variegata* at Holmwood in 1896, *Crossocerus walkeri* at Byfleet in 1913 and *Mimumesa spooneri* at Byfleet in 1913 and at Holmwood in 1890. He was evidently a wealthy man who had a chauffeur to drive him around the countryside and to hand him collecting boxes whilst he netted the next specimen. He collected almost every species known at that time in Surrey and his collection is in the BMNH. Unfortunately, like most Victorian and Edwardian collectors, all his specimens are labelled, mostly on pink card, either "Holmwood" or "Byfleet" although some of his specimens must have come from the North Downs, probably Box Hill and even further afield.

T.R. Billups (74 records) was another recorder collecting in the Woking, Chobham, Oxshott Heath and Box Hill areas and who recorded some of the great rarities of that time such as *Dufourea minuta* at Woking in 1881 and *Odynerus reniformis* at Chertsey in 1884. He published accounts of these finds in the EMM, together with others relating to Surrey, including a list of aculeates collected in a visit of two and a half hours to Oxshott Heath on 8 July 1890.

Also active at the same time and in the same area were the two brothers **H.G.** and **R.J. Champion**, who published in the EMM a list of 70 species collected at Horsell Common in 1914 and a report of their capture in 1914 of *Homonotus sanguinolentus* at both Chobham and Woking. **R.C.L. Perkins** added a few records, including the only one for the extremely rare *Andrena nana*.

O.H. Latter (280 records) was a pupil at Charterhouse from 1878 to 1883 and the senior science master there from 1890 till 1932, dying at Godalming in 1948; many of his records are mentioned by Saunders in his book and in the VCH. He himself wrote a short popular book *Bees and Wasps*, published in 1913. Many of his specimens were still at Charterhouse Museum in 2003, when they were donated to Haslemere Museum; unfortunately a large proportion of these have no data labels. He collected the only two known Surrey specimens of *Ancistrocerus antilope* at Godalming in 1932 (one specimen in Haslemere Museum). He also turns out to have been an unreliable hymenopterist. One of his pupils was **Guy M. Spooner**, who was inspired by Latter to study bees and wasps and later became an eminent hymenopterist himself in the 1950s to 1980s, collecting mainly in Devon and Cornwall. I have some correspondence between Spooner and Latter in which Spooner queries the identification of many of Latter's Surrey specimens in the school collection and Latter agrees that Spooner is probably right, e.g. *Podalonia hirsuta* from Thursley Common in 1890 and 1910, and *Megachile ericetorum*. Whilst at Charterhouse in 1938 Spooner recorded *Stelis phaeoptera* nesting there in an old fence.

After World War I very little collecting took place except by Mortimer, mentioned above, and a few well-known hymenopterists. **Professor Owain W. Richards** (54 records), the author of the handbook on sphecid and other wasps, taught at Imperial College, London, and at Silwood Park from where he often ventured into Surrey in the 1920s and after the war. On one of these collecting trips from Silwood Park he made the first inland record of the elusive *Euodynerus quadrifasciatus* at Bagshot Heath in 1950. He carried out an extensive survey of the aculeates of Oxshott Heath from 1922 to 1928, later publishing a paper on the results. **Ian H.H. Yarrow** (six records), who was head of the Hymenoptera Department at the British Museum (Natural History) (as it was known at that time), made a few interesting records. **John F. Perkins**, who lived at Claygate, also added a few records.

G. Fox Wilson (70 records) was the entomologist at the Royal Horticultural Society, Wisley, from 1919 to 1948, and in 1919 he started the RHS Wisley Collection which today still contains his specimens, including those of the now apparently extinct in Surrey *Andrena similis* and *Anthophora retusa*, and later ones of A.J. Halstead. **G.E. Frisby** (51 records) collected in the Redhill and Reigate area, a previously poorly recorded locality, between 1900 and 1916, and **E.G.B. Nevinson** (45 records) contributed some useful records from around Cobham between 1900 and 1922; his specimens are in the Hope Collection, Oxford, and the NHML. **G.H. Le Marchant** (32 records) formed a large collection, containing many Surrey specimens, which is now in the NHML, but nothing is known about him except that he was an army colonel.

In 1936 the London Natural History Society chose Limpsfield Common as a site for a long-term survey, although this was changed to Bookham Common after World War II. It was at this time that **Kenneth M. Guichard** (950 records), an amateur hymenopterist, started collecting at Limpsfield Common and published two papers on the aculeates of the Common. After the war he started his survey of three Surrey heaths, Chobham Common, Horsell Common and Oxshott Heath, culminating in his paper "*The Hymenoptera Aculeata of Chobham Common, the Woking area and Oxshott Heath, Surrey*" in the *Entomologist's Gazette* in 1977. In this paper he remarks that his list of aculeates "seems to form a basis for a County List which surprisingly does not exist for Surrey". This list, which excludes ants and dryinids, embolemids and bethylids, contains 315 species recorded from the three localities over the last 100 years. He also adds a list of 56 additional aculeate species recorded from other localities, in particular Byfleet and Weybridge, in the Administrative County of Surrey. His total number of bees and wasps for the county is therefore 407, compared with the present day list of 428. Although he lived in west London and spent time working abroad, he was a constant visitor to west Surrey, collecting from any area within easy access of a railway station, including Brookwood Cemetery and Weybridge. Amongst his records of species new to Surrey was *Hylaeus pectoralis* from Esher Common in 1967. He continued recording and collecting at Horsell Common until 1998, only four years before his death in 2002. He left his vast collection of aculeates, from all over Europe, the Middle East and Africa, as well as from Surrey, to the NHML, with duplicates to the Royal Scottish Museums, Edinburgh.

Donald B. Baker (100 records) lived at Cheam, and at Ewell where he died in 2004. Many of his Surrey records come from around these areas in the 1940s to 1980s but he also recorded extensively at Oxshott Heath between 1938 and 1985 (80 visits) and was a frequent visitor to Ashtead and Bookham Commons, Box Hill, Banstead and Epsom Downs and numerous other localities. He recorded *Dinetus pictus* from Oxshott Heath in 1950, only the third British record, and *Andrena niveata* from Ewell in 1957, this being only the second Surrey record. He made the first Surrey records of *Lasioglossum semilucens* at Oxshott in 1973, *Crossocerus exiguus* at Oxshott in 1962, *Andrena hattorfiana* at Coulsdon in 1949, *Ectemnius sexcinctus* from his garden at Ewell in 1982, *Lasioglossum cupromicans* on Banstead Downs in 1975, *Nitela lucens* from his garden at Ewell in 1982 and *N. borealis* a few days later at West Ewell Station. He kindly showed me some of his rarer Surrey specimens in his large collection of worldwide bees, which, shortly before his death, went to the University of Kansas, USA, where the world-famous bee specialist Charles Michener is still professor emeritus of entomology. His friend **P.W.E. Currie** (50 records) worked on the survey of Bookham Common from 1949 to 1951, making the first county record of *Dipogon bifasciatus*. Another friend, **Frank D. Lawton**, visited many localities in central Surrey, from before the war to the 1950s, and part of his collection was held by D.B. Baker. Other recorders at that period were **D.O. Boyd** (eight records) who collected in the Clandon area in 1937, and whose collection is in the NHML, **Peter F. Yeo** and **S.F. Imber** who collected briefly in the 1960s and made some important discoveries at Westcott Downs. **Alan E. Stubbs** visited Surrey regularly during the 1950s and 60s, as a hymenopterist rather than a dipterist, making the final record of *Anthophora retusa* in 1954 before it became extinct in Surrey.

By the start of the survey period in 1985, the following were the only four active bee recorders in the county, due mainly to a lack of any key with which to identify them:

Roger K.A. Morris (4,500 records) who not only made a large number of records from all over the county from 1984 to 1999 when he was also recording the distribution of hoverflies for his book on these flies, but also carried out an intensive survey of aculeates on Mitcham Common, south London in 1990/91, publishing his records in Morris (1992). He was the first to find *Ectemnius borealis* in Surrey.

Andrew J. Halstead (1,000 records), the Principal Entomologist at RHS Wisley, who had been recording bees, as well as other orders of insects, for some time and has continued to do so up to the present.

Stephen R. Miles (360 records) who was active in the 1980s and early 1990s, mainly on the western heaths, and who continues to send in records.

Michael Edwards (1,600 records) who, although living in Midhurst, West Sussex, was then, and is still, doing survey work on many of the best Surrey sites, including those owned by the National Trust. He was the first to record *Polistes dominulus* breeding in Britain, at Ham House.

Alan J.D. Morris also collected briefly from 1989 to 1992 in east Surrey, especially at Dawcombe and Reigate Heath.

It was only in 1996 that I (**David W. Baldock**, 18,500 records, including the first county records of *Andrena congruens* and *Stelis breviuscula*) started to study and record bees and wasps, but I soon realised that, because of its incredible diversity, Surrey needed to be surveyed in depth and Guichard encouraged me to write a book on the bees. I also realised that, although I could cover much of the western half of the county from my home at Milford, I would need assistance for the eastern half. Luckily the next two recorders came to the rescue immediately:

Graham A. Collins (6,500 records), living in South Croydon, who has covered most of the eastern side, including the previously unrecorded south-eastern corner. He made the first and only record of *Nomada conjungens* and the only modern Surrey records of *Sphecodes spinulosus* and *Nomada ferruginata*.

Roger D. Hawkins (3,000 records), living at Horley, who also surveyed the south-eastern corner as well as numerous other sites. He made the first and only record of *Andrena ferox* in Surrey and discovered *Lasioglossum sexstrigatum* new to Britain and Surrey in 2008.

Four other recorders who helped in the later stages of the survey were **Jonty S. Denton** (1,000 records), **Jeremy P. Early** (500 records), who made many interesting discoveries at Priory Park, Reigate, whilst photographing insects there, **Scott G. Dodd** who started on bees only in 2007 but added some interesting records from Brentmoor Heath, and **Derek A. Coleman** who added some useful records from Carshalton and Beddington Sewage Farm.

THE SURVEY

Strictly speaking the survey started in 1996. In 1995 I had decided to prepare an account of the bees and wasps of Surrey, which I thought might take about 20 years to complete. In December 1995 I sent a letter to all entomologists who might have Surrey records, informing them of my intention and asking them to let me have full details of any such records. This letter not only produced a good number of records but also provoked the faithful Surrey entomologists to start looking for bees and wasps. I started recording in 1996 and by 1997 I was able to produce some very provisional distribution maps for my own use, although I also distributed some to the Surrey recorders by way of encouragement. By the start of 1999 the number of records had increased threefold and a new set of maps was produced and circulated to all contributors in April. However, 1999 produced a bumper crop of records, many from previously neglected areas, and updated maps were therefore produced in early 2000, from a database of 18,500 records, and circulated to all recorders. These maps were already beginning to show characteristic patterns relating not only to habitat and geology, but also to individual recorder's home areas. In 2001 Roger Morris sent me over 5,000 records, many of which dated to the 1980s when he was going all over Surrey collecting data for his *Hoverflies of Surrey*. By this time I was adding about 2,500 records a year to the database and with the four main recorders living conveniently in each quarter of the county, the records were fairly evenly spread, although there were still some large gaps in the extreme south-east corner. Graham Collins was covering the north-east quarter, Roger Hawkins the south-east, Andrew Halstead the north-west and I myself the south-west. Roger Morris had records from most of Surrey, Mike Edwards was contributing large numbers from many survey sites across Surrey and Jonty Denton was sending in records from surveys in the north-west. By May 2003 the dry acid grasslands south of London had been properly worked and the database had 27,500 records so yet another set of maps was circulated, together with a note of the 12 new species that had been added since the previous maps, and a list of nine species that should be searched for. Recorders were also urged to concentrate on the obvious gaps in the maps. By May 2006 another 10,000 records had been added to the database and many of the gaps in the south-east corner had been surveyed, so another set of maps was circulated. The best way of encouraging recorders is to keep them up to date with what is happening, hence the large numbers of maps that were produced. In 2006 Jeremy Early appeared on the scene, busily photographing around Reigate at Priory Park and in a nearby garden and a disused sandpit, and adding many new records for this rather neglected area. During the last few years of the survey about 3,500 records were being received annually and the total number of records on the database, including historic ones, is about

45,000. A final set of maps was circulated in March 2008 with a coincidence map of all bees so that recorders could try to fill any remaining gaps.

All parts of *Provisional atlas of the aculeate Hymenoptera of Britain and Ireland* use a modern recording period from 1970 onwards for the distribution maps. Other county surveys have also tended to use 1970 as the starting point. However, 38 years is too long a period for a survey of insects because their distribution and frequency change over relatively short periods. It was therefore decided that the survey period should be only about 20 years and the starting date should be 1985. In the early 1980s only about 50 records a year were made and in the 1970s only about 30 a year, so not many records were excluded from the survey period and in any case these still appear on the maps as grey circles (denoting records from 1951 to 1984). Between 1985 and 1996 the number of records being made annually was about 300 so there are only about 3,000 records from the first half of the survey period, and the maps would look much the same if the survey period was shortened to 12 years, starting from 1996.

The vast majority of records have been made by netting bees at flowers or nest sites and then examining the specimens at home, usually under a microscope. Most rare or difficult to identify specimens were retained as vouchers by the recorders so that these could be checked at any time by experts. All extreme rarities have been examined by experts. A few bees are distinctive enough to be identifiable in the field, at least by experts and well practised amateurs, so there are a fair number of field records. Bees are notoriously difficult to identify from photographs and only those images about which there is no doubt as to the identity of the species have been accepted as records. Malaise traps can add many new species to a site and such traps have been operated at numerous localities around the county. A map showing these localities is overleaf.

A Malaise trap is rather like a small tent, made entirely of fine netting, but instead of sides it has a central partition into which the insects fly; they then fly up into the corner of the roof nearest the sun, in which there is a small hole leading into a bottle of alcohol. These traps tend to catch many more wasps than bees, especially spider wasps. Water, or pan, traps were only rarely used, except by Roger Morris on Mitcham Common. A few nest traps were occasionally put out. Searching for plant stems, mainly brambles, with holes in the end during the winter, known as 'brambling', can be an effective method of collecting bees. The stems are kept indoors and long series of adult bees emerge after a few weeks; this is the best method of collecting *Ceratina cyanea*, which hibernate as adults in bramble stems.

The coverage map overleaf shows that all the 450 or so complete tetrads

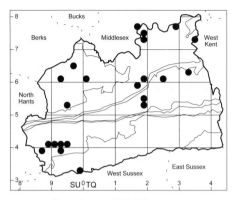

Locations of Malaise traps

have been visited and clearly indicates the best areas, such as the western heaths, as well as the poor ones, such as Inner London and the south-east corner of the county on the clay. This latter area is mainly agricultural and there are very few wild, undisturbed places and very few footpaths. There has been more recording in the west of the county than the east. There is a bias towards certain hotspots, mainly the western heaths such as Thursley, Horsell and Chobham Commons but also some in the east such as Mitcham Common and Reigate Heath as well as the northern Richmond Park, Kew Gardens complex. There is also a clear bias in the area around my home at Milford and especially in my own garden where I have recorded no fewer than 121 bee species.

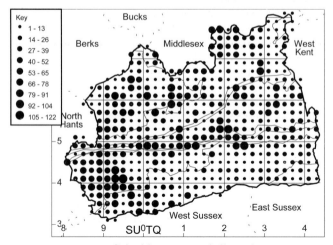

Coincidence map of all species

RESULTS OF THE SURVEY

The main object of the survey was to map the distribution of all the bees at a given point in time, from 1985 to 2008. The distribution maps in the Species Accounts hopefully show that this has been achieved. Another important object was to look at any changes in the bee fauna and this is dealt with in the next chapter. The third object was to identify the best sites for bees, bearing in mind that the older collectors had concentrated their efforts on sites convenient to the railway, mainly in the north-west of the county. Each year some entirely new site was found which, on further exploration, proved to be almost as good as the best of the older, well-known localities. These important sites are dealt with in a later chapter.

SPECIES FOUND NEW TO SURREY

As a result of of such an intensive survey by many entomologists over a 23 year period it was not surprising that some species were found which had never been recorded in Surrey before. Of the following 11 new species the first one and the last two are recent colonists. *Colletes hederae* was first recorded in Dorset in 2000 and is now spreading rapidly, *Bombus hypnorum* was first found in Wiltshire in 2001 but has also spread rapidly since then. The very large carpenter bee *Xylocopa violacea* has been turning up as a vagrant in southern England more and more frequently and actually bred successfully for the first time in 2006 in Kent and in 2006 and 2007 in Leicestershire. *Stelis breviuscula* was first found in Britain as recently as 1984 and appears to be spreading rapidly within the range of its host *Heriades truncorum*. *Colletes similis* must have been overlooked by all recorders prior to 1996 as it is not uncommon, both nationally and in Surrey; Saunders (1880) noted that it was very similar to other *Colletes* and "I expect that this is a common species, but overlooked". The other five species have always been nationally rare or very rare, and were possibly overlooked by earlier recorders in Surrey, although the late Victorian and Edwardian collectors missed very few species. *Sphecodes scabricollis* appears to be extending its range nationally in recent years and may therefore be a new arrival.

Colletes hederae	Only record 19 October 2007 at Reigate. JPE
Colletes similis	First record 1996 at Hogs Back. DWB
Andrena congruens	First record April 1997 at Wyke Common, Ash Ranges. DWB
Andrena ferox	Only record 11 May 1998 at Reigate Heath. RDH
Lasioglossum sexstrigatum	Found new to Britain and Surrey at Merstham 5 June 2008. RDH
Sphecodes scabricollis	First record 1993 at Chobham Common. RKAM

Stelis breviuscula	First record 19 August 1996 at Wyke Common, Ash Ranges. DWB	
Nomada conjungens	First and only record 5 June 2007 at Westcott Downs. GAC	
Nomada ferruginata	First and only record 26 April 1996 at Thorpe Hay Meadow. GAC	
Xylocopa violacea	First record 14 July 2003 at Guildford. D. Powell	
Bombus hypnorum	First record 28 May 2004 at Egham. T. Ings	

SPECIES REFOUND DURING THE SURVEY

Although there were many collectors from the end of the Edwardian era, in 1920, until the start of the survey period in 1985, there were a considerable number of species that had not been seen for some years prior to 1985. The following list shows the 23 species that were refound during the survey; column 1 gives the species, column 2 gives the date it was refound, column 3 gives the locality where it was refound, column 4 gives the finder and column 5 gives the number of years since it had last been recorded in Surrey. Most of these species are rare and very localised and could therefore have been easily overlooked.

Hylaeus pictipes	1996	Walton-on-Thames	RWJU	After 28 years
Andrena alfkenella	1996	Farthing Downs	RDH	After 39 years
Andrena falsifica	2004	Oxshott Heath	ME	After 36 years
Andrena hattorfiana	1998	Westcott Downs, Dorking	DWB	After 38 years
Andrena lapponica	1989	Friday Street	RKAM	After 68 years
Andrena nigrospina	2000	Papercourt Gravelpits, Send	ASD	After 36 years
Andrena niveata	2001	Ewell	DWB	After 42 years
Andrena proxima	1989	Fetcham	RKAM	After 109 years
Sphecodes niger	1996	Pewley Down, Guildford	DWB	After 46 years
Sphecodes rubicundus	1997	Sidney Wood, Dunsfold	DWB	After 95 years
Sphecodes spinulosus	1998	Westcott Downs, Dorking	GAC	After 61 years
Stelis ornatula	1998	Blatchford Down	ME	After 80 years
Osmia aurulenta	1997	Newlands Corner	DWB	After 21 years
Osmia pilicornis	1996	Oaken Wood, Dunsfold	DWB	After 73 years

Megachile dorsalis	2005	Wrecclesham Sandpit	DWB	After 92 years
Coelioxys conoidea	1997	Frensham Common	DWB	After 32 years
Nomada argentata	1984	Brookwood Cemetery	KMG	After 75 years
Nomada guttulata	2003	Richmond Park	DWB	After 63 years
Nomada lathburiana	1997	Ham Common	RDH	After 60 years
Eucera longicornis	1997	Hambledon Claypit	DWB	After 25 years
Ceratina cyanea	1986	Witley Common	KNAA	After 22 years
Bombus humilis	2003	East Dulwich	PRH	After 65 years
Bombus rupestris	1998	Guildford	DWB	After 35 years

SPECIES NOT REFOUND DURING THE SURVEY

Apart from the extreme rarities found by F. Smith and others on only one or two occasions, such as *Hylaeus punctulatissimus, Megachile ericetorum* and *M. lapponica*, the following 26 species have not been refound since 1985. Last recorded date, locality where last found and the collector of the last specimen are given for each species. Most of these species have suffered dramatic declines in the last few decades, or even earlier, and are not likely to be refound unless they increase again and expand their range. Some, for example *Melecta luctuosa* and *Bombus subterraneus*, have become extinct in Britain. But the seven species in the second part of the list might conceivably have been overlooked, some because they are very small, for example the two *Dufourea* species and *Lasioglossum cupromicans*, and the others because they have always been very rare in Surrey.

A. Species unlikely to be refound

Colletes marginatus	1890	Weybridge	T.A.Marshall
		The only Surrey record, doubtful	
Andrena nana	1915	Oxshott Heath	Anon.
		The only Surrey record. Specimen in OUM	
Andrena nitidiuscula	1974	Chobham Common	K.M.Guichard
Andrena rosae	1924	Holmwood	C.H.Mortimer
Andrena similis	1937	Clapham Common	K.M.Guichard
Andrena stragulata	1896	Chobham Common	E.Saunders
Halictus maculatus	1844	Weybridge	F.Smith
		The first and only Surrey record	
Lasioglossum sexnotatum	1888	Woking	E.Saunders
		The last of four Surrey records	

Nomada armata	c1850	Woking	F.Smith
		The only Surrey record and doubtful	
Nomada obtusifrons	1913	Byfleet	C.H.Mortimer
Nomada sexfasciata	1914	Horsell Common	Champion bros
Anthophora retusa	1954	Chobham Common	A.E.Stubbs
Melecta luctuosa	1901	Chobham Common	E.Saunders
Bombus distinguendus	1918	Chobham Common	R.C.Bradley
Bombus muscorum	1914	Godalming	O.H.Latter
		The only Surrey record	
Bombus ruderatus	1958	Clandon	D.B.Baker
Bombus soroeensis	c1880	Croydon	G.A.J.Rothney
Bombus subterraneus	1951	Hindhead	D.B.Baker
Bombus sylvarum	1929	Compton	C.Diver

B. Species that might possibly be refound

Lasioglossum cupromicans	1975	Banstead Downs	D.B.Baker
Dufourea halictula	1920	Byfleet	C.H.Mortimer
Dufourea minuta	1891	Chobham Common	E.Saunders
Stelis phaeoptera	1939	West Clandon	D.O.Boyd
Megachile circumcincta	1973	Chobham Common	K.M.Guichard
Coelioxys quadridentata	1982	Ewell	D.B.Baker
Nomada roberjeotiana	1972	Chobham Common	K.M.Guichard

SPECIES NEVER FOUND IN SURREY

Only 32 species on the British List have never been recorded in Surrey. Eleven of these have only ever been recorded once or twice and most of them not for over 100 years. Of the remaining 21 species, the first two in the following list could possibly occur in the future but the other 19 are most unlikely to be found, because 11 have an almost purely coastal distribution and eight are restricted to northern and western Britain.

A. Species that might occur in the future

Andrena gravida	Only known from Kent and East Sussex but could spread with climatic warming
Eucera nigrescens	Very few records for southern England, none since 1964. Possibly overlooked

B. Species unlikely to occur

Colletes cunicularius	Restricted to coastal dunes of west Britain
Colletes floralis	Restricted to coasts of north-west Britain
Colletes halophilus	Restricted to salt marshes on coasts of southern England
Hylaeus spilotus	South-east coast only
Andrena floricola	Only one British specimen, in 1939
Andrena lathyri	Known only from two sites in Wiltshire and Somerset and now possibly extinct
Andrena lepida	Only three British records, none since 1952
Andrena nanula	Only one doubtful British specimen in about 1875
Andrena pilipes	Almost entirely coastal
Andrena polita	Known only from two sites in Kent, none since 1934
Andrena ruficrus	Restricted to northern Britain
Andrena simillima	Very rare on southern coasts and Salisbury Plain
Andrena tridentata	Only old records for Dorset and Brecks
Andrena vaga	Only four British records
Halictus eurygnathus	Very rare and mainly found near coasts
Halictus subauratus	Only one British record, in 1855
Lasioglossum angusticeps	Restricted to coasts of Isle of Wight, Dorset and Devon
Lasioglossum laeve	Only two British specimens, in 1802
Lasioglossum laticeps	Restricted to coasts of Dorset and Devon
Lasioglossum rufitarse	Rarely found south of Midlands
Rophites quinquespinosus	Only two doubtful British specimens, in 1877 and 1888, from Hastings, East Sussex
Melitta dimidiata	Restricted to Salisbury Plain and Vale of Pewsey in Wiltshire
Osmia inermis	Restricted to the Scottish Highlands
Osmia parietina	Restricted to north-west Britain
Osmia uncinata	Restricted to Scotland
Osmia xanthomelana	Very rare and coastal, now known only from west Wales
Hoplitis leucomelana	Only one British specimen, in 1802
Coelioxys afra	Only one British record, in 1892

Coelioxys mandibularis	Entirely coastal
Nomada errans	Known only from Dorset coast near Swanage, probably now extinct
Bombus cullumanus	Formerly scattered over southern England, not recorded since 1941
Bombus monticola	Restricted to hills of north and west Britain
Bombus pomorum	Only four British specimens, in 19th century from East Kent

SURREY RARITIES

The survey has revealed that some species are so rare in Surrey that they have only been recorded once or twice since 1985, or only occur at one site. For instance *Megachile dorsalis* has only been found at Wrecclesham Sandpit but there it occurs in thousands. It is possible that the three small black *Andrena* species and the three small black *Lasioglossum* species have been overlooked because they look similar to other species.

Colletes hederae	Recorded once in 2007 at Reigate
Hylaeus pectoralis	Recorded twice, regularly at Esher Common and in 1999 at Lakeside Park, Ash
Andrena alfkenella	Recorded twice, in 1996 at Coulsdon and in 2001 at Thorpe Hay Meadow
Andrena falsifica	Recorded once in 2004 at Oxshott Heath
Andrena ferox	Recorded once in 1998 at Reigate Heath
Andrena nigriceps	Recorded once in 1994 at Burrowhill Green, Chobham
Andrena nigrospina	Recorded from one site, Papercourt Gravelpits
Andrena niveata	Recorded once in 2001 at Ewell
Lasioglossum nitidiusculum	Recorded once in 1993 at Chobham Common
Lasioglossum pauperatum	Recorded once in 1988 at Wisley Common
Lasioglossum semilucens	Recorded twice, in 1999 at Westcott Downs and in 2002 at Cobham Old Common
Sphecodes spinulosus	Recorded once in 1998 at Westcott Downs
Megachile dorsalis	Recorded from only one site, Wrecclesham Sandpit
Nomada conjungens	Recorded once in 2007 at Westcott Downs

Nomada ferruginata	Recorded once in 1996 at Thorpe Hay Meadow
Nomada guttulata	Recorded twice, in 2003 at Richmond Park and in 2004 at Horsell Common
Bombus humilis	Recorded once in 2003 at East Dulwich
Bombus barbutellus	Recorded once in 2003 at Whitebeech, Chiddingfold

SURREY SPECIALITIES

There are a few species which are common or frequent in Surrey but which are rare in the rest of Britain. The provisional national atlases produced by the Bees, Wasps and Ants Recording Society are prepared on a 10 kilometre square (hectad) basis. The four Surrey specialities below show the number of hectads in which they have been found in Surrey, compared with the total number of hectads in which they have been found outside Surrey.

Andrena florea	22 hectads in Surrey, 14 hectads outside Surrey
Stelis breviuscula	13 hectads in Surrey, 2 hectads outside Surrey
Heriades truncorum	19 hectads in Surrey, 15 hectads outside Surrey
Ceratina cyanea	17 hectads in Surrey, 19 hectads outside Surrey

CHANGES IN THE BEE FAUNA

One important object of the survey was to investigate any changes in the bee fauna since Edward Saunders produced details of Surrey's aculeate Hymenoptera in the *Victoria County History of Surrey* of 1902. Saunders' account consisted mainly of just a list of species; for the rarer and scarcer ones he did give localities and for the common species he noted that they were "Generally distributed". From this it is possible to estimate how rare or common most species were, over 100 years ago, and to compare their status in 1900 with their status in 2008. In the species accounts the VCH status is given and at the end of each account an opinion is given as to whether the species has remained the same, increased or declined since 1900. Of course coverage in 1900 was nowhere near as extensive as it is now. As mentioned in the earlier section on the history of aculeate recording, the Victorians relied on trains to move around the county and most of their recording was done from Chobham Common, Woking, Weybridge and Byfleet. Be that as it may, the following table shows the probable number of species in each category; for a few species it is impossible to estimate any change.

Species which have probably remained the same
since 1900..112, or roughly 50%

Species which have possibly or probably increased
since 1900..63, or roughly 30%

Species which have possibly or probably declined
since 1900..18, or roughly 10%

It seems therefore that bees, other than the bumblebees, most of which have declined dramatically, in Surrey at least, are doing better now than they were 100 years ago. This is probably due to two factors; first the climatic warming over the last few decades and secondly the fact that the four main habitats, heathland, dry acid grassland, chalk grassland and clay woodland, still survive to a considerable extent. This is remarkable when one realises that 40% of England's lowland heathland has been lost since 1950, dry acid grassland underwent a substantial decline in the 20th century and around 25% of the chalk grassland of the South Downs was lost between 1966 and 1980. Clearly it has been of crucial importance that many of Surrey's best sites for aculeates possess a designated conservation status and are owned and/or managed by organisations which take seriously their responsibilities for maintaining, improving and protecting the varied habitats. These include Surrey Wildlife Trust, the National Trust, local authorities and the Ministry of Defence, which owns more than half of Surrey's heathland.

It is also possible from the survey to compare the species which have probably become extinct in Surrey since 1900 with those which have probably arrived since 1900. It is reasonably easy to name the species which have been lost although one can never say for certain that a species is extinct. A few species became extinct before 1900, e.g. *Lasioglossum sexnotatum, Dufourea minuta* and *Bombus soroeensis*. All the lost species are ones which have declined nationally and their loss is not therefore unexpected. It is much more difficult to say which species have been gained. Some species have clearly colonised not only Britain but also Surrey since 1900, such as *Colletes hederae, Stelis breviuscula* and *Bombus hypnorum*. Others were localised residents but clearly present, even though they had not been recorded by 1900, e.g. *Colletes similis* (Saunders admitted it must have been overlooked), *Andrena hattorfiana, A. lapponica, Lasioglossum puncticolle, Sphecodes rubicundus*; they had been overlooked by the Victorians who never ventured into the Weald clay woods or the south-western heaths and rarely visited the North Downs. But there are a number of species which had either not yet been described, or had not been added to the British list by 1900, even though they had probably been resident in Surrey before then, e.g. *Andrena minutuloides*. There are a number of other species which were confused with other species by Saunders around 1900; most of these were clearly, or probably, resident before 1900, e.g. *Lasioglossum pauperatum*. A few were found since 1900 but then lost, and therefore appear in both lists, e.g. *Nomada obtusifrons* which was first found in 1920 but never seen again since then. In the following list only those species which were almost certainly, or probably, not resident before 1900 are included. The 17 losses are more than compensated numerically by the 26 gains (three since lost).

Species lost since 1900

Andrena nana	*Nomada roberjeotiana*
Andrena nitidiuscula	*Nomada sexfasciata*
Andrena rosae	*Anthophora retusa*
Andrena similis	*Melecta luctuosa*
Dufourea halictula	*Bombus muscorum*
Stelis phaeoptera	*Bombus ruderatus*
Megachile circumcincta	*Bombus subterraneus*
Coelioxys quadridentata	*Bombus sylvarum*
Nomada obtusifrons	

Species gained since 1900

Colletes hederae	Sphecodes niger
Hylaeus gibbus	Sphecodes scabricollis
Hylaeus pectoralis	Sphecodes spinulosus
Andrena alfkenella probably	Dufourea halictula but since lost
Andrena apicata	Stelis breviuscula
Andrena congruens	Nomada argentata
Andrena falsifica probably	Nomada conjungens
Andrena ferox	Nomada ferruginata
Andrena nigriceps	Nomada guttulata
Andrena niveata	Nomada lathburiana
Lasioglossum cupromicans	Nomada obtusifrons but since lost
but now possibly lost	Xylocopa violacea
Lasioglossum semilucens	only as a vagrant till now
Lasioglossum sexstrigatum	Bombus hypnorum

Many bee species fluctuate in numbers over a period of a few decades for various, mostly unknown, reasons. But during the last 30 years there has been a tendency for bees, as well as other insects, to increase and to expand their range northwards, due to climatic warming. The species which have shown such a tendency during the period of the survey are listed below, omitting two, *Andrena cineraria* and *Nomada lathburiana*, which have spread southwards from London, rather than northwards.

Species showing recent increases

Hylaeus cornutus	Sphecodes scabricollis
Andrena flavipes	Dasypoda hirtipes
Andrena florea	Stelis breviuscula
Andrena labiata	Heriades truncorum
Andrena proxima	Megachile maritima
Lasioglossum brevicorne	Coelioxys conoidea
Lasioglossum malachurum	Nomada fucata
Lasioglossum pauxillum	Nomada fulvicornis
Sphecodes niger	Ceratina cyanea
Sphecodes reticulatus	

COMPARISONS WITH OTHER COUNTIES

Until 1901 there were very few county reports of aculeate Hymenoptera. However, the publication of the first volumes of the *Victoria County History* changed all that when seven county volumes contained accounts of aculeates, including the account of Saunders and Morice in the Surrey volume, published in 1902. Other county volumes with similar accounts were Norfolk, Essex, Sussex (also by Saunders), Cornwall, Berkshire and Kent. Although no comparisons were given at that time Saunders commented in his Surrey account that the aculeates were "exceedingly well represented in Surrey, 312 species being recorded out of the 384 which have hitherto occurred in Britain". Various other county reports were published during the first half of the 20th Century but during the second half none appeared until 1990. Since then reports have been written on 13 counties or areas:

Leicestershire. Archer (1990)
Lists only solitary aculeates, so not suitable for comparison.

Dorset. Roberts (1993)
Lists only Nationally Rare and Scarce species.

Essex. Harvey (2007)
Full accounts and distribution maps on 5km scale.

Lancashire & Cheshire. Garland & Appleton (1997)
Limited species list so not suitable for comparison.

Surrey. Baldock & Collins (1999, 2000, 2003, 2006, 2008)
Distribution maps on tetrad scale.

Kent. Allen (2001)
Distribution maps on tetrad scale.

Staffordshire. Webb et al. (2002)
Full accounts but no maps.

Yorkshire. Archer (2002)
Accounts and maps at hectad scale.

Cumbria. Robinson (2005)
Full accounts but no maps.

Warwickshire. Falk (2005)
Species list only.

Worcestershire. Trevis (2006)
Species list with notes.

North-east England. Robinson (2007)
Full accounts but no maps.

Shropshire. Cheeseborough (2007)
Unpublished list.

As will be seen, some of these accounts are not suitable for comparison with Surrey. Even those that are suitable have other problems. Surrey consists of just one Watsonian vice-county (all vice-counties are of roughly similar size) but the only other comparable counties that consist of one vice-county are Staffordshire, Shropshire, Worcestershire and Warwickshire. Essex consists of two vice-counties, Kent of two and Yorkshire of five. Cumbria consists of two and a bit vice-counties, namely Cumberland, Westmorland and a small part of Yorkshire, whilst north-east England consists of three, namely County Durham, South Northumberland and North Northumberland. Some counties have been surveyed in more detail than others, as shown by the number of records on which the species figures are based. North-east England, Cumbria, Yorkshire, Dorset, Essex and Kent all have a coastline, a habitat which has a specialised aculeate fauna, whereas Surrey and the other four are purely inland counties.

The following table shows comparisons of ten counties with Surrey. The first column shows the county, arranged in order from north to south, with the year in brackets when the data was published or last updated. The second column shows the total number of aculeates, including ants, which have ever been recorded in the county; this total excludes the DEBs, (the *Dryinidae, Embolemidae* and *Bethylidae*) as these are rarely recorded. The third column shows the number of records on which the other figures are based. The fourth column shows the total number of bees (solitary and social) which have ever been recorded in the county. The fifth column shows the total number of bees recorded in the county since 1970.

County	Total aculeates	Total records	Bees all records	Bees post-1970
North-east England (2007)	197	2,700	86	77
Cumbria (2005+2007)	229	c.2,000	119	106
Yorkshire (2002)	299	c.20,000	136	121
Staffordshire (2002)	282	c.5,000	143	134
Shropshire (2007)	260	c.5,000	135	135
Warwickshire (2005)	307	?	143	132
Worcestershire (2006)	265	?	138	136
Essex (2007)	412	c.36,500	200	176
Dorset (1993)	436			
Kent (2001 + 2008)	448	c.40,000	217	199
Surrey (2008)	466	c.45,000	222	198

The table clearly shows how the number of species increases the further south the county is. It also shows that, in spite of its small size, Surrey has more species than all other counties in each column, except in the post-1970 bees column; Kent still has three more bumblebees than Surrey as well as two coastal species. Unfortunately the two vice-counties adjoining Surrey in the western Weald, West Sussex and North Hampshire, do not have published accounts or lists of their aculeates. They are both likely to have total numbers of species close to those of Surrey, because they both have dry sandy heathlands, even though these are not so extensive, as well as chalk downland.

HABITATS AND BEE ASSOCIATIONS

Many bees are closely associated with certain habitats and following the example of Roger Morris in his *Hoverflies of Surrey* I put forward proposed assemblages for each of the four main Surrey habitats. Each indicator species is graded from 1 to 3, 1 being the strongest and 3 the weakest. These indicator species are only relative to Surrey.

LOWLAND HEATHLAND

Dry heathland is by far the best habitat for bees and wasps but it is a rare and declining habitat, not only in England but also in the world. Fortunately, Surrey has a large proportion of the remaining heathland, including some of the best sites in England. To the south of the Chalk are the extensive dry heaths of the Upper and Lower Greensand, comprising the very large complex of Frensham, Churt, Hankley, Thursley, Witley and Mare Hill Commons, with a few outliers such as Tilford Woods (formerly Farnham Heath), Bricksbury Hill, Crooksbury Common, Puttenham Common and Heath, and Hambledon Common. Further east are the more isolated St Martha's Hill, Blackheath Common, Albury Heath, Leith Hill, Reigate Heath and Limpsfield Chart, as well as a few heaths on top of the Chalk such as Ranmore Common, Walton Heath and Headley Heath. To the north of the Chalk are the extensive damper heaths on Bagshot Sands such as the MOD Ash, Pirbright and Bisley Ranges, the famous Horsell and Chobham Commons, Wisley and Ockham Commons, and further east Oxshott Heath and the Esher Common complex and even a small heath in London at Wimbledon Common.

The main components of heathlands are heathers and gorse but it is not these that make them so rich in aculeates. It is the dry sand, which heats up quickly in the sun and is easy for bees to burrow in, that makes them so attractive to bees and especially to wasps. Only about seven bee species, *Colletes succinctus, Andrena argentata, A. fuscipes* and their respective cuckoos *Epeolus cruciger, Nomada baccata* and *N. rufipes,* as well as *Lasioglossum prasinum,* are actually associated with heather. Even two of these are sometimes found well away from heather, and the rest are found there because they are thermophilous, or heat-loving, insects. But heaths are so acid that very few flowers can grow there and it is only around the edges, where more flowers grow, that most of the bees are to be found. Two rare bees particularly associated with heathland edge are *Hylaeus gibbus* and *Halictus confusus.* Other scarce and interesting species which are found mainly on heathland, but also sometimes on dry acid grassland, are *Colletes fodiens, Andrena humilis* with its cuckoo bee *Nomada integra, Andrena lapponica* wherever bilberry grows*, Andrena ovatula, Panurgus calcaratus, Dasypoda hirtipes, Lasioglossum brevicorne* on yellow composites, *L. quadrinotatum, Megachile maritima* with its cuckoo bee *Coelioxys conoidea,* and *Bombus jonellus.*

Nomada argentata in Surrey is only found on damp heath with devil's-bit scabious.

Proposed heathland indicator species

Colletes succinctus	H1	*Dasypoda hirtipes*	H3
Hylaeus gibbus	H2	*Megachile maritima*	H2
Andrena argentata	H2	*Coelioxys conoidea*	H2
Andrena congruens	H1	*Nomada baccata*	H2
Andrena fuscipes	H1	*Epeolus cruciger*	H1
Halictus confusus	H1	*Bombus jonellus*	H2
Lasioglossum prasinum	H1		

LOWLAND DRY ACID GRASSLAND (OR GRASS HEATH)

Dry acid grassland is nationally a rare, but neglected and vulnerable, habitat and is now classified as a Biodiversity Action Plan habitat. In Surrey this habitat is virtually only found on the Thames Gravel Terraces, to the south and west of London. Here there are some large and valuable sites which are still rich in bees. Richmond Park is the largest, followed by the adjoining Wimbledon Common, which is about half the size. Barnes Common is another excellent site with a few old gravel workings producing very hot bare areas, as is the half a hectare of remaining open grassland at Ham Common, the rest of the Common having been so neglected that it has reverted to dense secondary woodland. Kew Gardens, although much altered by man, is still very rich in bees, some of which take advantage of the flowers cultivated there. Mitcham Common is a large site, with a golf course on it, which has been well studied for bees. Ditton Common consists entirely of a golf course, whilst Old Common at Cobham consists of only two hectares of old gravel workings. There are only a very few other small sites on different soils that contain this habitat. On the top of Ranmore Common, lying on the Chalk, is a small area of gravel and sand, on which grows an acid flora, including heather, gorse and bilberry. The former Brooklands Motor Racing Circuit, between Byfleet and Weybridge, until very recently consisted of a large area of dry acid grassland on alluvial sand from the River Wey, including a small patch adjoining the R. Wey which consisted of an extremely rare habitat known as 'parched acid grassland'. Unfortunately the whole of this has been destroyed by recent development by Mercedes Benz. At Seale there is a tiny site of one hectare on Lower Greensand, which was stripped of topsoil when a sandpit was opened up some years ago.

Dry acid grassland is characterised by drought-stressed grassland growing on well-drained gravel and sand, which heats up quickly in the sun; the grass tends to grow very sparsely, with plenty of bare patches in the heat of the summer for nest sites. The grassland is particularly rich in yellow composites, favourite forage flowers for many species of bees, particularly the small black halictines. It is similar in many respects to heathland, apart from the lack of heather, and most of the heathland bees, except for the four or five heather specialists, can be found on dry acid grassland. It is therefore difficult to identify indicator species for this habitat. *Andrena cineraria* and its cleptoparasite *Nomada lathburiana* are found more commonly on all the Thames Gravel sites than elsewhere in Surrey; at Ham Common they nest in tens of thousands. *Andrena tibialis* is also commoner on the London grasslands than on the heaths. *Panurgus banksianus, Heriades truncorum* and its cleptoparasite *Stelis breviuscula* are frequent on these grasslands because they forage from the abundant yellow composites, *Andrena florea* because its only forage plant white bryony flourishes on these well-drained sites, and *Andrena labiata* because its main forage plant germander speedwell also grows well here. *Andrena fulva* and *A. ovatula* are particularly common on the Thames Gravel sites, possibly because the well-drained soil provides good nesting sites. *Lasioglossum smeathmanellum, Osmia rufa, Anthophora plumipes* and *A. quadridentata* are all found more frequently on the Thames Gravel sites than in the countryside, probably because they use the old mortared walls and buildings surrounding these sites for nesting. Almost all the common species of *Lasioglossum* and the cleptoparasitic *Sphecodes* flourish on this habitat because of the abundance of yellow composites.

Proposed lowland dry acid grassland indicator species

Andrena cineraria	A2	*Panurgus banksianus*	A3
Andrena florea	A3	*Heriades truncorum*	A3
Andrena tibialis	A3	*Nomada lathburiana*	A2

CHALK DOWNLAND

Surrey has some of the finest steep, south-facing chalk slopes in the country, although many of them have recently become scrub-covered. A few of these scrubby areas have been cleared but it is difficult to restore the fine downland turf and flora once it has been shaded out by the dense scrub. The North Downs Chalk stretches from Farnham in the west, where the Hogs Back is only a narrow and low hill on which most of the chalk downland has been destroyed by agriculture or scrub invasion, to the Kent boundary in the east, where the chalk is considerably wider and higher. Along this stretch of south-facing escarpment, and in a few localities to the north of the escarpment, there are many areas which have a fine assemblage of aculeates; for instance

Pewley Down in Guildford, Newlands Corner above Albury, the Sheepleas near West Horsley, Colekitchen Down, White Downs, Westcott Downs (sometimes known as Denbies Hillside), Box Hill, Headley Warren and Farthing Downs at Coulsdon.

Bees, like most insects, prefer hot places and the steep slopes of the North Downs provide just the right microclimate for them. The majority of bees nest underground and they therefore prefer to nest in well-drained soil, either on sand or on chalk. The aerial nesters are not dependent on the soil type and their distribution maps show that they are fairly evenly spread over the whole county. But there are three aerial nesters (*Osmia aurulenta, O. bicolor* and *O. spinulosa*) which are almost restricted to the Chalk and that is because they specialise in nesting in old snail-shells which are more abundant there than elsewhere. Some bees are associated, for foraging purposes, with only one family of flowers, and a few of these specialists occur only or mainly on the Chalk. Both the very large *Andrena hattorfiana* and the much smaller *A. marginata* forage only from the flowers of scabious species, which are nowadays, in Surrey, almost restricted to the Chalk. *Melitta tricincta* forages only from red bartsia, which occurs mainly on the Chalk but occasionally in clay woodland rides and elsewhere. *Melitta haemorrhoidalis* is associated with the flowers of the bellflower family, mainly clustered bellflower and nettle-leaved bellflower, and since both are almost confined to the Chalk, this bee also occurs mainly on the Chalk; most records of this bee, away from the Chalk, are on harebell on heaths or on nettle-leaved bellflower on the Bargate Sands around Godalming, where it grows frequently. It will be seen from the maps that *Hylaeus signatus* is found mainly on the Chalk but with quite a few records off the Chalk. This bee is associated with flowers of the two species in the genus *Reseda*: wild mignonette, which is restricted to the Chalk, and weld, which occurs on roadsides and disturbed ground on any soil type, but especially on chalk. The map of *Andrena proxima* shows that this rare bee is mainly found on the Chalk. However, it forages from any white umbellifer, and these flowers are widespread both on and off the Chalk, although scarce on sand. The bee may therefore either be more widespread but overlooked, or it prefers the hot well-drained chalk escarpment for nesting. Nationally *Lasioglossum fulvicorne* is frequent on calcareous soils but also occurs much less frequently on sandy soils. In Surrey it is found almost entirely on the Chalk, with just a very few scattered records from the sand. Its cleptoparasite *Sphecodes hyalinatus* is only found on the Chalk in Surrey. Likewise the large *Lasioglossum xanthopus* is found nationally mainly on calcareous soils but also on coastal cliffs and landslips, and in Surrey all modern records of this scarce bee are from the Chalk. Its very rare cleptoparasite *Sphecodes spinulosus* has been found only once in Surrey and this was naturally on the Chalk also. The rare *Andrena minutuloides* obviously prefers the Chalk, where it is common, but it is occasionally found on the sand. It is not known why it favours calcareous soils because it is thought to forage from a wide variety of flowers, but chalk, like sand, drains easily and heats up quickly.

The following list of chalk indicator species only relates to Surrey. The maps for these species clearly show their strong preference for chalk.

Proposed chalk downland indicator species

Andrena hattorfiana	Ch1	*Sphecodes hyalinatus*	Ch1
Andrena marginata	Ch2	*Sphecodes spinulosus*	Ch1
Andrena minutuloides	Ch2	*Melitta tricincta*	Ch3
Andrena proxima	Ch3	*Osmia aurulenta*	Ch1
Lasioglossum fulvicorne	Ch2	*Osmia bicolor*	Ch1
Lasioglossum xanthopus	Ch1	*Osmia spinulosa*	Ch2

CLAY WOODLAND

Because clay can become waterlogged in winter and rock-hard in summer many ground-nesting bees shun this soil; the maps clearly show the ground-nesting species which avoid the clay and those which seem to tolerate it. However, where there are banks or slopes the clay is much better drained and becomes friable, and there are a few bees which are mainly found here. Much of the Weald Clay in the south of the county is wooded and some of the Forestry Commission woods are particularly good for aculeates because they have open rides with plenty of flowers; the large plantations are clear-felled in rotation, creating open, flower-rich areas for a few years. The clay here is also drier, perhaps because the trees soak up so much water, and there are plenty of banks along the rides, and large bare areas where clear-felling has occurred. There are therefore many suitable nesting sites for ground nesters. The best sites are in the south-west of the county: Sidney Wood near Dunsfold, Chiddingfold Forest (including Botany Bay, Oaken Wood and Fisherlane Wood), Holmens Grove and Stroud Wood, both just north of Haslemere, and Hambledon Claypit. In the south-east there are a few good clay woods near Charlwood, such as Glovers Wood and Edolphs Copse. The London Clay, lying to the north of the Chalk ridge, is lighter than the Weald Clay and much of it is overlain with sand deposits, but many species that occur on the Weald Clay will also be found on the London Clay.

The only bee which is nowadays restricted to the clay woodland is *Osmia pilicornis*, but this is an aerial nester in dead wood and it used to occur in other habitats, such as chalk woodland; presumably it favours clay woods because it is an early bee and the rides in spring are full of flowers, especially bugle, its favourite forage plant. The spectacular but decreasing *Eucera longicornis* used to be more widespread but in the last six years it has been found only along woodland rides in Chiddingfold Forest and in Hambledon Claypit. The large spring mining bee *Andrena labialis* is almost confined to the clay, but not always in woodland, whilst its cleptoparasite *Sphecodes rubicundus* is entirely confined to the Weald Clay. The rare *Sphecodes scabricollis* is found only on the Weald Clay and on a few of the western heaths, although its host bee *Lasioglossum zonulum* is much more widespread. *Lasioglossum puncticolle* is common in the south-western clay woodlands but occurs only very rarely elsewhere. *L. pauxillum* and *L. malachurum* are both found very commonly on the Weald Clay but the former is also just as common on the Chalk, whereas the latter is now widespread and common in all habitats. *Bombus hortorum* is more frequent on the Weald Clay than elsewhere, possibly due to the abundance of foxgloves in the woods there; its parasite *B. barbutellus* has been found only once, in the clay woodlands at Whitebeech. Of the scarcer species of aerial nesters, which are unaffected by the type of soil, *Heriades truncorum* (with its cleptoparasite *Stelis breviuscula*), *Hoplitis claviventris* and *Ceratina cyanea* are particularly common in the woodlands of the south-west, *Ceratina* being almost abundant. Because the rides, clearings and newly-felled areas are so floristically rich, most of the commoner bees, such as *Andrena, Lasioglossum* and their respective cleptoparasites *Nomada* and *Sphecodes*, are found in large numbers.

Proposed clay woodland indicator species

Andrena labialis	Cl2	*Sphecodes rubicundus*	Cl1
Lasioglossum malachurum	Cl3	*Sphecodes scabricollis*	Cl3
Lasioglossum pauxillum	Cl3	*Osmia pilicornis*	Cl3
Lasioglossum puncticolle	Cl2	*Eucera longicornis*	Cl1

GARDENS

Gardens, however small, are excellent places to observe bees because they are attracted by the continuous display of flowers throughout the year. In fact you are more likely to see a *Bombus terrestris* there in the depths of winter, foraging or sipping nectar from winter-flowering heather or jasmine, than anywhere else. There are many other species which are possibly more frequent in gardens than in the countryside and some of these, such as *Lasioglossum smeathmanellum, Osmia rufa* and *Anthophora quadrimaculata*, are commoner in urban, rather than country, gardens because they use crevices in walls for nest sites. *Anthophora plumipes*, accompanied by its cuckoo bee *Melecta albifrons*, is particularly common in gardens because its favourite flower lungwort is often grown there. One is more likely to see *Anthidium manicatum*, as well as its much scarcer cuckoo bee *Stelis punctulatissima*, in the garden than elsewhere because it comes to strip the hairs off leaves of lamb's-ear. Other interesting species frequently found in gardens are the rare little *Hylaeus pictipes, Osmia caerulescens* and *Andrena labiata*.

Most of these bees will probably only be visitors to the garden, coming for the flowers but nesting elsewhere. They can be encouraged to nest by putting up tube nests, introducing dead wood and making an area of bare ground, however small. And of course certain species can be attracted to the garden by planting their favourite flower. Urban as well as suburban gardens are important habitats for conserving bees in built-up areas because they provide plentiful forage and nectar sources at all seasons.

BROWNFIELD SITES

Surrey has hardly any post-industrial sites but it has plenty of disused mineral extraction sites. In the south there are old brickworks with their associated claypits on the Weald Clay, in the north, along the Thames Valley, there are the gravelpits and in the middle, along the greensand ridge, are the sandpits. All these sites are attractive to bees because they have many south-facing bare slopes for nest sites and a good selection of flowers, mostly ruderals. Bare ground, especially on slopes, is a rare habitat on the Weald clay; most of it is either grass-covered or cultivated, except for the woodlands.

The best of the claypits are Hambledon Claypit, Somersbury Brickworks at Ewhurst, and Cranleigh Brickworks, but all are likely to be developed for housing or industry in the near future. Hambledon is particularly good for rare bees, including a strong population of *Eucera longicornis* as well as of Wood White butterflies, and it should be conserved at all costs. Further east, North Holmwood Claypit is now a Local Nature Reserve but Capel Claypit still has some bare ground. The Thames Valley gravelpits are usually filled as soon as they are worked out and no survey work has been carried out on them. Unfortunately the old sandpits are also now being land-filled much more quickly than previously and most of them have completely disappeared. The best is Papercourt Gravelpit near Send Marsh; here there was a large complex of pits but all were land-filled except for a large one which is now a sailing lake and a small one which is now managed as a Nature Reserve by Surrey Wildlife Trust. This site had the only Surrey population of the very rare *Andrena nigrospina* for about four years but it may have died out due to lack of its main forage flower, hoary mustard; this plant flourishes on disturbed ground and now the pit has closed and there is no disturbance the plant is dying out.

IMPORTANT SITES FOR BEES

Surrey has some of the best sites in the country for bees as well as wasps. There are not many localities in Britain that can boast of having modern lists of more than 200 species of bees, wasps and ants but Surrey has nine such localities. Some sites are historically important, such as Horsell and Chobham Commons, and have been visited by almost all the famous hymenopterists. Four are National Nature Reserves, one is a World Heritage Site, some are Sites of Special Scientific Interest and many are designated for conservation at county, borough or local level. Others have no designated status but are important or interesting because of their bee fauna. It has been possible only to pick the best sites in each habitat but there are many other sites which have interesting bees. With the data collected for the survey it is easy to produce lists for the better sites from the database.

In the following list the sites are shown under the different categories of habitat, making comparisons easier. The first column gives the site and its status, if NNR, WHS or SSSI, the second gives the main habitat, the third gives the approximate area in hectares, the fourth gives the total number of aculeates (i.e. bees, wasps and ants) recorded since 1984, the fifth gives the number of wasps, both social and solitary, recorded since 1984, and the sixth gives the number of bees, again social and solitary, recorded since 1984. The list is followed by a very brief description of almost every site, with the total number of species, including bees, wasps and ants, together with number of RDB and Nationally Scarce species, and a note of some of the more interesting bees which are found there. The Red Data Book is now long out of date and is unlikely to be revised before this book is published; thus *Nomada fulvicornis* and *Sphecodes niger* have RDB status although they are now common and widespread in southern Britain, whilst *Lasioglossum prasinum* has no status although it is restricted to very few lowland heaths.

It can be seen very clearly from the list, not only that heathlands support the highest number of aculeates and clay the least, but also that heathlands, at the best-worked sites, are better for wasps than bees, whereas dry acid grassland, clay and chalk are far better for bees than wasps. The lists also show that the best sites on heathland, which have been well worked, preferably with Malaise traps, and are reasonably sized, support well over 200 species. Those on dry acid grassland support about 175 species, those on chalk grassland about 150 species and those on clay about 130 species. Surrey does not have many brownfield sites but the small selection of sites shows how rich they can be in aculeate fauna. Two inner London parks show that even in densely populated areas a diverse and interesting bee fauna can exist, while the very differently sized and situated gardens show how prolific these can be; my own garden probably has the highest number of aculeates of any site in Britain.

IMPORTANT AND INTERESTING SURREY SITES
FOR ACULEATES

Heathland

Site	Habitat	Hectares	Total species	Wasps	Bees
Thursley Common NNR	Heath	400	227	124	85
Chobham Common NNR	Heath	567	225	108	95
Mare Hill Common SSSI	Heath	40	225	122	89
Brentmoor Heath SSSI	Heath	60	217	110	92
Ash Ranges SSSI	Heath	1500	213	94	98
Bagmoor Common SSSI	Damp Heath	14	208	102	91
Hankley Common SSSI	Heath	500	202	96	88
Witley Common SSSI	Heath/ Woodland	150	200	95	91
Reigate Heath SSSI	Heath	150	187	82	92
Horsell Common SSSI	Heath	200	184	81	83
Esher/West End Commons SSSI	Heath	300	171	76	79
Priory Park, Reigate	Former Heath	100	169	90	74
Headley Heath SSSI	Heath/Chalk	100	167	65	92
Wisley/Ockham Commons SSSI	Heath	336	162	88	58
Frensham/Churt Commons SSSI	Heath	250	160	80	59
Brookwood Cemetery SSSI	Heath/ Grassland	200	152	49	90
Pirbright/Bisley Ranges SSSI	Heath	1000	144	51	71
Hambledon Common	Heath	30	142	60	70
Puttenham Common SSSI	Heath	190	125	53	64
Blackheath Common SSSI	Heath	100	119	57	48
Tilford Woods RSPB	Heath/ Woodland	200	104	42	53
Hindhead Common SSSI	Highland Heath	300	73	21	46

Dry Acid Grassland

Site	Habitat	Hectares	Total species	Wasps	Bees
Richmond Park NNR	Acid Grassland	700	**181**	**95**	**78**
Kew Gardens WHS	Acid Grassland	120	**180**	**83**	**84**
Mitcham Common	Acid Grassland	175	**178**	**80**	**89**
Brooklands, Byfleet	Acid Grassland	200	**142**	**57**	**79**
Barnes Common	Acid Grassland	50	**111**	**44**	**61**
Seale Lodge old sandpit	Acid Grassland	1	**101**	**33**	**59**
Windsor Great Park SSSI	Acid Grassland	300	**99**	**39**	**48**
Wimbledon Common	Acid Grassland/ Heath	350	**93**	**29**	**59**
Ditton Common	Acid Grassland	50	**79**	**34**	**42**
Ham Common	Acid Grassland	1	**79**	**34**	**41**
Old Common, Cobham	Acid Grassland	2	**66**	**21**	**40**
Ranmore Common SSSI	Acid Grassland	10	**61**	**24**	**34**

Chalk

Site	Habitat	Hectares	Total species	Wasps	Bees
Headley Warren SSSI	Chalk Downs	100	**165**	**75**	**77**
Sheepleas SSSI	Chalk Down/ Woodland	108	**162**	**67**	**84**
Westcott Downs SSSI	Chalk Downs	75	**123**	**37**	**78**
Pewley Down	Chalk Downs	10	**115**	**29**	**79**
Farthing Downs and Happy Valley SSSI	Chalk Downs	300	**107**	**26**	**74**
Banstead Downs SSSI	Chalk Grassland	200	**107**	**42**	**58**
Box Hill SSSI	Chalk Downs	200	**104**	**32**	**59**
Dawcombe SSSI	Chalk Downs	25	**92**	**22**	**63**
Colekitchen Down SSSI	Chalk Downs	3	**90**	**24**	**56**
Newlands Corner, Albury	Chalk Downs	100	**87**	**22**	**58**

Clay

Site	Habitat	Hectares	Total species	Wasps	Bees
Sidney Wood, Dunsfold SSSI	Clay Woodland	100	**140**	**50**	**82**
Holmens Grove/Stroud Wood	Clay Woodland	100	**138**	**46**	**85**
Chiddingfold Forest SSSI	Clay Woodland	250	**137**	**40**	**86**
Ashtead/Epsom Commons SSSI	Clay Woodland/ Grassland	200	**123**	**64**	**51**
Sayers Land, Dunsfold	Clay Woodland	3	**88**	**28**	**56**
Bookham Commons SSSI	Clay Woodland/ Grassland	200	**86**	**26**	**52**

Brownfield

Site	Habitat	Hectares	Total species	Wasps	Bees
Papercourt Gravelpits SSSI	Old gravelpits	10	**163**	**65**	**89**
Wrecclesham Sandpit	Old sandpit	20	**135**	**52**	**80**
Hambledon Claypit	Old claypit	20	**134**	**44**	**83**
Cranleigh Brickworks	Old claypit	25	**115**	**47**	**59**
Somersbury Claypit, Ewhurst	Old claypit	3	**92**	**30**	**59**

London Parks

Site	Habitat	Hectares	Total species	Wasps	Bees
Wandsworth Common	London Park Clay	20	**88**	**27**	**56**
Battersea Park	London Park Clay	20	**68**	**34**	**28**

Gardens

Site	Habitat	Hectares	Total species	Wasps	Bees
Milford	Country garden	1	**258**	**123**	**121**
RHS Wisley Gardens	Botanic garden	100	**127**	**58**	**63**
Reigate	Town/country garden	0.1	**119**	**51**	**63**
South Croydon	Suburban garden	0.05	**108**	**45**	**58**
Wandsworth	London garden	0.02	**32**	**7**	**24**

HEATHLAND

Thursley Common. SU9040. A National Nature Reserve consisting of about 400 hectares of dry and wet lowland heath, prone to devastating heath fires which help to keep the site open. Well visited and recorded, although not by the Victorian collectors except O.H. Latter. Malaise traps used for three seasons. **Total species 227, with 16 RDB and 33 Nationally Scarce. Bees 85**, with the whole of the heathland suite of species, as well as the very rare *Hylaeus gibbus* and *Halictus confusus* and the non-heathland *Andrena florea* and *Ceratina cyanea*.

Chobham Common. SU9664. A very large National Nature Reserve of undulating dry and wet heathland, unfortunately now bisected by the M3. Made famous for Hymenoptera by Saunders and Guichard. It is still one of the best sites in Surrey and Britain. Malaise trap used for 1 season. **Total species 225, with 12 RDB and 35 Nationally Scarce. Bees 95**, with the whole of the heathland assemblage of species, including *Halictus confusus* as well as other rarities such as *Andrena florea, Heriades truncorum, Sphecodes scabricollis, Stelis ornatula*. But a hundred years ago Saunders was finding greater rarities such as *Andrena rosae, Lasioglossum sexnotatum, Dufourea minuta, Stelis phaeoptera, Nomada roberjeotiana, N. sexfasciata* and *Melecta luctuosa*.

Mare Hill Common, Witley. SU9340. A small site of dry and wet heath, surrounded by woodland, owned and well-managed by Waverley B.C. Good dead-wood microhabitats: a dead beech tree and a large log pile. Well-trodden sandy paths, with many yellow composites. Much bilberry. Very well visited. Malaise trap used for two seasons, and also flower lures. One of the best sites in Britain in spite of its relatively small area, with **Total species of 225, with 20 RDB and 39 Nationally Scarce. Bees 89**, with all the usual heathland species, including *Andrena lapponica*, the very rare *Halictus confusus* (males of which were common in the Malaise trap), *Lasioglossum brevicorne, Dasypoda hirtipes, Megachile maritima* with its cleptoparasite *Coelioxys conoidea*, as well as *Sphecodes longulus, S. niger, S. reticulatus, Heriades truncorum* with *Stelis breviuscula, Nomada sheppardana, Ceratina cyanea* and *Bombus hypnorum*.

Brentmoor Heath, West End. SU9361. Medium-sized area of dry and wet heathland, managed by Surrey Wildlife Trust. Malaise trap used in 2007, adding 45 species to the list. **Total species 217, with 13 RDB and 34 Nationally Scarce. Bees 92**, with all the usual heathland species, as well as the very rare *Hylaeus gibbus* and *Halictus confusus, Sphecodes longulus, Macropis europaea* and *Anthidium manicatum* with *Stelis punctulatissima*.

Ash Ranges. SU9153. One of the finest large areas of unspoilt heathland in the country. Owned and managed by MOD, access is very restricted so the site is under-recorded. Many ridges and much bare ground, especially around the butts. Variety of flowers round the edges. **Total species 213, with 17 RDB and 38 Nationally Scarce.** Bees **98**, the highest site number, with many unusual species, such as *Andrena congruens, A. florea, A. tibialis, Halictus confusus, Lasioglossum quadrinotatum, Sphecodes niger, Macropis europaea, Heriades truncorum, Stelis breviuscula, Eucera longicornis* and *Nomada flavopicta.*

Bagmoor Common, Elstead. SU9242. Small area of damp heathland, almost adjoining Thursley Common. Owned and managed by SWT, which cleared invading pine and birch in 1988. Many root plates after 1987 gale provide dry nest sites. **Total species 208, with 13 RDB and 21 Nationally Scarce. Bees 91**, with a few heathland species such as *Lasioglossum quadrinotatum* and *Sphecodes longulus* but, because of the damp ground, many aerial nesters such as *Hylaeus gibbus, Stelis breviuscula* with its host *Heriades truncorum, Ceratina cyanea*; *Macropis europaea* nests and the very local *Andrena tarsata* occurs.

Hankley Common, Elstead. SU8840. A vast swathe of dry heathland, owned and managed by the MOD, which has cleared large areas of invading pine, and with a golf course on the western side. Many ridges and bare ground but few flowers. Malaise trap for one season. **Total species 202, with 14 RDB and 33 Nationally Scarce. Bees 88**, with the usual heathland species but also *Halictus confusus, Heriades truncorum, Hylaeus gibbus, Lasioglossum puncticolle, Sphecodes longulus* and *S. scabricollis.*

Witley Common. SU9240. The very dry and heathy western part is owned and well-managed by the Herpetological Conservation Trust, which has created many sandy tracks for sand lizards and much bare ground for nesting bees. Malaise trap used for half a season. The larger eastern part, owned and managed by the National Trust, is mainly damper and more wooded. **Total species 200, with 14 RDB and 25 Nationally Scarce. Bees 91,** with most of the heathland species and a few others such as *Andrena florea, Dasypoda hirtipes, Heriades truncorum, Sphecodes longulus, S. niger* and *Ceratina cyanea.*

Reigate Heath. TQ2350. A small, undulating, dry heathy site, most of which consists of a golf course, with much well-trodden bare ground due to the golfers. A very long distance from the main heathland area of the south-west. A large area of dead willows has produced a good selection of dead-wood-nesting species. **Total species 187, with 19 RDB and 24 Nationally Scarce. Bees 92**, with most of the heathland species, in spite of its relative isolation, such as *Andrena bimaculata, A. trimmerana, A. tibialis* and *Sphecodes longulus*. Species of sandy, but not heathy, soil include *Andrena florea, A. minutuloides* and *Andrena cineraria* with its cuckoo *Nomada lathburiana*. The dead-wood species include *Heriades truncorum, Stelis breviuscula, S. punctulatissima*. But its two great rarities are *Andrena ferox*, with a tantalising singleton in May 1998 at its only Surrey locality, and *Nomada signata*, which was found in good numbers all over the site in 2006 and 2007.

Horsell Common, Woking. TQ0060. One of the most famous entomological sites, with its sandpit, which was worked intensively by Saunders and his circle of hymenopterists, and later by Guichard in the 1960s, and where the Martians landed in H.G. Wells' *The War of the Worlds*. The pit has become degraded by invasive pines, and the surrounding heathland now has little open bare ground. Malaise trap used one year. **Total species 184, with 7 RDB and 27 Nationally Scarce. Bees 83**, with the usual heathland species including *Andrena bimaculata, Dasypoda hirtipes, Lasioglossum quadrinotatum, Sphecodes longulus* as well as *Andrena tibialis* and *Sphecodes scabricollis*. None of the Victorians' great rarities have been refound, e.g. *Dufourea halictula, D. minuta, Stelis phaeoptera, Nomada armata, N. roberjeotiana, N. sexfasciata*.

Esher, Fairmile, West End and Arbrook Commons and Oxshott Heath. TQ1262-1461. Large area of adjoining dry and damp heathy commons. Much of it was planted with conifers in the 1950s, which destroyed much of the best habitat but many pines are now being felled by Elmbridge B.C. which manages it. Oxshott Heath, which has an old sandpit and a steep south-facing slope, was intensively surveyed by O.W. Richards in 1930s and by Guichard and Baker from 1940s to 1970s, when it was open heathland, and they recorded another 50 or so species which have not been refound in the survey. It was also well known to Edwardian collectors, due to the railway station on the edge of the heath. **Total species 171, with 9 RDB and 19 Nationally Scarce. Bees 79**, with the usual assemblage of heathland species but also *Hylaeus pectoralis* in the reeds at Black Pond, *Andrena falsifica, A. florea, Lasioglossum fratellum, Macropis europaea* by the River Wey, *Stelis breviuscula* with its host *Heriades truncorum*.

Priory Park, Reigate. TQ2549. A greensand ridge with steep south-facing slope but mainly covered in trees which need opening up. To the east an old disused sandpit, mainly overgrown but with a very small south-west-facing open sandy cliff. Heather grew until 50 years ago. Owned and managed by Reigate B.C. **Total species 169, with 11 RDB and 15 Nationally Scarce. Bees 74**, with the usual sand-loving species but also some rarities. The first and only Surrey record of *Colletes hederae* came from the old sandpit in October 2007, where *Bombus hypnorum* has also been recorded. *Stelis breviuscula* occurs with *Heriades truncorum,* and *Andrena florea* and *Ceratina cyanea* are also found.

Headley Heath. TQ2053. An isolated patch of sand drift over chalk, so the western part is chalk grassland and the eastern is heathland. **Total species 167, with 7 RDB and 22 Nationally Scarce. Bees 92**, with a curious mixture of chalk species, such as *Andrena marginata, A. minutuloides, Osmia bicolor, Nomada hirtipes,* and heathland species such as *Andrena bimaculata, A. humilis, Sphecodes miniatus, Nomada integra.* Others include the very localised *Andrena apicata,* the rare *Nomada signata* and *Ceratina cyanea.*

Wisley and Ockham Commons. TQ0859. Large area of heathland on either side of the A3, damp heath on the west and dry on the east. Ockham was almost entirely covered in mature pinewoods but these have now been felled and the heath is recovering. Under-recorded. **Total species 162, with 8 RDB and 27 Nationally Scarce. Bees 58**, with most of the usual heathland species including *Lasioglossum pauperatum, L. quadrinotatum, Sphecodes longulus* and *Nomada baccata* with its host *Andrena argentata* but also *Andrena florea* and *Macropis europaea.*

Frensham and Churt Commons. SU8540. A very large area of undulating dry and wet heathland, with an interesting small patch of almost dune-like, bare sand around the Great Pond, and a small sand cliff which attracts many nesters; few flowers. **Total species 160, with 6 RDB and 22 Nationally Scarce. Bees 59**, with most of the commoner heathland species but few rarities except *Hylaeus gibbus* and *Andrena florea,* possibly due to lack of recording.

Brookwood Cemetery. SU9556. One of the largest cemeteries in the world, created in the 1880s on heathland, and containing the graves of Saunders and Morice. Remnant dry and damp heath, with many flowers including acres of devil's-bit scabious. **Total species 152, with 11 RDB and 18 Nationally Scarce. Bees 90**, many more than wasps, with many heathland species and also *Andrena florea, A. tarsata, A. labiata, Heriades truncorum, Ceratina cyanea* and most importantly a strong population of *Andrena marginata* with its very rare cuckoo bee *Nomada argentata* on the devil's-bit scabious.

Pirbright and Bisley Ranges. SU9358. A vast area of about 1,000 hectares of dry and wet lowland heath, owned by MOD and in almost constant use as firing ranges, so very difficult of access and under-recorded. The northern, wetter half has been closed to the public for 100 years, but recently a few visits have been allowed. Much bare ground and plenty of flowers, when not mown by the National Rifle Association. **Total species 144, with 13 RDB and 23 Nationally Scarce. Bees 71.** It has the usual suite of heathland species including *Halictus confusus, Lasioglossum brevicorne, Dasypoda hirtipes, Megachile maritima, Coelioxys conoidea* as well as a large population of *Eucera longicornis, Ceratina cyanea, Sphecodes niger* and *S. scabricollis.* The most interesting bee is the very rare *Nomada argentata*, which is here found in September on devil's-bit scabious, with its host *Andrena marginata.*

Hambledon Common. SU9638. Two miles south-east of Witley. An isolated site of about 15 hectares of mainly steep south-facing dry heathland, merging into Weald Clay at the bottom. Twenty years ago the whole site had become overgrown with dense birch and pine, with no heather or bare sand, and it was almost devoid of aculeates. However the owner, almost single-handedly, has slowly cleared the trees, the heather and bilberry have regenerated and the heathland aculeates have returned, presumably spreading from the nearest heathland at Witley and Mare Hill Commons, three or four miles away. Not many flowers except heather and bilberry, so better for wasps than bees. **Total species 142, with 8 RDB and 20 Nationally Scarce. Bees 70.** It has the usual assemblage of heathland bees including *Andrena argentata, A. lapponica, Lasioglossum brevicorne, L. prasinum, Coelioxys conoidea, Nomada baccata* as well as *Sphecodes niger* and *Ceratina cyanea.*

Puttenham Common. SU9146. Rather isolated from the other south-western heaths, it has much coarser sand, with only little heather and more trees. **Total species 125, with 8 RDB and 21 Nationally Scarce. Bees 64**, with many heathland and sandy species including a strong population of *Andrena humilis* with its cuckoo bee *Nomada integra, Halictus confusus, Lasioglossum brevicorne, Sphecodes longulus, Dasypoda hirtipes, Ceratina cyanea.*

Blackheath Common. TQ0346. South-east of Guildford. A large, isolated area of very hot dry heathland, which is separated from the western block of heaths by about eight miles. Through lack of management the whole Common had become entirely overgrown with pine by the 1980s, with hardly any heather or aculeates surviving. It is now managed by Waverley B.C. and large areas of dense pine have recently been clear-felled, leaving plenty of bare ground with heather regenerating. There are far more species present now than there were 10 years ago when pine clearance started and each year more species are found. It seems that they are recolonising the site from the nearest heaths, eight or ten miles to the south-west. If so, it shows that bees and wasps do move long distances to find new breeding sites, and that if suitable habitat is provided they will eventually find it. The total of only **119 species (with 4 RDB and 13 Nationally Scarce)** of aculeates so far recorded is well below those of similar heaths in the south-west, such as Thursley and Hankley, so many species have not yet managed to recolonise it but hopefully will do so in time, especially if more pines are cleared. Due to lack of flowers, other than gorse and heather, only **48 Bees** have so far been found, with most from the usual heathland assemblage including *Andrena argentata*, with its cleptoparasite *Nomada baccata*, *Dasypoda hirtipes*, *Lasioglossum brevicorne* and *L. prasinum*.

Tilford Woods. SU8543. A large hilly area of former heathland, known as Farnham Heath, which was planted with pines in the 1950s. These mature pine plantations were purchased by RSPB in 2002 and are now being clear-felled, the heather is recovering and the heathland birds are returning and with them the aculeates. **Total species 104, with 7 RDB and 11 Nationally Scarce. Bees 53**, with many of the heathland species already, but more will colonise as the open heath spreads. Rarer and local species include *Hylaeus gibbus*, *Andrena congruens*, *A. lapponica*, *Lasioglossum brevicorne*, *Dasypoda hirtipes*, *Nomada baccata* and *Ceratina cyanea*.

Hindhead Common. SU9036. A huge area of high ground around the Devil's Punchbowl, rising to almost 1,000 ft at Gibbett Hill, and owned by the National Trust. Because of its height it provides an interesting comparison with the much lower and hotter heathland, only a mile to the north, at Thursley Common. With a total of only **73 species (with 3 RDB and 5 Nationally Scarce)** of bees and wasps it has about a third of those at Thursley, due mainly to the colder and wetter climate at Hindhead but also to the coarser and harder sand. I prefer to call the habitat, consisting mainly of heather and bilberry, Highland Heathland, which also occurs at a similar height around Leith Hill. Only **46 bees** have been recorded, including 12 bumblebees, which are better suited to colder climates due to their large size and hairy bodies. There are two species, *Lasioglossum fratellum* and *Bombus bohemicus*, which are often found at high altitudes in Surrey and which are much commoner in the north than in the south of Britain. *Andrena lapponica*, another northern bee, is common on the bilberry and, rather surprisingly, *Lasioglossum prasinum* has been seen nesting at about 800 ft, this bee being considered a species of hot lowland heaths.

DRY ACID GRASSLAND

Richmond Park. TQ2073. Designated as a National Nature Reserve in 2002 for its internationally famous dead-wood beetle fauna. About 700 hectares of undulating grassland, much of it covered in thick bracken, with many woodland enclosures and ancient trees, some dead and some half-dead. Apart from the enclosures it is overgrazed by deer and floristically very poor. There are very many hard-packed paths and other bare ground. The best sites are in the enclosures and in particular the area behind Holly Lodge, consisting of rough ground and horse paddocks with old fence posts; this area has a variety of flowers including speedwell, ragwort and hogweed. Surveyed in depth with many visits and Malaise traps operated at Oak Lodge, Pen Ponds and Holly Lodge. **Total species 181, with 13 RDB and 23 Nationally Scarce. Bees 78** including *Andrena bimaculata, A. florea, A. labiata, A. varians, Lasioglossum pauxillum, Sphecodes crassus, Stelis breviuscula, Heriades truncorum, Nomada flavopicta, N. fulvicornis, N. guttulata, N. lathburiana.*

Kew Gardens. TQ1877. 120 hectares. A World Heritage Site since 2003, being the grounds of the Royal Botanic Gardens. Much open woodland and dead wood. Little bare ground. Floristically very rich. Malaise trap operated for two seasons in the Conservation Area. **Total species 180, with 10 RDB and 28 Nationally Scarce. Bees 84** including *Hylaeus cornutus, Andrena bucephala, A. florea, A. labiata, Lasioglossum pauxillum, Sphecodes crassus, S. reticulatus, Macropis europaea, Melitta haemorrhoidalis, Heriades truncorum, Stelis breviuscula, S. punctulatissima, Anthophora quadrimaculata, Nomada flavopicta, N. hirtipes, N. lathburiana, Bombus hypnorum.*

Mitcham Common. TQ2967. 175 hectares. Much of it golf course. Scattered heather. Much bare ground. Little dead wood. Surveyed intensively by Roger Morris in 1990/91 but hardly revisited since. Pan traps used. **Total species 178**, with **5 RDB and 20 Nationally Scarce. Bees 89** including *Hylaeus cornutus, Andrena bimaculata, A. florea, A. fulvago, A. minutuloides, A. tibialis, A. trimmerana, Nomada fulvicornis.*

Brooklands, Byfleet and Weybridge. TQ0662. 200 hectares of floodplain next to the River Wey, with alluvial sand and rich in spring ephemeral plants. Prior to 2005 this was an extremely rich area for aculeates but it has been entirely destroyed by the recent development of a car test circuit by Mercedes Benz. The company, in spite of its self-proclaimed green policies, has levelled the ground, destroyed the rabbits which kept the ground disturbed, and finally sown the whole site with grass which is mown regularly. There is now hardly a bee or rare plant to be seen. **Total species (before 2005) 142, with 9 RDB and 19 Nationally Scarce. Bees 79** including *Hylaeus pictipes*, *H. signatus, Andrena argentata* with its parasite *Nomada baccata* away from heathland, *A. florea, A. bimaculata, Lasioglossum brevicorne, Sphecodes longulus, Dasypoda hirtipes, Heriades truncorum* with *Stelis breviuscula, Ceratina cyanea.*

Barnes Common. TQ2276. About 50 hectares of open grassland and scrub surrounded by woodland, but dissected by many roads and a railway. It had

SSSI status until about 1993 when this was removed because the site had degenerated, having lost much of its open grassland habitat due to encroachment by trees and scrub; it is now a Local Nature Reserve. Since then 'The Friends of Barnes Common' have carried out much conservation management, clearing scrub, Turkey oak and other invasive trees. There are many well-trodden footpaths providing valuable nesting sites, and an area of old small-scale gravel workings, known locally as "the ups and downs", which has very sparse, drought-prone grass cover and much bare ground. This area becomes very hot in the summer and attracts large quantities of nesting aculeates. There is plenty of standing dead timber, mainly birch trees killed by fire and drought, providing nest sites for many dead-wood species. It is floristically rich, with a very prolific yellow composite flora as well as other flowers such as ragwort, yarrow, rosebay willowherb and labiates around the edges. **Total species 111, with 7 RDB and 13 Nationally Scarce. Bees 61** including *Andrena bimaculata, A. humilis, A. tibialis, Sphecodes longulus, S. reticulatus, Stelis breviuscula* with its host *Heriades truncorum, Nomada flavopicta, N. fulvicornis, N. lathburiana*.

Wimbledon Common. TQ2372. About 350 hectares. Large areas of heather. Golf course on acid grassland. Much bare ground and open sandy paths. Little dead wood. **Total species 93, with 5 RDB and 9 Nationally Scarce. Bees 59** including *Andrena bimaculata, A. humilis, A. labiata, A. tibialis, Nomada fulvicornis, Sphecodes niger, S. reticulatus.* Historic records include *Andrena argentata, A. similis, Nomada signata, Anthophora retusa.*

Ditton Common. TQ1466. Two miles south of Bushy Park. About 20 hectares of mainly unimproved golf course, with many well-trodden footpaths and bare ground providing good nest sites. There are many trees, mainly oak, but no dead wood. There is a small relict patch of heather and a good variety of flowers around the edges and abundant yellow composites on the golf course. **Total species 79, with 7 RDB and 5 Nationally Scarce. Bees 42** including *Andrena labiata, A. tibialis, Lasioglossum brevicorne, Nomada fulvicornis* and *N. lathburiana*.

Ham Common.TQ1871. Half a mile west of Richmond Park. One hectare of unimproved grassland, rich in yellow composites, surrounded by dense oak woodland. The area is only kept open by people exercising horses which creates much bare ground; no dead wood. It has the largest aggregation of *Andrena cineraria* in Surrey, possibly 50,000 pairs in an area of only about 30 square metres, with about 10,000 pairs of its cleptoparasite *Nomada lathburiana*. **Total species 79, with 6 RDB and 9 Nationally Scarce. Bees 41**, including *Andrena florea* and *Nomada fulvicornis*.

Old Common, Cobham. TQ1161. 2 hectares. A tiny relict site of old small-scale gravel workings with drought-stressed acid grassland. Neglected and mostly overgrown with trees and scrub but now partially cleared. Still under-recorded but it has a very high proportion of rarities. **Total species only 66, but these include 10 RDB and 9 Nationally Scarce species. Bees 40** including *Andrena bimaculata, A. florea, Sphecodes niger, Heriades truncorum, Nomada lathburiana, N. fulvicornis* and, most importantly, the very small and rare *Lasioglossum semilucens* at one of its two modern sites in Surrey.

CHALK GRASSLAND

Headley Warren. TQ1954. Privately owned, south-facing scrubby downland. Well recorded, with Malaise trap run for two seasons. The best chalk site. **Total species 165, with 6 RDB and 19 Nationally Scarce. Bees 77**, with the usual chalk species including *Hylaeus cornutus, Andrena bucephala, A. florea, A. marginata, A. minutuloides, Melitta haemorrhoidalis, M. tricincta* and *Osmia bicolor.*

Sheepleas, West Horsley. TQ0851. A large, well-recorded SSSI on the north-facing dip slope of the North Downs, managed by Surrey Wildlife Trust. The open grassland is flower-rich but much of the site is wooded, although many trees were blown down or damaged in the 1987 gale, leaving many south-facing root-plates and dead beeches, which have created an excellent dead-wood microhabitat. Unfortunately most of these dead and half-dead beeches have now been cut down on safety grounds. **Total species 162, with 12 RDB and 20 Nationally Scarce. Bees 84** including most of the chalk grassland specialities such as *Hylaeus signatus, Andrena minutuloides, Osmia bicolor, Melitta haemorrhoidalis* and *M. tricincta* with *Nomada flavopicta,* the dead-wood species *Stelis breviuscula* and its host *Heriades truncorum.* Other rarer species include the very local *Andrena apicata, A. florea, A. proxima, Stelis ornatula* and *Ceratina cyanea.*

Westcott Downs (Denbies Hillside), Dorking. TQ1450. The finest large area of hot south-facing scarp slope on the North Downs. **Total species 123, with 11 RDB and 15 Nationally Scarce. Bees 78**, with all the chalk grassland species including *Andrena minutuloides, Melitta haemorrhoidalis* and *M. tricincta* and *Osmia bicolor* with *O. aurulenta,* and a remarkable series of rarities, including the only records for the very rare *Sphecodes spinulosus* and *Nomada conjungens,* both with their respective hosts *Lasioglossum xanthopus* and *Andrena proxima,* the very rare little *L. semilucens,* recorded from only one other site, the rare and impressive *A. hattorfiana, Nomada hirtipes* with its host *A. bucephala, A. florea, Sphecodes niger* and *Ceratina cyanea.*

Pewley Down, Guildford. TQ0049. A small steep south-facing slope, with allotments on the top, on the edge of Guildford, owned and managed by Guildford B.C. Forty years ago it had a fine downland turf but through lack of management much of it became invaded by scrub and tor grass; in the last five years Pewley Down Volunteers have done a remarkable job of restoring it to its former state. Very flower-rich, with short and long grass areas. **Total species 115, with 8 RDB and 12 Nationally Scarce. Bees 79**, with most of the chalk grassland species including *Melitta haemorrhoidalis* and *M. tricincta,* with the cleptoparasite *Nomada flavopicta,* and *Andrena minutuloides,* with others such as *A. proxima, A. florea, Stelis breviuscula* with its host *Heriades truncorum, Osmia bicolor, Anthophora quadrimaculata* and *Bombus ruderarius.*

Farthing Downs and Happy Valley, Coulsdon. TQ3057. A large area of partly south-west-facing downland, Farthing Downs, owned and managed by the City of London, and Happy Valley, owned by Croydon B.C. **Total species 107, with 4 RDB and 16 Nationally Scarce. Bees 74** including the very rare *Andrena alfkenella, A. hattorfiana, A. marginata, Lasioglossum xanthopus,* all three Surrey species of *Melitta, Nomada flavopicta* and *Osmia bicolor.*

Banstead Downs. TQ2561. Flat, mainly scrub-covered chalk grassland owned by the local council. Malaise trap operated for one season. **Total species 107, with 3 RDB and 12 Nationally Scarce. Bees 58** including *Hylaeus cornutus, Andrena marginata,* all three Surrey species of *Melitta, Osmia bicolor* and *Stelis punctulatissima.*

Box Hill, Dorking. TQ1852. A very famous entomological site, with very steep south-facing scarp slope, owned and managed by the National Trust. **Total species 104, with 6 RDB and 14 Nationally Scarce. Bees only 59**, this low number probably being due to under-recording and lack of flowers on the south slope which suffers from tor grass invasion. Interesting species include *Andrena bucephala* with its cleptoparasite *Nomada hirtipes, A. minutuloides, A. proxima, Melitta haemorrhoidalis, M. tricincta, Osmia bicolor* and the very rare *Nomada signata.*

Colekitchen Down, Abinger. TQ 0848. A tiny, steep, south-facing site with typical downland flora, managed by Surrey Wildlife Trust. Under-recorded. **Total species 90, with 5 RDB and 11 Nationally Scarce. Bees 56** including *Hylaeus cornutus, Sphecodes niger, Osmia bicolor, Heriades truncorum* and *Stelis ornatula.* There is an ancient record for *Lasioglossum xanthopus,* which might well still be there.

Newlands Corner (Abinger Down), Albury. TQ0449. A well-known beauty spot on south-facing scarp slope, managed by Surrey Wildlife Trust. **Total species 87, with 4 RDB and 19 Nationally Scarce. Bees 58** including *Hylaeus cornutus, Andrena marginata, A. minutuloides, Lasioglossum quadrinotatum, Melitta tricincta, Osmia bicolor, O. aurulenta* and *Nomada flavopicta.*

CLAY WOODLAND

Sidney Wood, Dunsfold. TQ0234. A large area of Forestry Commission woodland on Weald Clay, with many flower-rich rides and dry banks with friable clay. **Total species 140, with 9 RDB and 17 Nationally Scarce. Bees 82**, with the usual clay species, such as *Andrena labialis,* with *Sphecodes rubicundus,* and *Lasioglossum puncticolle,* as well as the rare *Hylaeus gibbus* and *Osmia pilicornis, Andrena bucephala* with *Nomada hirtipes* nesting on the bank of the old canal, *Heriades truncorum* with *Stelis breviuscula, Sphecodes scabricollis* and *Ceratina cyanea.*

Stroud Wood and Holmens Grove, Grayswood. SU9235 and 9236. Two adjoining Forestry Commission Weald Clay woodlands, with many flower-rich rides, and areas which are clear-felled in rotation, producing a temporary profusion of wood spurge, foxgloves, broom, etc. **Total species 138, with 8 RDB and 14 Nationally Scarce. Bees 85**, with most of the usual clay woodland species, including the rare and declining *Osmia pilicornis, Lasioglossum puncticolle,* and *Sphecodes scabricollis* as well as *Andrena cineraria, A. labiata, Heriades truncorum, Sphecodes niger* and *Ceratina cyanea.*

Chiddingfold Forest. SU93. A large area of Forestry Commission oak woodland with conifer plantations on Weald clay, comprising Botany Bay, Tugley Wood, Fisherlane Wood and Oaken Wood, all famous for their woodland butterflies. Many flowery rides and clear-felled sites. Malaise trap used in Oaken Wood for one season. **Total species 137, with 7 RDB and 19 Nationally Scarce. Bees 86**, with most of the same rarities as Sidney Wood but also *Melitta tricincta* with *Nomada flavopicta, Sphecodes niger,* and *Eucera longicornis* all along the main ride.

Ashtead and Epsom Commons. TQ1759-1860. A mosaic of oak woodland and neutral grassland on London Clay, Ashtead Common NNR being owned and managed by the City of London, Epsom Common by Epsom and Eweli B.C. Malaise traps operated for three seasons. An under-recorded site. **Total species 123, with 6 RDB and 14 Nationally Scarce. Bees 51**, with few rarities except *Andrena florea, Melitta tricincta* and *Nomada flavopicta.*

Sayers Land, Dunsfold. TQ0136. A very small, privately owned site of 3 hectares of Weald Clay woodland, which was mostly clear-felled in 1997 and then replanted. For two years, in 1999 and 2000, there was much bare ground and a profusion of flowers before it became overgrown with brambles, and later shaded out as the new trees grew. Only a few visits made but in those two years many typical clay woodland and rarer species moved in to take advantage of the newly created nesting sites and abundance of forage and nectar plants. **Total species 88, with 4 RDB and 8 Nationally Scarce. Bees 56** including *Andrena labialis* and *Sphecodes rubicundus, A. labiata, Eucera longicornis, Sphecodes niger, Nomada fulvicornis* and *Ceratina cyanea*.

Bookham Common, Leatherhead. TQ1256. A mosaic of oak woodland and open grassland on London Clay, this classic SSSI has been intensively surveyed for all living organisms since 1945 by the London Natural History Society, but it is heavily under-recorded for aculeates, with only very few recent visits. **Total species 86, with 5 RDB and 7 Nationally Scarce. Bees 52** including *Andrena coitana*, at one of its three Surrey sites, A. *minutuloides*, rare away from the Chalk, *A. florea* and *Ceratina cyanea*.

BROWNFIELD OR POST-INDUSTRIAL SITES

Papercourt Gravelpits, Send. TQ0356. Old disused gravelpits, mostly land-filled, but the part managed by Surrey Wildlife Trust, still with bare ground, is an SSSI. **Total species 163, with 6 RDB and 26 Nationally Scarce. Bees 89**, with the only modern Surrey nesting locality of the very rare *Andrena nigrospina* (if still surviving), *A. florea, A. bimaculata, A. proxima, A. trimmerana, Lasioglossum quadrinotatum, Melitta tricincta, Dasypoda hirtipes, Ceratina cyanea* and *Osmia bicolor*, far from the Chalk but possibly just a wanderer.

Hambledon Claypit. SU9737. Nutbourne Brickworks closed down about 20 years ago, leaving a derelict site of ponds and south-facing, slipping clay cliffs surrounded by oak woodland. Great variety of flowers. The cliffs, similar to coastal clay cliffs, are a unique habitat in Surrey. The site has no protection although the cliffs are part of an Site of Nature Conservation Importance. The best clay site in Surrey but likely to be developed in the near future. **Total species 134, with 9 RDB and 22 Nationally Scarce. Bees 83**, with most of the same species as nearby Chiddingfold Forest but here nesting in the cliffs in large numbers. Strong nesting aggregations of *Eucera longicornis, Andrena labialis* with *Sphecodes rubicundus, Lasioglossum puncticolle*. Others of interest include *Andrena proxima, Melitta tricincta, Heriades truncorum, Stelis ornatula, Nomada hirtipes* and *Ceratina cyanea*.

Wrecclesham Sandpit. SU8144. A large and deep, disused sandpit with a long, high, south-facing cliff and a seam of Gault Clay. Good variety of flowers. Surveyed for only 2 years. Western end has now been opened up for further quarrying and the pit will probably be land-filled. **Total species 135, with 7 RDB and 23 Nationally Scarce. Bees 80**, with most species of sandy habitats, including a large nesting aggregation of the coastal *Megachile dorsalis* at its only Surrey locality, and some species normally associated with heaths, although miles from the nearest heather, such as *Andrena argentata* and *Nomada baccata*; also a few clay species, such as *Andrena labialis* with *Sphecodes rubicundus, Lasioglossum puncticolle.*

Cranleigh Brickworks. TQ0635. Another disused claypit, ripe for redevelopment, with much bare earth and a few low cliffs and spoil heaps. Under-recorded with only one season's survey. **Total species 115, with 5 RDB and 11 Nationally Scarce. Bees 59**, with similar, but fewer, species as Hambledon claypit. *Hylaeus pictipes* frequents a tiny patch of weld, in company with *H. signatus, H. communis and H. hyalinatus*; other aerial nesters include *Heriades truncorum, Ceratina cyanea.*

Somersbury Claypit, Ewhurst. TQ1037. Small disused claypit with only one bare bank. **Total species 92, with 2 RDB and 12 Nationally Scarce. Bees 59**, with similar species to those at Cranleigh Brickworks but also *Hoplitis claviventris* with its cuckoo bee *Stelis ornatula,* and *Melitta tricincta.*

LONDON PARKS

Wandsworth Common. TQ2774. Large open area in inner London, on London Clay with small areas of sand and gravel drift deposits. Western part is woodland with open glades and dead-wood microhabitats, the rest is mainly mown grass and playing fields but with small areas of long grass and other wildlife habitats created by Wandsworth Borough Council, which manages the site. **Total species 88, with 5 RDB and 7 Nationally Scarce. Bees 56**, with a surprisingly diverse suite of species, including *Andrena fulvago,* both *Panurgus* species*, Lasioglossum smeathmanellum, Heriades truncorum* with *Stelis breviuscula, S. punctulatissima* with *Anthidium manicatum, Anthophora quadrimaculata* and even a singleton *Eucera longicornis* (probably only a straggler).

Battersea Park. TQ2877. Typical London park with mown grass, flower beds and ornamental trees on London Clay, and as a result a poor aculeate fauna compared with Wandsworth. Malaise trap for 2 seasons. **Total species 68, with 1 RDB and 7 Nationally Scarce. Bees 28** including *Anthidium manicatum* and *Anthophora plumipes.*

GARDENS

Milford. SU942415. My own garden of about 2 hectares on greensand, next to heathland of Witley Common. Very well recorded over 10 years, Malaise and water traps used for one season. Improved for aculeates by judicious planting, a few square metres stripped of turf, a south-facing sand bank created and dead wood introduced, thus ensuring a wide variety of nesting bees and wasps. It probably has the highest total for any site in Britain, due to constant observation. **Total species 258, with 14 RDB and 39 Nationally Scarce. Bees 121,** with most of the heathland species including *Andrena bimaculata, A. trimmerana, Halictus confusus, Lasioglossum brevicorne, L. quadrinotatum, Sphecodes longulus, S. niger, Dasypoda hirtipes and Megachile maritima,* as well as dead-wood and generalist species such as *Hylaeus cornutus, Andrena florea, A. labiata, A. proxima, Melitta haemorrhoidalis, Heriades truncorum, Anthophora quadrimaculata, Ceratina cyanea* and even a single male *Macropis europaea* which came to a newly planted yellow loosestrife in the small pond.

RHS Gardens, Wisley. TQ0658. A very large flower garden! Intensively managed for horticulture but with a wildlife area by the River Wey. **Total species 127, with 5 RDB and 14 Nationally Scarce. Bees 63** including *Andrena florea, Lasioglossum puncticolle, L. quadrinotatum, Macropis europaea* and *Nomada flavopicta.*

Park Lane East, Reigate. TQ254494. A garden of 700 sq. ms. on sandy soil backing on to deciduous woodland. Dead wood introduced. Worked for only one full season so under-recorded. **Total species 119, with 5 RDB and 2 Nationally Scarce. Bees 65,** with many of interest such as *Andrena florea, A. labiata, Stelis punctulatissima, S. breviuscula* with *Heriades truncorum, Nomada lathburiana, N. signata, Melecta albifrons* and *Bombus hypnorum.*

Hurst Way, South Croydon. TQ333636. A typical suburban garden of about 500 sq. ms. Malaise trap for one season. **Total species 108, with 3 RDB and 12 Nationally Scarce. Bees 58** including *Andrena tibialis, A. trimmerana, Melitta haemorrhoidalis, Stelis punctulatissima, Nomada fulvicornis* and *Anthophora quadrimaculata.*

Airedale Road, Wandsworth. TQ280736. A typical garden for a terraced London house, of only about 200 sq. ms. Under-recorded with a few, brief visits. **Total species 32, with 1 RDB and 1 Nationally Scarce. Bees 24.** Even the smallest of London gardens can have a surprising variety of species, most of them crevice nesters and some probably nesting in walls, such as *Andrena nitida, Anthidium manicatum, Chelostoma campanularum, Hylaeus hyalinatus, Lasioglossum smeathmanellum, Osmia caerulescens, Megachile centuncularis, Anthophora furcata, A. plumipes* and *A. quadrimaculata.*

BEE CONSERVATION AND BIODIVERSITY

Bees are thermophilous, or warmth-loving, insects with a mainly southern distribution and many have therefore profited from the recent climate warming, especially from the long run of warm, sunny late summers and autumns. Some of the rarer and scarcer species have increased dramatically and expanded their range, not only in Surrey but throughout Britain. Only a very few have decreased in the last 25 years.

In order to conserve bees it is vital to conserve their habitats. The three most favoured habitats for bees in Surrey are Lowland Heath, Lowland Calcareous Grassland and Lowland Dry Acid Grassland, all of which are included in the UK List of Priority Habitats for conservation action under the UK Biodiversity Action Plan. Much of Surrey's heathland has been transformed over the last few years by the Surrey Heathland Project which has been instrumental in the clearance of hundreds of acres of encroaching pine, birch and bracken from previously open heath. The RSPB is clearing pine plantations from 400 hectares of former heathland and the MOD has cleared large areas of their heaths. Heather regenerates very easily and quickly after clearance of woodland and during the early stages of succession there is plenty of bare earth for the bees to nest in. The Herpetological Conservation Trust, which owns, leases and manages about 35 sites in west Surrey, carries out works on these sites, primarily to conserve Sand Lizards, but these works, consisting of tree, scrub and bracken clearance as well as creation of sandy strips, also help bees by providing bare ground for nest sites. Most of the best bee localities on heathland are on sites managed by this Trust. Heathland bees are probably doing better now than at any time in the last 60 years. Two of Surrey's largest heaths, Thursley and Chobham Commons, are National Nature Reserves, and most of the remaining larger heaths have some form of protection as Sites of Special Scientific Interest (SSSI).

Lowland Dry Acid Grassland is rather more vulnerable because at first sight it does not look a very exciting habitat. Most sites of this habitat in Surrey are protected because they are SSSIs; Richmond Park is a Royal Park and a National Nature Reserve, and Kew Gardens is a World Heritage Site. Nesting sites for bees are provided in all these sites by the sandy paths which are kept open by the large numbers of visitors.

There is plenty of Lowland Calcareous Grassland in Surrey provided by the North Downs which stretch from west to east across the county. But very little of this is protected and it has suffered badly over the last 60 years from lack of grazing which has encouraged scrub invasion and the spread of tor grass and other coarse grasses to the detriment of finer downland grasses and flowers. Once this habitat has become scrub-covered the fine matrix of chalk turf disappears and, when the scrub is cleared, this turf does not regenerate unless it is grazed. The National Trust, which owns much of the south-facing scarp, has cleared large areas of scrub but these sites may require years of management before they return to their former habitat of fine downland turf, rich in wild flowers. The best remaining site is Westcott Downs (or Denbies Hillside) near Dorking, which has never suffered from much scrub invasion; this is an SSSI and is owned by the National Trust.

In the latest UK List of Priority Species for conservation action under the UK BAP, 20 species of British bees are included. Many of these are bumblebees, which have declined dramatically in the last 20 years, but there are four species in this list which still occur in Surrey.

Andrena ferox	Found only once in Surrey, at Reigate Heath.
Andrena tarsata	Always rare, now declining.
Bombus ruderarius	Never common, but still found occasionally.
Eucera longicornis	Previously widespread but now very local. Now rare inland in England.

FINDING BEES

The most important thing to remember, when looking for bees, is that they are warmth-loving insects, and will be found only in hot sunny places. Except for the bumblebees, they will not be seen unless the sun is shining; as soon as the sun goes behind a cloud they disappear, unless the day is extremely hot, only to re-emerge as soon as the sun shines again. Bees can be found in almost every type of habitat so long as there are flowers for the females to forage from and for both sexes to nectar at. One of the best places to search is the garden, whether a small town garden or a large one in the country, as most gardens have a large variety of flowers in bloom from March to October.

Bees can best be found at four different places, all of which relate to their life-history. First is their nest site, where females, and sometimes males, and also parasitic bees, will be found, frequently in large numbers. Second is their mating site; this may be an isolated bush or tree trunk or a hedge where males congregate, waiting for females to arrive. Third is their forage site, where the females come to collect pollen for their nests. The fourth is their nectar site, where both males and females come to sip nectar to supply them with energy.

NESTING SITES

More than half the species of bees nest in the soil and most of these make their nest burrows in bare, or lightly vegetated, ground. Some prefer level ground whereas others like sloping or vertical banks but all demand well-drained, dry, south-facing ground. So look for any sunny bare ground but particularly hot, south-facing banks and rootplates and you will almost certainly find bees nesting. Some species nest in large, dense aggregations and these are usually easy to find because of the numbers of bees flying in and out; males are often present, as they wait for virgin females to emerge from their burrows. Parasitic bees can also frequently be seen at these aggregations, sometimes in large numbers, searching for nest entrances and crawling in and out of their host's burrows. Other species nest solitarily, often under cover of plants, and these nest sites are very difficult to find.

On the other hand many species nest above ground, in old beetle holes in dead wood or in other cavities, or in dead plant stems or even in old snail shells. Sunlit, dead, standing tree trunks or old fence posts are preferred by many bees, particularly if these are riddled with old beetle holes. Stem nests are more difficult to find although 'brambling' in winter can be profitable. 'Brambling' consists of searching for holes in the cut ends of brambles or wild roses, cutting off the last ten inches of the stems, bringing them home and putting them in jars or tubes in the warmth. After about three weeks or later, depending on the species, bees (and many wasps) may emerge from their nests. The rare and beautiful *Ceratina cyanea* is best found using this method, but others that can be found are *Hylaeus brevicornis, H. communis* and *Megachile centuncularis.*

MATING SITES

Sometimes one comes across a bush, a small tree or even a clump of heather, round which a mass of small bees are flying very fast. These are males waiting for females to arrive, and these congregations are similar to leks in the bird world. Certain species of males can also be seen flying back and forth along hedges, while others can be seen flying in zigzag fashion up sunlit tree trunks in the early spring. Because these males fly so fast and rarely settle they are difficult to identify and it is usually necessary to catch a few for identification.

FORAGE SITES

Certain species of bee gather pollen from a single species of flower (monolectic bees) or from only a few closely related flowers (oligolectic bees). These bees are relatively easy to find as long as one knows the flowers on which they specialise. Almost every plant of white bryony in Surrey will have the rare *Andrena florea* foraging from the flowers, most stands of bilberry will have *Andrena lapponica*, red bartsia is almost bound to have *Melitta tricincta* and most yellow loosestrife will have *Macropis europaea*. Any species of *Campanula*, including garden species, will attract the oligolectic *Chelostoma campanularum* and *Melitta haemorrhoidalis*, any scabious will attract *Andrena marginata* (and its cleptoparasite *Nomada argentata*) and occasionally the large and rare *A. hattorfiana*. Similarly four species of bee are found collecting pollen only from heathers, whilst most of the early spring mining bees forage only from sallow blossom. But most of the commoner bees are more catholic in their choice of pollen (polylectic bees) and the best place to find these is a well-stocked flower garden, where there is a wide range of flowers to suit many such bees. Even so certain bees will be attracted to labiate flowers, such as the striking Wool-carder Bee, *Anthidium manicatum*, whilst others, such as the small black halictine bees and the various *Colletes*, will forage on composite flowers and some, such as the leaf-cutter bees, prefer the pollen of flowers of the pea family.

NECTAR SITES

Both sexes need a supply of nectar to give them the energy required for their very active life, not least because they possess comparatively short wings which they beat at very high frequency. They therefore spend much of their time sipping nectar from suitable flowers, the long-tongued bees, such as the leaf-cutters, from labiates and leguminous flowers, and the short-tongued bees, such as *Colletes*, from flowers of the daisy family. It is sometimes difficult to tell whether females are foraging or taking nectar as they frequently take nectar and pollen from the same flower. Again, a garden is one of the best places to find bees at nectar sources, but in the wild it is easy to find good sites if one knows which flowers are attractive to bees. The Species Accounts give lists of flowers visited, for nectar as well as pollen, by different bees but there are clear favourites; in the spring these are sallow, blackthorn, hawthorn, wood spurge and forget-me-not, and in the summer those in the bellflower and pea families, thistles and brambles, but especially the yellow composites such as hawkbits and cat's-ears. It is ironic that ragwort, probably the most attractive flower for the majority of summer bees, is the only flower to have had its own Act of Parliament, Ragwort Control Act 2003, passed with the aim of eradicating it from many areas; luckily this is most unlikely to happen.

THE BEE YEAR

March   Search sallow blossom and especially sunlit tree trunks for early species *of Andrena*, and in gardens *Anthophora plumipes* on lungwort, and queen bumblebees.

April   Search blackthorn for spring *Andrena* and female *Lasioglossum*, bilberry for *A. lapponica*, gardens for *Osmia rufa,* dandelions, buttercup, bugle and apple blossom for various bees.

May   Search hawthorn, cow parsley, spurge, speedwell and ground ivy for *A. haemorrhoa, A. labiata*, etc.

June   Late *Andrena*. Summer bees start emerging.

July   The height of season. Search for leaf-cutter bees on leguminous flowers, *Chelostoma campanularum* and *Melitta haemorrhoidalis* on bellflowers, *Colletes, Heriades, Dasypoda* on ragwort.

August   A busy month unless it is too hot, when all goes quiet. The heather specialists are out.

September   A good month for searching heaths.

October   Search ivy for *Colletes hederae.*

Winter   Look for *Bombus terrestris* at winter-flowering shrubs in gardens on any warm day. Go brambling, especially for hibernating *Ceratina* in dead bramble stems.

BEES NESTING

The bees, wasps and ants are the only insects in Britain that build nests and provision these for their young. All other orders of insects lay eggs without any form of nest construction, except for some of the dung and burying beetles which construct very simple chambers in the soil. Grasshoppers and crickets deposit eggs into the ground or into plant stems; dragonflies lay eggs on plants or scatter them in water; butterflies and moths deposit eggs on plants or scatter them randomly; flies and beetles lay eggs on the ground or on other animals.

All species of bees, except the cuckoo or parasitic bees, construct some form of nest for their offspring, this being one of the reasons that they are armed with such strong mandibles for burrowing into the earth and cutting stems and leaves. The type of nest varies enormously from one species to another (see Plate 46). The majority of bees dig underground nests, some in level ground and others in banks, but some, known as aerial nesters, use existing cavities above ground, in old beetle holes and natural holes in wood or walls etc. The young in their cells are thus kept safely away from predators until they emerge as adults, although many insects, including other bees, have found ways of attacking them. But because they live the whole of their pre-adult life in a cell underground or in a hole, the mother has to ensure that their offspring have enough food in their cell for them to grow from an egg to maturity.

Most species of bees are solitary but some are social in varying degrees. Solitary bees make a burrow, or use a cavity, in which they construct a series of cells; they provision each cell with pollen and nectar on which they lay an egg before closing the cell. When all the cells are provisioned the burrow is sealed and the female then starts constructing another burrow and she continues to do this until she dies after a few days or weeks. She will never see her offspring, which emerge from the cell in the following spring, or later that year if the species is double-brooded. A few solitary species may share a nest entrance with other females but they are not social.

A few of the mainly solitary, halictine bees, the small black *Halictus* and *Lasioglossum* species, are primitively social. The queen rears a small brood of worker females, which guard the nest and help the queen to rear a larger second brood of queens and males. The bumblebees have reached a more advanced state of sociality, having a life cycle similar to the social wasps. The mated queen hibernates underground or in a hole, and in the spring makes a nest in an underground hole or in leaf litter on the surface in which she constructs a honey pot from wax glands in her body. She fills this with nectar and then lays some eggs on a mass of pollen which she then incubates. The emerging adults are all female workers which build more cells and forage for pollen and nectar. After more broods of workers have emerged, and the nest has grown to its maximum size, males and queens emerge. The new queens mate and hibernate, but the males and the old queen and workers die. The honey bee *Apis mellifera* is the most complex social bee. Unlike the bumblebees the nest is perennial and a new colony is formed by the old queen leaving the nest with a swarm of workers. Honey bee nests are occasionally found in the wild, usually in a hollow tree or hanging from a tree branch, and such nests can contain as many as 50,000 workers at the height of the season.

All the solitary mining bees, i.e. the Halictinae, the Mellitinae and all species in the genera *Andrena, Colletes* and *Panurgus,* are subterranean nesters. The female digs a burrow in the soil, using her mandibles for digging and her legs for pushing the soil out of the burrow, sometimes forming conspicuous mounds of earth at the nest entrance. The cells are lined with a wax-like substance, or in the case of the *Colletes* waterproofed with a cellophane-like material; the cells of *Macropis europaea*, the nests of which are often constructed in damp ground, are lined and waterproofed with a unique yellow material made from the oils of yellow loosestrife. Some species, such as *Andrena barbilabris* and the spectacular *Dasypoda hirtipes*, nest in bare, level, hard-packed soil, such as paths, while others, like *Andrena argentata*, nest only in very soft, level sand. Some, such as most *Colletes*, nest only in vertical banks while others, like *Andrena bimaculata*, prefer sloping banks. The beautiful spring-flying mining bee *Andrena fulva* usually nests in flat grass-covered ground, such as lawns, throwing up characteristic spoil heaps. Although most species prefer nesting in well-drained soil, such as sand or chalk, there are some that are normally found nesting in clay, for example *Lasioglossum malachurum* and *Andrena labialis*. Some species nest close together in aggregations and these nests are easily found, but many others nest solitarily in herbage and these nests are almost impossible to find; nests of certain species are still unknown.

All the species of Megachilinae, or leaf-cutter bees, are solitary bees but they differ from the mining bees in collecting pollen on brushes of hair beneath their abdomens, rather than on their hind legs. These leaf-cutter bees are mostly aerial nesters, using a great variety of holes and crevices. The large and robust *Anthidium manicatum*, commonly known as the Wool-carder Bee, nests in dead wood, hollow stems and mortar crevices and lines its cells with silk hairs shaved from plants. Most species of *Osmia* nest in various crevices, making cell walls and partitions from chewed leaf pulp or mud. *Osmia rufa* often nests in crumbling mortar of house walls and is commonly known as the Red Mason Bee. *Osmia bicolor* and *O. aurulenta*, as well as their close relative *Osmia spinulosa*, specialise in nesting in old snail shells; after the snail shell has been filled with cells and sealed with leaf mastic, the female *O. bicolor* covers it with grass stems and other debris, presumably to hide the nest from predators. *Heriades truncorum* and both species of *Chelostoma* nest in old beetle burrows in dead trees or posts. All the species of the genus *Megachile* cut pieces of leaves and petals with their mandibles to use in making their nests; they can sometimes be seen flying to their nests carrying these leaves rolled up beneath them. Each cell is lined with many rolled-up large pieces of leaves and the ends of the cells are made from smaller circular pieces (see Plate 37). Most species are crevice nesters but some make holes in the ground.

The solitary bees in the genus *Anthophora* carry pollen on their hind legs and nest in a variety of places; some are aerial nesters in crevices in walls or in dead wood while others are subterranean nesters, burrowing into the ground. They often nest in aggregations. The beautiful small blue *Ceratina cyanea* is the only British representative of the 'small carpenter bees', so called because the female excavates its nest burrow in dead pithy stems, usually of bramble; the cell partitions are made from wood dust. Except for *Xylocopa violacea*, this bee is unique amongst British bees because in late summer the adults of both sexes enter the old nest stem and hibernate there till the spring, sometimes as many as ten in a stem.

About one third of the solitary bees are parasites of other solitary bees. They are not strictly parasites, as they do not consume their hosts, but are cuckoo bees, or cleptoparasites, because they steal the nests of other bees. They all, in varying ways and depending on the species, crawl into the nest burrow of their host when the host is away from the nest, and enter a fully- or partly-provisioned cell; they lay an egg on the pollen ball and then crawl out again. The cuckoo bee larvae, on emerging, destroy the host's egg or larva and then proceed to eat the pollen and nectar provision, eventually emerging as adults in the spring. The cuckoo bees can often be seen around the nest sites of their hosts, especially of those nesting in large aggregations. Six species of bumblebee are social parasites of other bumblebees, and have no workers of their own; the cuckoo queen enters the colony of its host, kills the host queen, and the host workers rear the new cuckoo queens and males.

GARDENING FOR BEES

A garden, as already mentioned above, is the best place to watch bees, especially the commoner species, but rare ones will always turn up. Bees are attracted to gardens because there is a continuous supply of pollen and nectar from a variety of different plant species which flower in succession throughout the year. And, of course, being literally on the doorstep it is possible to observe the bees at close quarters at all times of the day; if the sun only comes out for a few minutes it is easier to pop into the garden, rather than drive to some local site only to find the sun has gone in again. But it is possible to make a garden even more attractive to bees in a few simple ways.

The first is to plant flowers which are attractive to bees. Some plants, such as St John's Wort *Hypericum,* never seem to attract any bees whereas others, such as lavender, will have an endless stream of visitors. The labiates, such as catmint, rosemary and lavender, are excellent for bumblebees as well as for smaller solitary bees. Flowers of the daisy family are good for *Andrena* and small black *Lasioglossum*, tansy being especially good for all species of *Colletes.* Apple blossom is attractive to many *Andrena*, especially *A. haemorrhoa*, and the early *Osmia rufa*; spurges, especially wood spurge, are similarly attractive to spring *Andrena* species. Bellflowers attract many species but especially the two *Campanula* specialists *Chelostoma campanularum* and *Melitta haemorrhoidalis.* Pea-flowers are excellent for all leaf-cutter species, whilst umbellifers, such as angelica, fennel and sea hollies are good for the small *Hylaeus* and *Lasioglossum*. Lungwort is certain to attract *Anthophora plumipes* in the early spring, with its very territorial brown males and all-black females. The garden forms of shrubby cinquefoil *Potentilla fruticosa* are covered in smaller bees and some larger *Andrena* throughout their long flowering season. Even exotic shrubs such as *Cotoneaster, Escallonia, Pyracantha, Cistus, Hebe* and *Ceanothus* are highly attractive to many species, at least for nectar. Winter-flowering plants, such as yellow jasmine, *Mahonia* and heathers will almost certainly encourage bumblebees (mainly *Bombus terrestris*) into the garden throughout the winter; it is not unusual to see these on New Year's Day if the weather is mild. A few species of bee collect pollen only from a single species of plant or from one genus or family of plants and it is worthwhile planting some of these plants to see if the specialist bees will come to them. It is an excellent way of finding out whether these bees are in the area because they will almost certainly locate the plants. I have tried this in my own garden and have been amazed how quickly these bees find the plants. For instance I put a single plant of yellow loosestrife in my garden pond and within a week of it flowering a male *Macropis europaea* appeared although I know of no nesting site of this very specialised bee, nor any locality for the plant, within two miles of my garden. Other people have planted wild mignonette or weld and soon the very local

Hylaeus signatus has come to the flowers, even though the bee was not previously known in the area. Other flowers which might be planted for such specialised bees are lamb's-ear *Stachys byzantina* for *Anthidium manicatum*, speedwells for *Andrena labiata* (but this also comes to star-of-Bethlehem) and ragwort for *Heriades truncorum* and its cleptoparasite *Stelis breviuscula* (but these will also come to other yellow composites).

Another way of improving the garden for bees is to provide them with nest sites. Most of the bees coming to the flowers will not be nesting there, especially in small gardens, because of a lack of suitable nest sites. Town gardens may have various crevice-nesting bees, such as the little green *Lasioglossum smeathmanellum* or the larger *Anthophora quadrimaculata*, because there are plenty of old walls in which they like to nest; these bees are scarcer in country gardens because of a lack of walls. Bees that nest in old beetle holes in dead wood can easily be encouraged to nest in the garden by importing old tree trunks, logs or wooden fence-posts which have been attacked by beetles, and standing these upright in a hot sunny sheltered spot. Almost instantly a variety of bees (and wasps) will be seen emerging from, flying round and investigating the holes, and within days will be nesting. It is best if the logs or posts are in different stages of decay because some species prefer hard wood while others require softer rotting wood. Pine is not good because very few beetles can cope with the resin, oak is usually too hard and birch rots too quickly, but lime is excellent and beech is probably the best. It is quite possible to have up to a dozen different bee species nesting in these logs, and two or three times that number of wasp species. Many bees will also use these logs for basking in the sun, which will give good opportunities for getting a close look at them while they are still for a moment.

But the majority of bees nest in the soil and they require mainly bare ground for this. In most gardens the only bare ground is in flower or vegetable beds but these are constantly being disturbed by digging, forking or hoeing which makes them unsuitable as nest sites. So it is usually necessary to find a sheltered sunny spot and remove any turf or loose topsoil in order to expose the more compacted subsoil. Even a square metre will be enough although the larger the area the better; it is best if the site is on a south-facing slope and the soil needs to be well-drained and friable, preferably on sand or chalk. If the soil is damp or of clay consider importing a bag or two of sand. The turf or soil which has been removed can be piled up on the north side of the site to create a vertical or sloping bank, facing south; some species, such as *Colletes* and *Anthophora*, prefer nesting in steep banks rather than in flat ground. The bees will start burrowing into the newly exposed soil within hours, but make sure the site is in the sun for at least half the day. It is well worth sacrificing a small corner of the lawn as the reward will be hours of pleasure all season watching the bees building their varied nests and provisioning them with pollen and nectar, as well as the cuckoo bees, such as *Nomada* and *Sphecodes*, hanging around the nest entrances waiting for their chance to crawl in and lay their eggs.

Another method of attracting crevice-nesting and hole-nesting bees, such as *Osmia rufa* and the leaf-cutters, is to put out artificial nest sites, sometimes known as bee boxes. These can be bought in garden centres or they can be made at home. The bought ones are usually made of hollow tubes of man-made material stuffed into a container but home-made ones can be made of different sizes of bamboo tubes or other hollow plant stems. These are hung up in a sheltered site in the sun and protected from rain by an overhanging board. The bees will choose tubes with different-sized diameters according to their size. When a tube has been filled with cells the female will cap the end of the tube, either with an earth plug in the case of *Osmia rufa*, or with a mastic plug made of chewed leaves in the case of the leaf-cutters. It is then possible at a later stage to slice open a tube to examine the contents or to leave the tubes *in situ* until the adults emerge next season. A more sophisticated bee box uses glass tubes mounted in a small box with a moveable cover. The advantage of this is that it is possible not only to watch the female constructing each cell, filling it with pollen, laying her egg, making the cell partitions and finally plugging the end, but also to observe the development of the larva, pupa and emerging adult. A diagram of this bee box, developed by BWARS member Kim Taylor of Albury, is shown overleaf, whilst the photographs on Plate 46 show the box with nests and a glass tube with a female *Osmia rufa* laying an egg on the pollen mound. For more information see Useful Addresses in Appendix 5.

I have used all these methods in my own garden over the last ten years and as a result I have recorded 258 species of aculeates there, of which 121 are bees, roughly two-thirds of the Surrey total. Probably 90% of these have been seen breeding in the garden, mostly on the bare patch of sand which I created, and in a dead trunk of lime which I imported.

THE BEE BOX

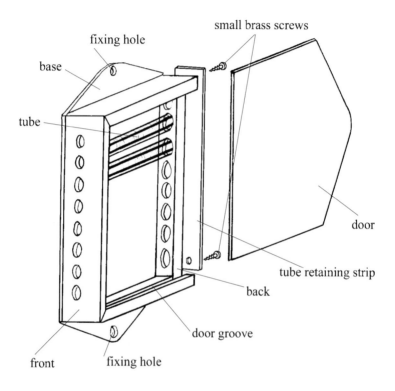

Tube length: 125mm
Tube OD: 10mm
Tube ID: 8mm

IDENTIFYING BEES

Here is the great stumbling block in the study of bees. So many amateurs and professionals have tried studying these fascinating insects but have given up when they find that they cannot identify them because there are no modern identification keys. It is impossible to identify bees without such keys because so many species appear at first sight to be similar. The only book about bees, which contains identification keys and illustrations, is the classic *The Hymenoptera Aculeata of the British Islands* by Edward Saunders, published in 1896 in separate versions, with and without the plates. This book is not only expensive and difficult to find, but is also, not unnaturally, slightly out of date! It is still a very useful book but since 1896 many more species have been either found or recognised, and a number of new species have colonised this country. In addition most species now have names different from those used in Saunders, which can cause confusion.

R.C.L. Perkins published, in a journal, *The British species of Andrena and Nomada* in 1919, *The British species of Halictus and Sphecodes* in 1922 and *The British species of Megachile* in 1925. These contained more modern identification keys but few or no drawings; they are still used today by a number of hymenopterists, through lack of anything else, but they are difficult to obtain and the specific names used are still confusing, and of course Perkins dealt with only about three quarters of the total number of British bees. In 1974 K.M. Guichard published, again in a journal, a short key to British species of *Colletes*. Keys to all the bumblebees, with drawings, were published in *Bumblebees* by O. Prys-Jones and S.A. Corbet in 1991, *Field Guide to the Bumblebees of Great Britain and Ireland* by M. Edwards & M. Jenner (with keys) was published in 2004, and, in 2006, further keys, with drawings, were published in the New Naturalist edition of *Bumblebees* by Ted Benton. The only other key to a genus of bees, *Identification. Leaf-cutter bees,* by G.R. Else, was published in *British Wildlife* in 1999.

George Else, however, has been preparing the *Handbook of the bees of the British Isles and Channel Islands*, and when this is published the stumbling block should disappear. This handbook will have identification keys to all the British bees, with drawings illustrating the diagnostic characters. Fortunately, early drafts of these keys, without drawings, have been circulating amongst a small number of members of BWARS for some years, and these few members have been able to identify bees and thus make records for the national mapping scheme. Without these draft keys there would be almost no dots for the bees in the provisional atlases. In recent years BWARS, in conjunction with the British Entomological and Natural History Society, have been running workshops on identification of the different groups of bees; these can be invaluable to beginners as well as to more experienced students.

Meanwhile, on the European mainland there has been a recent spate of books with identification keys to various families (now subfamilies) of bees, all with drawings. There are three Polish ones, *Megachilid Bees of Europe* (1998), *Bees of the Family Halictidae of Poland* (2000), and *Melittidae of Poland* (2005), all of which are in English. There are five Swiss ones in the *Fauna Helvetica* series, which have excellent drawings and keys, in German and French, and which now cover most subfamilies of bees, except Andreninae. There are also three German books with illustrated keys to many of the bee families, but only in German, a Spanish one in the *Fauna Iberica* series, in Spanish, covering the subfamilies Colletinae, Melittinae and Apinae, and a Dutch one on the genus *Hylaeus*, in Dutch. All of these are useful to those who can read German, French, Dutch and Spanish, but the keys contain many species that are not found in Britain, making them much harder to follow. These foreign keys can be very enlightening as the authors often use different characters, for separating species, from those used in British keys. With the number of new species arriving in Britain recently these keys are proving to be very useful for checking specimens for possible colonists from mainland Europe.

It is of course possible, after a short while, to identify in the field some of the larger and more distinctive species, such as *Macropis europaea, Dasypoda hirtipes* and *Anthidium manicatum*, most of the commoner bumblebees, and even a few of the 68 species of *Andrena*, for instance the beautiful *Andrena fulva* and the little red-bodied *A. labiata*. With the invaluable aid of a reference collection of pinned and named specimens the beginner should be able to identify a few more by matching his or her bee with the named specimen. But for the vast majority of species a key is essential. Having 68 species of *Andrena* is bad enough but, because most males and females are entirely different from each other, there are in reality 136 *Andrena* to identify. Their cleptoparasites, the *Nomada*, are an even more difficult genus to sort out, with 32 species, and again the males differ from females. The little black *Lasioglossum*, with 23 species, can be a nightmare for beginners, as well as for professionals, because the characters used for separating the species rely on amounts and positions of hair patches and punctation which are visible only under a reasonably high-powered microscope. Their cleptoparasites, the *Sphecodes* which number 16 species, all look very similar with their red and black abdomens, and the females are mostly separable only by minute differences in punctation, etc.; many of the males can only be identified by dissecting their genitalia. Even the best photographs cannot show most of these microscopic characters, especially if these are situated on the underside of the bee. Photographs can form valuable records of the more distinctive bees which, as the plates in this book show, are very photogenic; but for the great majority of species it is vital to catch the specimen which has just been photographed in order to identify it at home under a microscope, or possibly with a field lens. Unfortunately this is not an easy task because the bees do not often stay long enough for the photographer to net them.

My advice, therefore, to anyone interested in bees is first of all to get hold of an identification key, then, if possible, acquire a reference collection of named specimens from a friend or contact, and then buy or borrow a microscope or go to a museum where you can use one. Then persuade a local bee expert to name the bees which you have collected, and have hopefully tried to name. Once you can identify even 20 bees, you will be able to add a few new ones each year. This is difficult advice to follow but you will be hooked for life if you do take it.

KEY TO BEE GENERA

INTRODUCTION

The key presented here should enable almost all bee specimens to be assigned to a genus. It is designed for the beginner and complex technical terms are kept to a minimum. A glossary is provided and most features used in the key are illustrated in the relevant couplet. Ease of use is paramount and long, complex couplets allowing for every eventuality have been avoided – so from time to time a particular specimen might prove difficult or impossible to key out, especially when only a few genera have been encountered. Put it to one side and try again when more material has been accumulated and you have more experience. The key will only work with British examples of the genera and other works will need to be consulted for European material. [The genus *Dufourea*, until recently considered extinct in Britain, is omitted from the key.]

CHECKLIST – IS IT A BEE?

Many insects mimic bees while at the same time a number of bees, mostly cleptoparasitic species, are distinctly wasp-like. Before working through the keys it is sensible to check that your insect is a bee!

- Two pairs of membranous wings; the forewings with 9-10 enclosed cells, the hindwing with a row of hooks on its front edge which connect it to the forewing in flight.

- Mandibles present, between which a tongue is usually visible.

- Antennae with 12-13 segments (be careful, the second segment can be very short and partially hidden within the first; however, the third is usually long and distinctly conical, differing from the following segments).

- Distinct constriction between thorax and abdomen ("wasp-waist"), not easy to see in very hairy species.

- Plumose hairs: branched hairs adapted to carry pollen, these are usually obvious in non-parasitic species but in parasitic bees only a few remain, particularly on the propodeum and below the thorax. Simple hairs may also be present.

- First segment of hind tarsus usually flatter and wider than following segments.

KEY TO BEE GENERA

HOW TO USE THE KEY

Having killed the bee, preferably in the fumes of ethyl acetate but, at a pinch, by a few hours in a domestic freezer, it should be mounted. Continental pins are recommended to facilitate handling and to allow multiple labelling. Appendages should be moved away from the body, the mandibles opened if possible (don't force them, the jaw muscles are much stronger than the neck muscles and loss of the head is almost inevitable). In addition, if the bee is a male (see KEY 1), the genital capsule should be extracted from the abdomen using a pin. Ideally it will be fully visible but still attached to the body. If it is necessary to remove it completely, it can be mounted on a piece of card attached to the same pin as the bee.

All specimens should be labelled with collecting data (at least site, vice-county, full grid reference, full date and collector), and, once identified, a determination label with the name of the species, the determiner and the date determined.

Separate keys are given to males and females. In many cases males and females of the same species are distinctly more different than the same sexes of closely related species. Identifying a bee to genus is only the first step in the process, identification to species is the ultimate aim and most published keys, and those in the long-awaited *British Bees* book, treat the sexes separately. It is thus sensible to get used to recognising males and females from the start. Failure to do so correctly will cause problems as different characters are used in the two keys.

Check that the insect agrees with the characters listed above and move on to KEY 1. Each key consists of couplets which list alternative character states. In this key they are subdivided into clauses, with, for example, the alternatives being **a** or **aa**, **b** or **bb**. Where possible the description is accompanied by a figure which illustrates the position and state of each character, but a separate glossary is also given.

Clauses are presented in order such that easy to see, definitive characters are used before more variable and comparative ones. Tongue characters, used in a number of other keys, are only used where absolutely necessary as the tongue may well be hidden. Characters of wing venation are used widely. They are generally very constant, but occasionally particular veins can be wholly or partially absent, although often traces remain, especially at the junction with other veins; it is best to check both wings.

Starting at couplet 1, read each clause <u>and</u> its alternative before making a decision – each half of the couplet will then lead on to either another couplet or the answer. If there appears to be a conflict between the two halves of a couplet you may have gone wrong earlier. You have two options. Either follow each lead and see if the situation resolves, or go back to the previous couplet and check it again. The number of the previous couplet is given in brackets next to the current couplet number.

KEY – GLOSSARY

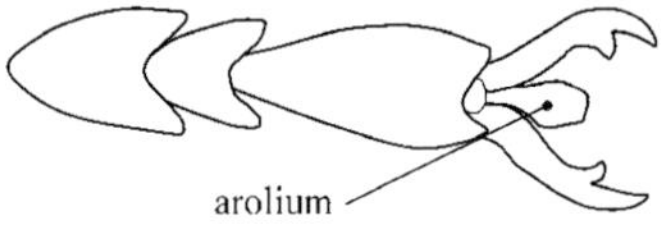

fig. 1 – tarsus

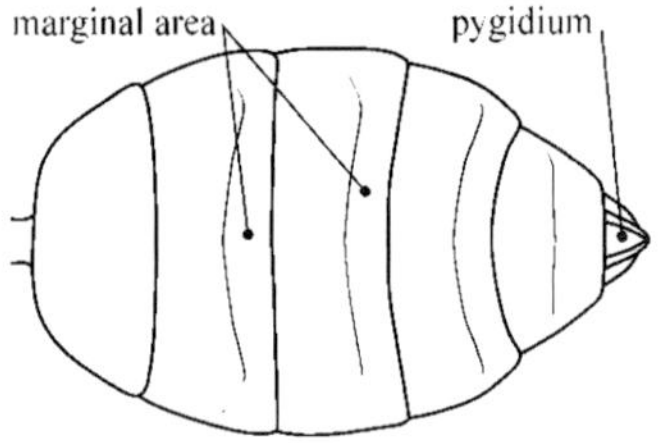

fig. 2 – abdomen

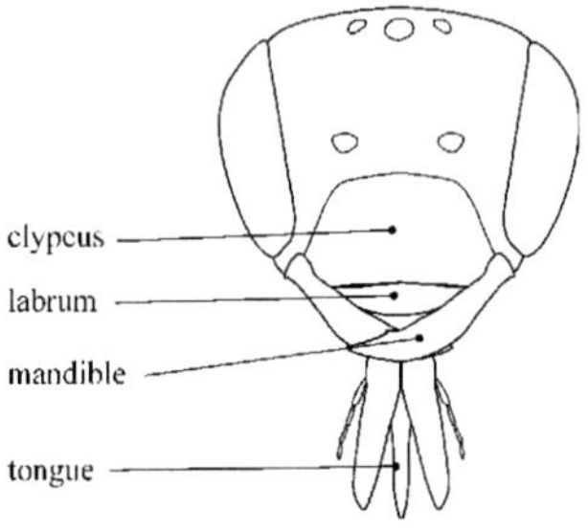

fig. 3 – face

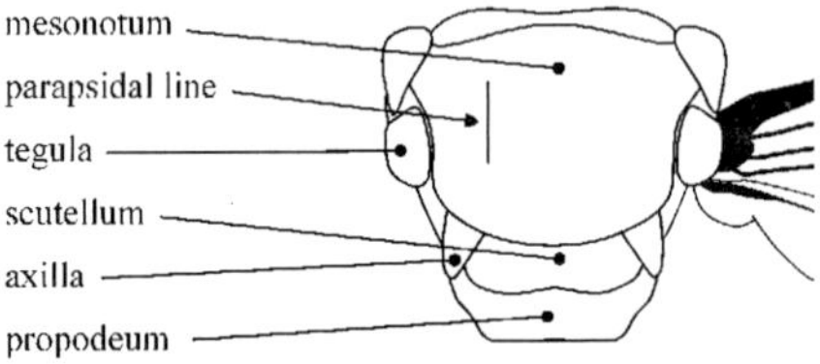

fig. 4 – thorax

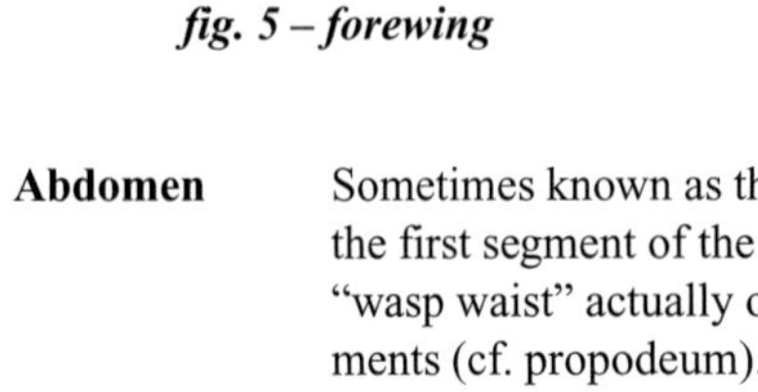

fig. 5 – forewing

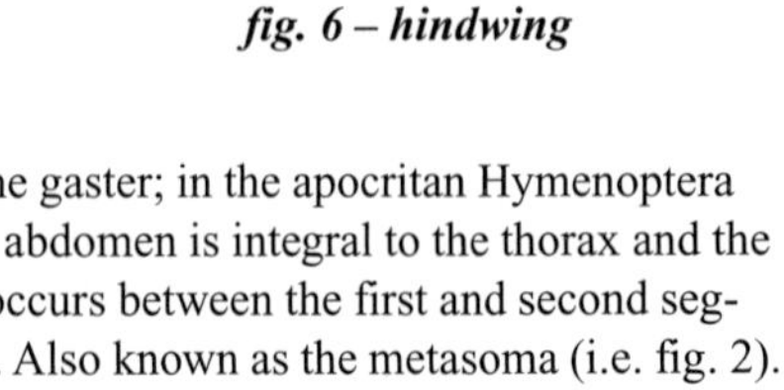

fig. 6 – hindwing

Abdomen	Sometimes known as the gaster; in the apocritan Hymenoptera the first segment of the abdomen is integral to the thorax and the "wasp waist" actually occurs between the first and second segments (cf. propodeum). Also known as the metasoma (i.e. fig. 2).
Arolium	A small pad which projects between the two claws of the foot (fig. 1).
Axillae	Small triangular plates on either side of the scutellum, usually inconspicuous but in some genera enlarged and projecting backwards as teeth (fig. 4).
Claval lobe	see Jugal lobe (fig. 6).

KEY – GLOSSARY (continued)

Cleptoparasite	A species that steals the nest of another. The host species creates and stocks a nest and lays her egg in it. The parasite opens the nest and lays her own egg which eats the host's resources. The host egg is destroyed by the parasite female or her larva.
Clypeus	The central plate of the face (fig. 3).
Cubital cell	see Jugal lobe (fig. 6).
Integument	A hard external covering.
Jugal lobe	The lowermost longitudinal vein of the hindwing, if followed to the wing margin, reaches a point where the wing border is excised. The lobe thus formed behind the vein is the claval lobe. If the margin is followed back to the wing base a second incision may be present marking off the jugal lobe. The presence and length of the jugal lobe relative to the claval lobe and the cubital cell is an important character in the key; in comparison, both are measured from the wing base (fig. 6).
Labrum	The plate at the base of the tongue, just below the clypeus (fig. 3).
Marginal area	The apical part of each tergite, usually one third to one half its total length, often with different vesture or punctation to the basal part (fig. 2).
Mesonotum	The top of the central part of the thorax, between the wing bases (fig. 4).
Parapsidal line	A modified area on the mesonotum, usually linear, lying level with the wing-base and half way between base of wing and mid-line (fig. 4).
Propodeum	The back of the "thorax" (or mesosoma) is actually the first segment of the abdomen (fig 4).
Pygidium	A modified, usually triangular, area on the last tergite of the abdomen, usually in females where it is used to remove material when nest-building (fig. 2).
Scape	The elongate, basal segment of the antenna.
Scopa	The pollen-collecting apparatus of the female, consisting of dense and long hairs. In some genera it is present below the abdomen, in others on the hind leg, particularly the tibia and first tarsal segment. It is lacking in cleptoparasitic species.
Scutellum	The part of the thorax behind the mesonotum (fig. 4).
Sternites	The plates that make up the lower surface of the abdomen.
Tegula	A small plate covering the base of the wing (fig. 4).
Tergites	The plates that make up the upper surface of the abdomen.

KEY 1 – MALE OR FEMALE?

a   Antennae with 12 segments

b   Abdomen with six visible tergites

c   Sting present, which may protrude after death

d   Scopa, or pollen-collecting apparatus, often present, either on the hind legs or below the abdomen (absent in the parasitic, usually wasp-like, species)

.... **FEMALES – KEY 2, page 81**

aa   Antenna with 13 segments

bb   Abdomen with seven visible tergites (but in some genera, the apical ones folded beneath the end of abdomen)

cc   Complex internal genitalia present in the form of a capsule (which should be hooked out with a pin to facilitate identification in certain genera)

dd   Never with scopa (although incidental collection of pollen may occur through feeding on nectar)

.... **MALES – KEY 3, page 93**

KEY 2 – FEMALES

1

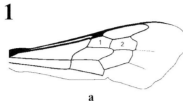 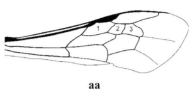

a	aa

a   Forewing with two submarginal cells **2**

aa   Forewing with three submarginal cells **14**

2 (1)

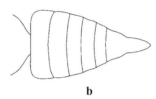

b

a   Surface of eyes with long dense hairs

b   Abdomen strongly narrowing to pointed apex .... ***Coelioxys*** (page 230)
     Medium-sized to large bees (9-16 mm); abdomen rather shining and
     with pale bands or wedge-shaped spots formed of flattened hairs;
     scutellum with rearward-pointing projections either side; no scopa.
     Cleptoparasitic on *Megachile* and *Anthophora*.

aa   Surface of eyes bare

bb   Abdomen more-or-less parallel-sided or oval, rounded at apex **3**

3 (2)

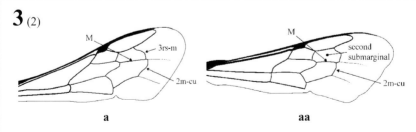

a	aa

a   Vein 2m-cu meets M beyond point where 3rs-m does **4**

aa   Vein 2m-cu meets M opposite second submarginal cell **5**

KEY 2 – FEMALES (continued)

4 (3)

arolium

c   cc

a Abdomen black or at most with cream-coloured spots or bands; face and legs without colour

b No scopa present

c Arolium present between tarsal claws .... ***Stelis*** (page 210)
Small to medium-sized species (5-11 mm); black, sometimes with pale markings on abdomen; rather shining, heavily-armoured species. Cleptoparasitic on *Osmia*, *Hoplitis*, *Anthidium* and *Heriades*.

aa Abdomen with bright yellow spots; similar colour present on face and legs

bb Dense golden-yellow scopa on underside of abdomen

cc No arolium between tarsal claws .... ***Anthidium*** (page 209)
One British species – *manicatum*. Large (11-15 mm); black with yellow spots on abdomen, tibiae, sides of mesonotum, tegulae, top of head, face and mandibles.

5 (3)

arolium

a   aa

a Arolium present between tarsal claws **6**

aa Arolium absent .... ***Megachile*** (page 225)
Medium-sized to large species (9-18 mm); head large, mandibles triangular with broad cutting edge carrying several teeth; scopa present on underside of abdomen. "Leaf-cutter Bees".

KEY 2 – FEMALES (continued)

6 (5)

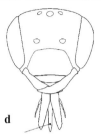 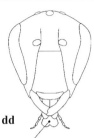

d   **dd**

a Scopa (pollen-collecting hairs) present, either on hind leg or underside of abdomen

b Face black beneath any hairs

c Legs black, without yellow markings

d Tongue pointed at apex, fairly short to long **7**

aa No obvious scopa present

bb EITHER yellow markings present on face OR face black with projecting lobes at lower corners of clypeus and a bulge below antennal bases forming a triangular concavity

cc Legs almost hairless and with clear yellow markings

dd Tongue short and bilobed at apex .... *Hylaeus* (page 124)
  Small to medium-sized species (4-8 mm); very sparsely-haired
  bees; black with yellow on legs and (usually) face.

7 (6)

a Scopa on hind legs **8**

aa Scopa on underside of abdomen **11**

8 (7)

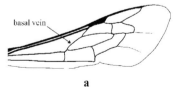 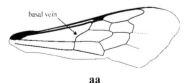

basal vein   basal vein

a   **aa**

a Basal vein (second section of M) almost straight **9**

aa Basal vein (second section of M) fairly strongly arched **10**

KEY 2 – FEMALES (continued)

9 (8)

c   cc

a Mesonotum very sparsely haired; surface brightly shining between the punctures

b Abdomen sparsely haired, except for the apical tergites, without hint of pale bands

c Pygidium triangular with a blunt or rounded apex and raised median keel .... *Panurgus* (page 168)
  Medium-sized species (7-10 mm); shiny black with pale, long-haired scopa.

aa Mesonotum densely haired with a mixture of black and golden-yellow hairs; surface matt between the punctures

bb Abdomen with apical half of tergites 2-4 covered with dense, pale flattened hairs, contrasting with the sparser black hairs of the basal halves, thus appearing banded

cc Pygidium long triangular with a deeply notched apex, its surface flat
  .... *Dasypoda* (page 208)
  One British species – *hirtipes*. Large (13-15 mm); banded bee with conspicuous scopa, the hairs of which are considerably longer than the thickness of the tibia.

10 (8)

a Medium-sized species, not over 10 mm

b First tergite smooth and shining, with small widely-spaced punctures, almost hairless

c Marginal area of tergite 2 smooth and impunctate .... *Macropis* (page 206)
  One British species – *europaea*. Shining black bee, with pale hair-bands on the apical tergites. Associated with yellow loosestrife.

aa Large species, 13-15 mm

bb First tergite densely covered with deep punctures, from which arise long hairs

cc Marginal area of tergite 2 rather densely punctate and with surface dulled .... *Eucera* (page 256)
  Large, dull species, with pale bands on apical tergites.

KEY 2 – FEMALES (continued)

11 (7)

a   b   aa

a First tergite of abdomen with a strongly raised sharp ridge at front, separating dorsal surface from anterior face

b Viewed from above, this ridge distinctly concave .... ***Heriades*** (page 214)
One British species – *truncorum*. Medium-sized (7-8 mm), rather slender bee; body shining with dense, deep punctures; clypeus with paired median apical tubercles.

aa First tergite of abdomen more-or-less smoothly curved from dorsal surface to anterior face, without a distinct transverse keel

bb If change in surface texture between dorsal surface and anterior face gives the impression of a vague ridge, this ridge viewed from above almost straight **12**

12 (11)

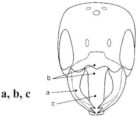
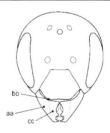

a, b, c   **aa, bb, cc**

a Mandibles long and narrow, tapering towards apex

b At rest, upper edge of mandibles nowhere near clypeus, but leaving an opening through which the labrum is clearly visible

c Labrum very long, so that its tip is visible below apices of closed mandibles

d Thorax elongate, area behind scutellum horizontal, almost as long as vertical posterior face of propodeum .... ***Chelostoma*** (page 216)
Small to medium-sized species (5-11 mm), shining black with elongate abdomen.

aa Mandibles shorter, length less than twice basal width, parallel-sided or widening towards apex

bb At rest, upper edge of mandibles fitting closely against edge of clypeus

cc Labrum longer than wide but not projecting below apices of closed mandibles

dd Thorax short, falling away vertically immediately behind scutellum **13**

KEY 2 – FEMALES (continued)

13 (12)

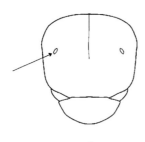 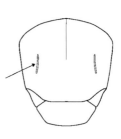

a   aa

a   On mesonotum, parapsidal lines short, scarcely longer than wide, appearing as a raised, flattened area usually distinct from surrounding punctures (move specimen relative to light-source to create reflections), AND/OR

b   Scopal hairs golden-reddish or black .... ***Osmia*** (page 218)
Medium-sized to large species (7-14 mm); many either with long,
dense red hair or metallic integument. "Mason bees".

aa   On mesonotum, parapsidal lines linear, many times longer than wide, not always obvious, AND

bb   Scopal hairs white .... ***Hoplitis*** (page 224)
Medium-sized species (6-10 mm); sparsely haired with black
integument.

14 (1)

marginal cell

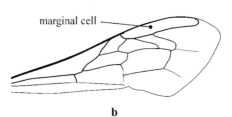

b

a   Surface of eyes with long dense hairs

b   Marginal cell long and narrow .... ***Apis*** (page 280)
The Honey Bee.

aa   Surface of eyes bare

bb   Marginal cell usually shorter and broader **15**

KEY 2 – FEMALES (continued)

15 (14)

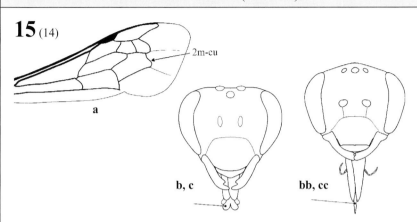

- **a** Vein 2m-cu strongly S-shaped, the lower end bulging outwards
- **b** Tongue short and bilobed at apex
- **c** Head, viewed from in front, rather triangular, the inner margins of
the eyes converging ventrally .... *Colletes* (page 120)
  Medium-sized to large bees (8-16 mm), most species with dense
  flattened hairs covering the marginal areas of the tergites, producing
  a banded effect; scopa on hind legs.

- **aa** Vein 2m-cu usually straight, at most slightly curved and then not bowed
outward at lower end (illustration, next couplet)
- **bb** Tongue variable in length but always pointed at apex
- **cc** Head more rounded or oval, inner margins of eyes usually more parallel **16**

16 (15)

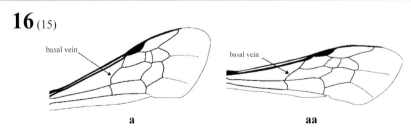

- **a** Basal vein strongly arched with a distinct bend towards lower end,
forming almost a right angle where it meets the longitudinal vein **17**

- **aa** Basal vein almost straight or slightly and evenly arched, the lower end
meeting the longitudinal vein at an acute angle **20**

KEY 2 – FEMALES (continued)

17 (16)

a

a Fifth tergite with a specialised hair patch, the rima, in the form of a central, longitudinal bare area surrounded on each side by dense, flattened hairs

b Scopa on hind legs

c Integument wholly black or metallic blue or green **18**

aa Fifth tergite without rima, either almost bare or with flattened hairs forming a complete apical band

bb No obvious scopa

cc Integument either metallic blue or with some tergites clear blood-red **19**

18 (17)

a Abdomen with bands or spots of whitish flattened hairs situated on the marginal areas of the tergites (glossary, fig. 2), often extending beyond the apical margin and thus masking it

b Outer cross-veins similar in thickness and pigmentation to adjacent wing veins .... *Halictus* (page 170)
  Small to medium-sized species (6-11 mm); integument black or metallic bronzy green.

aa If abdomen with patches of whitish flattened hairs, these are situated basally, often originating below the apical margin of the preceding tergite which is thus obvious; in some species these hair patches absent or indistinct

bb Cross-veins towards wing tip usually finer and less obviously pigmented than adjacent longitudinal veins .... *Lasioglossum* (page 172)
  Small to medium-sized species (5-11 mm); integument black or metallic greenish to bluish.

19 (17)

a Integument obviously metallic bluish .... *Ceratina* (page 264)
  One British species – *cyanea*. Fairly small (6-7 mm), shining metallic blue bee. Nests, and overwinters, in bramble stems. The "Blue Carpenter Bee".

aa Integument black, with several tergites completely blood-red ....
  .... *Sphecodes* (page 191)
  Very small to medium-sized species (4-12 mm); abdomen black with more-or-less extensive red belt, usually rather shining; heavily punctured head and thorax. Cleptoparasitic on species of *Lasioglossum*, *Halictus* and *Andrena*.

KEY 2 – FEMALES (continued)

20 (16)

a Wings strongly purplish-iridescent

b Very large species, over 18 mm, with entirely black hairs on body
and legs .... *Xylocopa* (page 265)

One species – *violacea* – until recently a vagrant to Britain, but
seen more often in recent years and has now become established.

aa Wings usually clear, at most smoky brownish

bb Often smaller, if as large as 18 mm then body usually with bands or
spots of lighter coloured hairs **21**

21 (20)

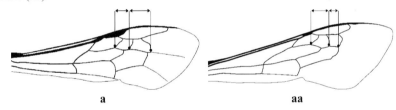

a   aa

a Lower border of third submarginal cell (measured between intersection
with its bordering cross-veins) distinctly longer than that of second
submarginal cell **22**

aa Lower border of third submarginal cell more-or-less equal in length to
that of second or even shorter **24**

22 (21)

a Fairly distinct scopa on hind legs

b Integument dark or with reddish marks or bands, not metallic **23**

aa No evident scopa

bb Integument distinctly metallic bluish .... *Ceratina* (page 264)

One British species – *cyanea*. Fairly small (6-7 mm), shining
metallic blue bee. Nests, and overwinters, in bramble stems.
The "Blue Carpenter Bee".

KEY 2 – FEMALES (continued)

23 (22)

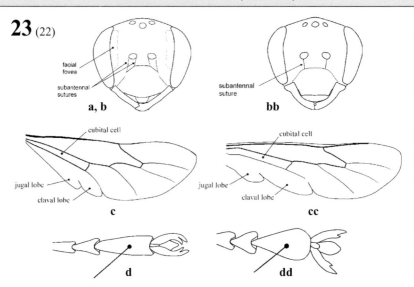

a Facial foveae present – distinct depressions just inside inner border of eyes and lined with very short, dense hairs giving a velvety appearance

b Two subantennal sutures present, showing as shining lines descending from antennal socket to meet upper border of clypeus, the shining suture defining the clypeus slightly thickened at these points

c Jugal lobe of hindwing long, its length, measured from base of wing, distinctly more than half the length of claval lobe, usually reaching as far out as the vein closing the cubital cell [care needed – it may be folded under]

d Last tarsal segment slender, at least three times as long as wide ....
....*Andrena* (page 131)

Small to large species (6-15 mm); a very large and diverse genus with species ranging from almost hairless to densely haired, shining to dull, some banded, and some with reddish markings on abdomen.

aa Facial foveae absent, the face inside eyes not depressed or lined with velvety hairs

bb One subantennal suture present

cc Jugal lobe of hindwing short, less than half length of claval lobe, and not nearly reaching vein closing the cubital cell

dd Last tarsal segment broad, about twice as long as wide ..... *Melitta* (page 204)
Medium-sized to large species (10-15 mm); integument dark; abdomen with either whitish hair bands or an orange tail.

KEY 2 – FEMALES (continued)

24 (21)

a One or more pairs of legs marked with or completely yellow or reddish-orange **25**

aa All legs with integument entirely black **26**

25 (24)

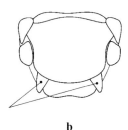 

          b   **bb**

a Abdomen with paired pale spots formed from dense flattened hairs

b Axillae, on either side of scutellum, large and triangular, projecting backwards as a pair of teeth .... *Epeolus* (page 254)
      Medium-sized species (6-11 mm); cleptoparasites of *Colletes*.

aa Abdomen without patches of dense flattened hairs, instead patterned by yellow, red or brownish spots or bands due to pigmentation of the integument

bb Axillae, on either side of scutellum, small and inconspicuous, not projecting backwards as teeth .... *Nomada* (page 235)
      Small to large species (4-15 mm); abdomen patterned with red or yellow and shining (thus wasp-like); head and thorax often heavily punctured. Cleptoparasites of *Andrena*, *Lasioglossum*, *Melitta* and *Eucera*.

KEY 2 – FEMALES (continued)

26 (24)

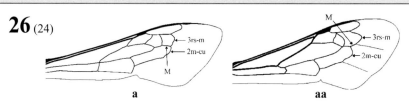

| a | aa |

a Veins 2m-cu and 3rs-m touching where they meet vein M

b Scopa present on hind leg .... *Anthophora* (page 258)
Fairly to very large species (10-17 mm); usually rather hairy; abdomen with
hair bands in some species; eyes, in life, sometimes rather greenish.

aa Vein 2m-cu meeting M clearly nearer base of wing than 3rs-m does

bb Scopa either entirely absent, or pollen-collecting apparatus present
in the form of a corbiculum – the hind tibia flat and shiny and
bordered by long hairs 27

27 (26)

a, b   **aa, bb**

a Cheek (malar space) short; distance from lower margin of eye to
mandibular base less than one fifth of width of mandible here

b Face strongly protruding, clypeus at about 45° to vertical

c Abdomen mainly sparsely haired and shining, with very long hairs
confined to base; tergites with paired lateral white spots formed
from flattened hairs .... *Melecta* (page 262)
Large to very large bees (12-16 mm), black with greyish-white hair;
scutellum with paired apical prongs (difficult to see beneath hair).
Cleptoparasites of *Anthophora*.

aa Cheek (malar space) long, equal to or longer than width of mandibular base

bb Face almost flat, clypeus vertical

cc Abdomen relatively densely long-haired, especially towards apex, never
with rounded spots but often with complete bands of coloured hair ....
.... *Bombus* (page 266)
Medium-sized to very large species (10-35 mm); Bumblebees, with
pollen-basket, and Cuckoo Bumblebees, without. [Includes the former
genus *Psithyrus* now considered a subgenus of *Bombus*].

KEY 3 – MALES

28

a   **aa**

a   Forewing with two submarginal cells **29**

aa   Forewing with three submarginal cells **41**

29 (28)

a   Antennae exceptionally long, at least as long as forewing ....
.... ***Eucera*** (page 256)
      Large species (12-16 mm); rather hairy; face yellow.

aa   Antennae normal, rarely more than half as long as forewing **30**

30 (29)

a   Face with yellow markings **31**

aa   Face with integument black, although it may be covered with dense
     pale hairs **33**

31 (30)

a   Abdomen with paired, lateral, bright yellow spots
b   Tergites 6 and 7 of abdomen with prominent, hook-like projections ....
.... ***Anthidium*** (page 209)
      One British species – *manicatum*. Large (11-15 mm); black with yellow
      spots on abdomen, tibiae, tegulae, top of head, face and mandibles.

aa   Abdomen completely black
bb   Apical tergites usually unadorned, at most with a median, down-curved
      projection on last tergite **32**

KEY 3 – MALES (continued)

32 (31)

cc

a Legs with yellow spots on at least tibiae or tarsi

b Legs slender, hind tibia oval in cross-section

c Apex of abdomen simple .... *Hylaeus* (page 124)
   Small to medium-sized species (4-8 mm); very sparsely-haired
   bees; black with yellow on legs, face and sometimes parts of
   thorax; tongue short with bilobed apex.

aa Legs completely black

bb Legs robust, hind femur and tibia strongly swollen, the latter rather
   triangular in cross-section

cc Last tergite of abdomen with median, down-curved, tongue-like
   projection .... *Macropis* (page 206)
   One British species – *europaea*. Shining black bee, with pale
   hair-bands on the apical tergites and yellow face. Associated
   with yellow loosestrife.

33 (30)

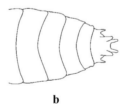

b

a Surface of eyes with long dense hairs

b Tergite 6 (apparent apex) of abdomen with three pairs of posteriorly
   projecting spines .... *Coelioxys* (page 230)
   Medium-sized to large species (9-14 mm); head and thorax densely
   and deeply punctured; abdomen black and shiny, tapered towards apex,
   with bands of white, flattened hairs; scutellum with rearward-pointing
   hooks either side. Cleptoparasitic on *Megachile* and *Anthophora*.

aa Surface of eyes bare

bb Tergite 6 without three pairs of spines, at most with roughened rim **34**

KEY 3 – MALES (continued)

34 (33)

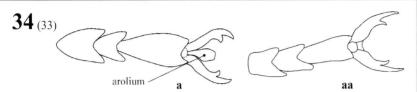

arolium   **a**   **aa**

a   Arolium present between tarsal claws **35**

aa   Arolium, between tarsal claws, absent .... ***Megachile*** (page 225)
Medium-sized to large species (9-15 mm); mandible with broad
cutting edge with 3-4 teeth; tongue long; some species with front
tarsus modified, expanded and pale-coloured. "Leaf-cutter Bees".

35 (34)

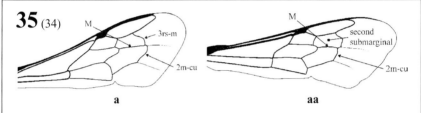

a   **aa**

a   Vein 2m-cu reaching vein M at or beyond the point that vein 3rs-m
does .... ***Stelis*** (page 210)
Small to medium-sized species (5-10 mm); abdomen black, black with
narrow pale margins to tergites or black with pale lateral spots; rather
shining, heavily-armoured species. Cleptoparasitic on *Osmia, Hoplitis,
Anthidium* and *Heriades.*

aa   Vein 2m-cu reaching vein M before 3rs-m does, thus entering second
submarginal cell **36**

36 (35)

a   **aa**

a   First tergite of abdomen with a strong transverse ridge at front,
separating dorsal surface from anterior face .... ***Heriades*** (page 214)
One British species – *truncorum.* Medium-sized (7-8 mm),
rather slender bee; body shining with dense, deep punctures.

aa   First tergite of abdomen with dorsal surface smoothly rounded into
anterior face **37**

KEY 3 – MALES (continued)

37 (36)

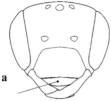 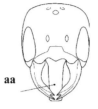 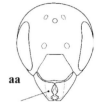

a   aa   aa

a   Labrum much wider than long, easily seen even when sickle-shaped mandibles are closed **38**

aa   Labrum longer than wide; in some species concealed by broad, triangular mandibles **39**

38 (37)

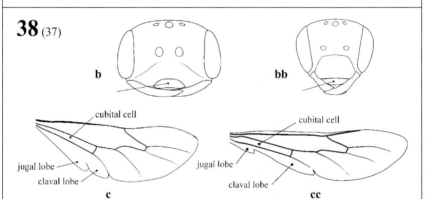

b   bb

cubital cell   cubital cell

jugal lobe   jugal lobe

claval lobe   claval lobe

c   cc

a   Mesonotum black and shining with distinct but sparse punctures

b   Labrum fitting into excision in lower part of clypeus so that the lower borders of each are level

c   Jugal lobe of hindwing long, well over half length of claval lobe, and extending as far as or beyond vein closing cubital cell .. ***Panurgus*** (page 168)
     Medium-sized species (7-9 mm); deeply black and shiny; rather hairless.

aa   Mesonotum brownish-black, surface matt with indistinct punctures

bb   Labrum hinged below level of clypeus

cc   Jugal lobe of hindwing very short, much less than half length of claval lobe and not reaching anywhere near as far as vein closing cubital cell .... ***Dasypoda*** (page 208)
     One British species – *hirtipes*. Large (12-14 mm); banded bee with long hairs on abdomen, thorax, legs and face.

KEY 3 – MALES (continued)

39 (37)

a   aa

a   Parapsidal lines short, scarcely longer than wide, appearing as a raised, flattened area usually distinct from surrounding punctures (move specimen relative to light-source to create reflections), OR sternite 1 with a long ventral spine

b   Abdomen with sternite 2 flat and unmodified

c   Integument may be slightly metallic but black in some species ....
.... ***Osmia*** (page 218)
Medium-sized to large species (7-13 mm); many either with long but sparse red hair or metallic integument. "Mason bees".

aa   Parapsidal lines linear, many times longer than wide, not always obvious

bb   Abdomen with sternite 2 modified into a raised welt

cc   Integument always black **40**

40 (39)

a   aa

a   Tergite 7 of abdomen ending in two downward-pointing projections with a deep notch between them (view from behind)

b   Rim of tergite 6 with smooth outline

c   Thorax elongate; propodeum long, with a distinct division between dorsal and posterior surfaces, the dorsal area with a series of raised longitudinal keels .... ***Chelostoma*** (page 216)
Small to medium-sized species (5-11 mm); rather shining, black, elongate body.

aa   Tergite 7 of abdomen ending in a single median point, this segment somewhat curved beneath the end of the abdomen and partially concealed by tergite 6 (view from behind)

bb   Rim of tergite 6 with small lateral teeth

cc   Thorax compact; propodeum short and rounded, almost vertical with no obvious dorsal surface .... ***Hoplitis*** (page 224)
Medium-sized species (6-10 mm); abdomen shining, sparsely haired with black integument.

KEY 3 – MALES (continued)

41 (28)

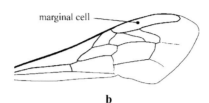

marginal cell

b

  a Surface of eyes with long dense hairs

  b Marginal cell long and narrow .... *Apis* (page 280)
      The Honey Bee; drones infrequently found.

aa Surface of eyes bare

bb Marginal cell usually shorter and broader **42**

42 (41)

  a Wings strongly purplish-iridescent

  b Very large species, over 18 mm

  c Body covered with dense, blackish-purple hairs .... *Xylocopa* (page 265)
      One species – *violacea* – until recently a vagrant to Britain, but
      seen more often in recent years and has now become established.

aa Wings usually clear, at most smoky

bb Often smaller, if as large as 18 mm then body with bands or spots
      of lighter coloured hairs

cc If covered with dense, black hairs then marginal cell divided in two
      by an extremely fine vertical false vein and jugal lobe entirely absent **43**

KEY 3 – MALES (continued)

43 (42)

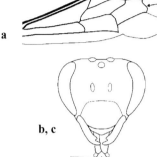

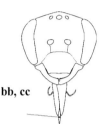

a

b, c

bb, cc

a Vein 2m-cu strongly S-shaped, the lower end bulging outwards

b Tongue short and bilobed at apex

c Head, viewed from in front, rather triangular, the inner margins of the eyes converging ventrally .... ***Colletes*** (page 120)

Medium-sized to large bees (7-15 mm), most species with dense flattened hairs covering the marginal areas of the tergites, producing a banded effect; sternum 7 modified with lateral extensions (needs to be fully visible for identification).

aa Vein 2m-cu usually straight, at most slightly curved and then not bowed outward at lower end

bb Tongue variable in length but always pointed at apex

cc Head more rounded or oval, inner margins of eyes usually more parallel **44**

44 (43)

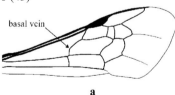

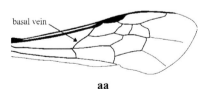

basal vein

basal vein

a

aa

a Basal vein strongly arched with a distinct bend towards lower end, forming almost a right angle where it meets the longitudinal vein **45**

aa Basal vein almost straight or slightly and evenly arched, the lower end meeting the longitudinal vein at an acute angle **48**

KEY 3 – MALES (continued)

45 (44)

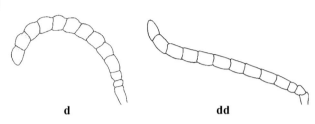

d   dd

a Usually, one or more tergites of abdomen marked with reddish or orange-brown, shining, with sparse punctures and almost hairless - but may be completely black

b Face with integument black (except, perhaps, tips of mandibles)

c Legs black, at most tarsi translucent reddish-brown

d Antenna with segments short and usually with ventral surface of apical segments with a pubescent depression basally, thus appearing "knobbly" ....***Sphecodes*** (page 191)
Very small to medium-sized species (4-11 mm); abdomen black, usually with more-or-less extensive red belt but melanic examples occur; usually rather shining; heavily punctured head and thorax. Cleptoparasites of species of *Lasioglossum*, *Halictus* and *Andrena*.

aa Tergites usually black or dark-metallic; if red-marked then often with patches of whitish, flattened hairs and legs with yellow markings

bb Face nearly always with yellow markings, at least at apex of clypeus

cc Legs black or with yellow markings on tibia and/or tarsus

dd Antennae variable, but segments usually more-or-less cylindrical and with even covering of pubescence **46**

KEY 3 – MALES (continued)	

46 (45)

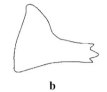
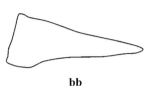

b — bb

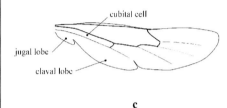
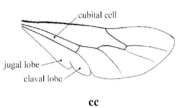

c — cc

a Integument metallic blue AND legs black except for a minute yellow spot at base of each tibia

b Mandibles rather short and narrowing abruptly towards apex, ending in three teeth, black

c Jugal lobe of hindwing very short, much less than half length of claval lobe and not reaching anywhere near as far as vein closing cubital cell .... *Ceratina* (page 264)
One British species – *cyanea*. Fairly small (6-7 mm), shining metallic blue bee. Nests, and overwinters, in bramble stems. The "Blue Carpenter Bee".

aa Integument black, or if metallic then legs either entirely black or more extensively yellow

bb Mandibles sickle-shaped, narrowing evenly from base to a simple point, sometimes yellow-marked

cc Jugal lobe of hindwing long, well over half length of claval lobe, and extending as far as or beyond vein closing cubital cell 47

KEY 3 – MALES (continued)

47 (46)

a Bands or spots of whitish flattened hairs, if present, situated on apical
part of each tergite, usually extending beyond the apical margin and
thus masking it; sometimes with basal bands AS WELL

b Outer cross-veins of similar thickness and pigmentation to adjacent veins

c IF head and thorax metallic bronze or green, then legs predominantly
yellow or orange .... *Halictus* (page 170)
<small>Small to medium-sized species (6-11 mm); integument black
or metallic greenish; legs extensively yellow.</small>

aa Bands or spots of whitish flattened hairs, if present, situated basally
and often originating beneath the apical margin of the previous tergite

bb Outer cross-veins thinner and less well pigmented than adjacent veins
(less distinct than in females and sometimes very difficult to appreciate)

cc IF head and thorax metallic bronze or green, then legs dark with at
most tarsi yellow .... *Lasioglossum* (page 172)
<small>Very small to medium-sized species (4-12 mm); integument black or metallic
greenish to bluish; legs usually less extensively yellow than in *Halictus*.</small>

48 (44)

a Face and/or mandibles with clear yellow or reddish-yellow markings
on the integument **49**

aa Face, and mandibles, except perhaps extreme apex, black (but may
have yellow hair) **53**

49 (48)

b **bb**

a Integument shining metallic blue

b Mandibles rather short and narrowing abruptly towards apex ....
.... *Ceratina* (page 264)
<small>One British species – *cyanea*. Fairly small (6-7 mm), shining
metallic blue bee. Nests, and overwinters, in bramble stems.
The "Blue Carpenter Bee".</small>

aa Integument black or marked with yellow or reddish-yellow

bb Mandibles long, narrowing evenly from base to apex (sometimes
with an accessory tooth) **50**

KEY 3 – MALES (continued)

50 (49)

a Some part of front or mid femora or tibiae clear yellow or reddish-yellow, usually fairly extensively (if, very occasionally, front and mid femora and tarsi apparently brownish-black, then abdomen with yellow spots on the integument of one or more tergites) **51**

aa Front and mid femora and tibiae completely black or brownish-black **52**

---

51 (50)

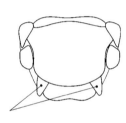

b	bb

a Abdomen with paired pale spots formed from dense flattened scale-like hairs

b Axillae, on either side of scutellum, large and triangular, projecting backwards as a pair of teeth .... ***Epeolus*** (page 254)
    Medium-sized species (6-11 mm); cleptoparasites of *Colletes*.

aa Abdomen without scale-like hairs, instead patterned by yellow, red or brownish spots or bands due to pigmentation of the integument

bb Axillae, on either side of scutellum, small and inconspicuous, not projecting backwards as teeth .... ***Nomada*** (page 235)
    Small to large species (4-15 mm); abdomen patterned and shining
    (hence wasp-like); head and thorax often heavily punctured.
    Cleptoparasites of *Andrena*, *Lasioglossum*, *Melitta* and *Eucera*.

KEY 3 – MALES (continued)

52 (50)

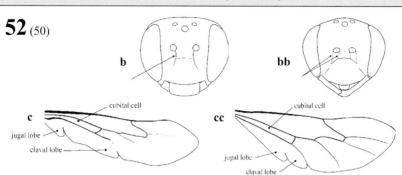

a First segment of antenna (scape) with a yellow mark on front surface, contrasting with rest of antenna

b One subantennal suture present, visible as a black line cutting through yellow facial mark above clypeus

c Jugal lobe of hindwing very short, much less than half length of claval lobe [care needed – may be folded under] .... ***Anthophora*** (page 258)
  Fairly to very large species (9-16 mm); usually rather hairy; abdomen with hair bands in some species; eyes, in life, sometimes rather greenish.

aa First segment of antenna (scape) brownish-black, like rest of antenna

bb Two subantennal sutures present, showing as shining lines descending from antennal socket to meet upper border of clypeus, the shining suture defining the clypeus slightly thickened at these points

cc Jugal lobe of hindwing long, more than half length of claval lobe and reaching as far as the vein closing the cubital cell .. ***Andrena*** (in part) (page 131)
  Fairly small to large species (6-15 mm); a small section of this large genus has the face marked with yellow; one species with tergites 2 and 3 blood-red.

53 (48)

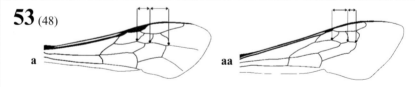

a Lower border of third submarginal cell (measured between intersection with its bordering cross-veins) distinctly longer than that of second submarginal cell **54**

aa Lower border of third submarginal cell more-or-less equal in length to that of second or even shorter **55**

KEY 3 – MALES (continued)

54 (53)

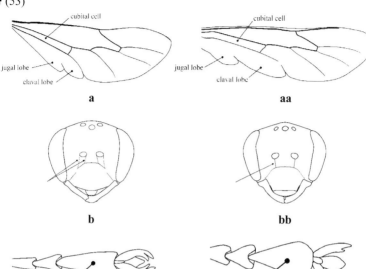

a   aa

b   bb

c   cc

a Jugal lobe of hindwing long; its length, measured from base of wing, distinctly more than half the length of claval lobe, usually reaching as far out as the vein closing the cubital cell [care needed – may be folded under]

b Two subantennal sutures present, showing as shining lines descending from antennal socket to meet upper border of clypeus, the shining suture defining the clypeus slightly thickened at these points

c Last tarsal segment slender, at least three times as long as wide ....
....*Andrena* (page 131)
Small to large species (5-15 mm); a very large and diverse genus with species ranging from almost hairless to densely haired, shining to dull, some banded, and some with reddish markings on abdomen.

aa Jugal lobe of hindwing short, less than half length of claval lobe, and not nearly reaching vein closing the cubital cell

bb One subantennal suture present

cc Last tarsal segment broad, about twice as long as wide ..... *Melitta* (page 204)
Medium-sized to large species (8-13 mm); integument dark; some species with whitish hair bands on abdomen; most species with antennal segments long and concave below, the antennae appearing "knobbly".

KEY 3 – MALES (continued)

55 (53)

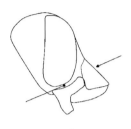

| a, b | aa, bb |

a Cheek (malar space) short, distance from lower margin of eye to mandibular base less than one fifth of width of mandible here

b Face strongly protruding, clypeus at about 45° to vertical

c Abdomen mainly sparsely haired and shining, with very long hairs confined to base, tergites with paired lateral spots formed from flattened hairs .... *Melecta* (page 262)

> Large to very large bees (12-16 mm), black with greyish-white hair; scutellum with paired apical prongs (difficult to see beneath hair). Cleptoparasites of *Anthophora*.

aa Cheek (malar space) long, equal to or longer than width of mandibular base

bb Face almost flat, clypeus vertical

cc Abdomen relatively densely long-haired, especially towards apex, never with rounded spots but often with complete or interrupted bands of coloured hair .... *Bombus* (page 266)

> Large to very large species (12-17 mm); Bumblebees and Cuckoo Bumblebees. [Includes the former genus *Psithyrus* now considered a subgenus of *Bombus*].

PREDATORS, PARASITES AND OTHER ENEMIES

Bees, in all their stages from egg to adult, are under constant attack from a large range of enemies. Because they produce very large numbers of offspring they, like all insects, have to be checked or their numbers would get out of control. Their enemies range from mammals, birds, spiders, wasps, flies and mites to, rather surprisingly, other bees. See Plate 45.

Badgers and foxes can cause serious losses to bumblebees by digging up their nests to consume the larvae and honey, but they also dig out nests of solitary bees in a bank in my garden. The honey-buzzard, which is a rare breeder in south-west Surrey, digs out the nests of bumblebees and social wasps, eating the combs and larvae. Many insectivorous birds take smaller bees but probably avoid the larger ones for fear of being stung; bee-eaters get round this problem by rubbing the bees on a stick to get rid of the sting. Hobbies have been seen catching and eating bumblebees over Thursley Common, and woodpeckers probably eat a proportion of larvae and pupae of dead-wood-nesting species. The crab spiders in the family Thomisidae are the best-known of the bee-killing spiders. They are cryptically coloured and lie in wait for their prey on flower-heads; when a bee alights on the flower it is grabbed by the spider's front legs, immediately injected with venom and then slowly consumed by sucking out the body contents; the perfectly preserved husk of a bee can often be found on flowers. Although relatively small they often take bumblebees. On heathlands the pink-bodied *Thomisus onustus* perfectly matches the colour of the heather flowers on which it sits in wait, whilst the common *Misumena vatia*, in white, yellow or green colour forms, is mainly seen in gardens on daisy flowers. Bees are also often caught in the webs of orb-web spiders, such as the garden spider *Araneus diadematus*. A few species of social and solitary wasps prey on bees; the hornet *Vespa crabro* occasionally takes honey bees and probably some solitary bees, whilst the female bee-wolf *Philanthus triangulum* preys solely on the honey bee, which she grabs in flight, slings under her body and places in each cell in her underground nest burrow. This solitary wasp is now abundant in Surrey, mainly on heathland, and must exact a large toll on the beleaguered honey bee population because each female can have as many as 50 cells and some nesting aggregations consist of thousands of nests. Another solitary wasp *Cerceris rybyensis* preys on solitary bees, mainly the small halictine species of *Halictus* and *Lasioglossum* but sometimes *Andrena* species; Surrey prey records of this wasp include *Andrena argentata, A. bicolor, A. dorsata, A. flavipes, A. fuscipes, Halictus rubicundus, H. tumulorum, Lasioglossum calceatum, L. fulvicorne, L. malachurum, L. morio* and *L. prasinum*. Of the flies only the larger robberflies, such as *Asilus crabroniformis* and *Machimus atricapillus*, have been known to capture adult bees in flight. Mites, sometimes in large numbers, are commonly found on larger bees, especially bumblebees, and these can eventually kill the bees by sucking their body fluids; dead bumblebees are often found covered in hundreds of mites. The introduced Asian mite *Varroa jacobsoni* has recently become a serious parasite of honey bee colonies in this country, destroying large numbers of hives.

The stored food, which all bees provide for their young, attracts various insects. The females of the four, large, fat and flightless oil beetles in the genus *Meloe* dig a pit in the soil in which they deposit huge numbers of eggs. The resulting small larvae, or triungulins, swarm up plant stems; some of these reach flowers where they climb onto incoming bees and a few are carried in to the bees' nests. There they develop by feeding on the pollen provision, thus starving the bee larva. All species of these *Meloe* are probably now extinct in Surrey although the reason for this decline is not known. There are various flies which are parasites or predators of bees but the one most likely to be seen at nesting aggregations of solitary bees is the female shadow fly, a species in the *Miltogramma* genus. This small, dull fly 'shadows' an incoming pollen-laden mining bee to its nest burrow and then loiters around the entrance until the bee flies off. She then enters the nest and lays an egg on the pollen mound; on hatching, the fly larvae feed on the pollen and if there are many of them the bee larva is starved to death.

Various insects attack the larvae and pupae of bees; for instance, several species of parasitic wasps of the families Ichneumonidae, Gasteruptiidae and Pteromalidae lay their eggs in bee larvae which are later consumed by the parasitic larvae; some species are equipped with very long ovipositors for reaching the larvae of dead-wood-nesting bees. A few species of the brilliantly metallic ruby-tailed wasps, or jewel wasps, are parasitoids of mason bees; the common blue and green *Trichrysis cyanea* probably preys on *Heriades truncorum* and *Chelostoma florisomne* as well as on solitary wasps, such as *Trypoxylon* species, but the larger, red and blue *Chrysura radians* can usually be seen on dead trees where *Osmia* species, particularly *O. leaiana*, are nesting. This latter wasp enters the bee's nest and lays an egg on the pollen in a cell; the wasp larva starts to eat the bee larva very slowly but as soon as the full-grown bee larva makes a cocoon it quickly eats the whole larva and makes its cocoon inside the bee cocoon. It is a parasitoid, because it kills its prey, rather than a parasite, which merely lives off its prey. The two primitive wasps in the family Mutillidae, commonly known as velvet ants because the females are wingless and hairy, are parasitoids of bees; the large *Mutilla europaea* parasitises bumblebees and the tiny, ant-like *Smicromyrme rufipes* can often be seen on sandy banks where it attacks the nests of small *Lasioglossum* bees and ground-nesting sphecid wasps.

Female bee-flies, like the common spring-flying *Bombylius major*, scatter their eggs around the nest entrances of mining bees such as *Andrena* and *Lasioglossum*. The eggs hatch quickly into tiny larvae which enter the nest where they develop as ectoparasites of the bee larvae. Certain species of flies in the family Conopidae develop as internal parasites of adult bees. The conopid fly waits on vegetation and attacks a foraging bee with a quick pounce, momentarily grasping it whilst inserting an egg between two abdominal segments. The larva eats the internal organs of the bee, eventually killing it, and then pupates inside the husk of the body of its host. The black and yellow, wasp-like *Conops flavipes* and *C. quadrifasciatus* are parasitic on bumblebees, as are the very common reddish-brown *Sicus ferruginatus* and the slender *Physocephala rufipes*. The smaller and duller *Myopa buccata* is probably a parasite of mining bees whilst the very small, black *Thecophora atra* is usually found flying around nesting aggregations of *Lasioglossum morio,* of which it is probably a parasite.

The strangest of all the internal parasites of adult bees are the curious species of *Stylops* in the insect order Strepsiptera. Little is known about these insects, which were until recently thought to be related to beetles but due to recent DNA investigation are now believed to be more closely related to flies. The winged male can fly but the female remains in the host bee, her body consisting mainly of a sac full of eggs and larvae, with only her head and thorax sticking out between the bee's abdominal segments; the male pupa also projects from the bee's abdomen in the same way. Stylopised bees, mainly those in the genus *Andrena*, often have their sexual characters changed around so that males appear more female and vice-versa; they frequently become sterile and the size and proportions of their body are altered so that they become difficult to identify. The mated female *Stylops* produces thousands of tiny, active larvae (known as triungulins), which have emerged from eggs inside her, and these are carried by the host bee to flowers and eventually, by hitching a ride on another bee, to a larva in the nest of this new host bee. The stylopid larva enters the larva of the bee and moults into a legless maggot which lives in the host bee larva, absorbing food from its blood.

But the most extraordinary fact is that in Surrey almost 28% of the species of bees, i.e. 54 out of 193, are parasites of other bees; they are social parasites and cleptoparasites (meaning nest-stealers), commonly known as cuckoo bees, because they lay their eggs in the nests of other bees, and their larvae eat the host bee's pollen. The female cuckoo bees can often be seen flying slowly around the nest sites of the host bees, locating the nests by smell; the cuckoo waits for the host female to leave the nest and then crawls in and lays an egg in a fully provisioned cell, and, in the case of *Sphecodes*, destroys the host's egg, replacing it with its own. In most other cases, after hatching from the egg the parasitic larva uses its large, sickle-shaped mandibles to kill the host's egg or larva, and then develops by eating the pollen mass in the cell. The female cuckoo bumblebee enters the nest of its host bumblebee when the colony is already well formed with plenty of workers, and then either drives out or kills the queen, destroys any of the host eggs and lays her own eggs in the cells. Her larvae are then cared for and fed by the host workers; she produces only males and future queens, but no workers. None of the different cuckoo bees need to forage for pollen, so they have no pollen-gathering hairs, brushes or pollen baskets. Most of them have very tough cuticles to avoid attack by their hosts, and many are brightly coloured or have colour patterns resembling their host bees.

Cleptoparasitism (nest-stealing) is more widespread in bees than in any other group of insects, because they store food for their young in nests. In Britain, and in Surrey, there are seven genera, or subgenera, of cuckoo bees:

1. **Sphecodes**
   Fourteen red-bodied species parasitic on various species in the genera *Lasioglossum* and *Halictus*, and two which parasitise species of *Andrena*.

2. **Stelis**
   Only four (one now extinct in Surrey) black species which parasitise various species of megachiline bees in the genera *Anthidium, Osmia, Hoplitis and Heriades*.

3. **Coelioxys**
   Five (one now extinct in Surrey) species with distinctive white hair-bands on a black body, which parasitise various species in the genera *Megachile* (leaf-cutters) and some *Anthophora*.

4. **Nomada**
   Twenty-six (four now extinct in Surrey) highly coloured species, many wasp-like with black and yellow bands and some with red bodies; they parasitise various subterranean-nesting species in the genera *Andrena, Lasioglossum, Melitta* and *Eucera*.

5. **Epeolus**
   Two black and red species which parasitise various species of *Colletes*.

6. **Melecta**
   Two (one now extinct in Surrey) white-spotted, black species which parasitise two species of *Anthophora*.

7. **Bombus (Psithyrus)**
   Six species of cuckoo bumblebees which are social parasites of various species of bumblebees.

Many of these cuckoo bees parasitise only one species, i.e. they are host specific, but others will parasitise a number of different species in the same genus. There is still a lack of evidence in some cases as to exactly which cuckoo species parasitise which hosts. Most of the 138 non-parasitic bee species are parasitised by cuckoo bees, the exceptions being all of the *Hylaeus* and a very few species of *Andrena*, such as *A. florea*.

But the worst enemy of bees is man who not only destroys their specialised habitats by intensive agricultural methods and by development, but also kills them and their nectar and pollen sources by the use of insecticides and herbicides.

MIMICRY

Predators of insects, such as birds, avoid eating bees and wasps because of their stings. But many stingless insects also avoid being eaten because they are mimics of wasps, most of them having black and yellow bands. Many bees are rather cryptically coloured, by being covered in brown or black hairs, except for most of the cuckoo bees which either have warning red colours, such as *Sphecodes* and some *Nomada*, or are banded black and yellow, as in most *Nomada* species, which are clearly wasp mimics.

Many species of hoverflies are mimics of bees and bumblebees (see Plate 44 and Stubbs & Falk, 2002). Species with brown, hairy bodies, such as those in the genus *Cheilosia* and *Eristalis*, are mimics of brown bees, *Eristalis tenax* (commonly known as the drone-fly) and *Criorhina asilica* closely resemble honey bees, whilst *Volucella bombylans*, *Merodon equestris* and three species of *Criorhina* are bumblebee mimics. *V. bombylans* and *M. equestris* even come in three different colour forms, one of which is black-haired with a red tail resembling *Bombus lapidarius*, another has yellow and black hair with a white tail resembling *Bombus lucorum,* and the third is brown-haired like *Bombus pascuorum*; *Criorhina ranunculi* has two colour forms, red-tailed and white-tailed. Female *V. bombylans* crawl into bumblebee nests to lay their eggs, the larvae being scavengers on debris below the cells, possibly also attacking the bumblebee larvae. Another bumblebee mimic, but in an entirely different family, is the bee-fly *Bombylius major*, which has already been mentioned as a bee parasite; this fly is brown-haired and resembles *Bombus pascuorum* especially as it hovers in front of flowers.

SOCIALITY IN BEES

The great majority of bees are solitary, that is, the female almost never lives to see her offspring; she will make a nest, provision the cells with pollen and nectar, lay an egg in each cell, close up each cell and then go off to repeat the process until she dies after a week or two. Many species of solitary bees nest close to each other in aggregations which might at first sight appear to be a social colony, but each female has her own nest and there is no cooperation with others. Very few species, for instance *Andrena bucephala* and *A. ferox*, may share a nest entrance but probably each female has her own nest burrow leading off the entrance burrow. The carpenter bees, *Ceratina cyanea* and *Xylocopa violacea*, hibernate together as adults, often with two generations sharing the same hole, which may be the old nest-hole.

However, some species of *Halictus* and *Lasioglossum* and all the non-parasitic bumblebees are social bees, whilst the honey bee *Apis mellifera* has the most highly complex social structure. In Britain there are a small number of halictine species which are primitively social, such as *Halictus rubicundus, Lasioglossum malachurum* and *L. pauxillum*. In *L. malachurum* the overwintered female, or queen, makes a burrow with about six cells in the spring and rears her first brood of workers. The workers, which are smaller than the queen, help to build a new burrow with more cells and to forage while one worker guards the nest entrance. This second, or sometimes even a third, nest produces males and queens in late summer; the new mated queens hibernate and the old queen dies. Bumblebees have an annual life cycle very similar to that of social wasps. Mated queens overwinter in underground burrows, in leaf litter or under bark. In the spring the queen starts a nest either underground, usually in an abandoned small mammal burrow, or at the surface of the ground, under dry leaf litter. The queen makes a space in the nesting material and then builds a honey pot from wax secreted from below her abdomen. She fills her honey pot with regurgitated nectar and some eggs are then laid on a mass of pollen which is surrounded by a wax cell. The queen incubates the cell by lying across it. The larvae are progressively fed on a pollen-nectar mixture, the wax cell being gradually enlarged to accommodate the growing larvae. The first adults are workers which build further cells and forage for food. Some species, called 'pocket-makers', build wax pockets near the base of the cell, into which the foragers deposit their loads of pollen to feed the larvae. This diet is supplemented by a pollen-nectar mixture regurgitated to the larvae through a small hole in the cell. In other species, called 'pollen-storers', the foraged pollen is stored in empty pupal cocoons or specially built wax cylinders. A pollen-nectar mixture is squirted into the larval cell through a hole in the wax covering. Further wax cells make an irregular-shaped nest. At pupation the larva spins a silken cocoon. The wax from the cell is then removed and used to build further cells. The workers carry out all the work in the nest as well as foraging whilst the queen merely lays eggs. Some mature bumblebee colonies may have from 100 to 400 workers, depending on the species, and at this stage males and future queens are produced. These leave the nest and after mating the males die and the queens find a place in which to hibernate. The colonies of the honey bee are much larger, comprising up to 50,000 workers, and they are perennial because the queen does not die at the end of summer but may live for up to 20 years, laying up to a thousand eggs a day. Another difference is that new colonies are formed by a swarm, consisting of an old queen and about 10,000 workers, splitting off from the old colony and flying to a new site. The social life in the colony is highly complex and cannot be dealt with her but there are many books on the matter, one of the best and most readable being *Bees of the World* by Christopher O'Toole and Anthony Raw, which also discusses sociality.

Sociality has arisen in only four orders in the insect world; in the ants and termites, where all species are highly social, and in the wasps and bees, where only a few species are social in varying degrees. In the bees sociality has evolved independently at least eight times world-wide but in Britain only in the two subfamilies Halictinae and Apinae. But sociality poses many questions, many of which are still unresolved. For instance, why has it evolved in so few insects? If ants and termites are probably the most successful insects in the world why have other insects not followed suit? But the question which caused Charles Darwin the greatest problem, and nearly caused him to reject his theory of evolution by natural selection, was how infertile worker bees could pass on their traits to the next generation. Knowing nothing of genetics he thought that social insects were different and one had to look at the whole colony rather than the individual. It was not until 1964 that W.D. Hamilton put forward the theory of 'kin selection', based on his findings that, because female bees have mothers and fathers but males have only mothers, all infertile worker sisters and their fertile sisters are 75% related, but mothers and daughters are only 50% related. Thus it pays infertile workers to sacrifice themselves if it will help their fertile sisters to succeed in rearing their offspring.

CLASSIFICATION OF BEES

Insects, like all other living organisms, are classified by taxonomists into groups, in order to try to show the the relationships and differences between the various Orders, Families, Genera and Species into which they are divided. Bees all belong to the family Apidae in the Order Hymenoptera. The classification of the bees of Surrey, down to genus level, is shown below.

Class **INSECTA**
  Order **HYMENOPTERA**
    Suborder **APOCRITA** (Section Aculeata)
      Superfamily **APOIDEA**
        Family **Apidae**
          Subfamily **Colletinae**
            Genus *Hylaeus*
            Genus *Colletes*
          Subfamily **Andreninae**
            Genus *Andrena*
            Genus *Panurgus*
          Subfamily **Halictinae**
            Genus *Halictus*
            Genus *Lasioglossum*
            Genus *Dufourea*
            Genus *Sphecodes* (cleptoparasitic)
          Subfamily **Melittinae**
            Genus *Macropis*
            Genus *Dasypoda*
            Genus *Melitta*
          Subfamily **Megachilinae**
            Genus *Anthidium*
            Genus *Stelis* (cleptoparasitic)
            Genus *Heriades*
            Genus *Chelostoma*
            Genus *Osmia*
            Genus *Hoplitis*
            Genus *Megachile*
            Genus *Coelioxys* (cleptoparasitic)
          Subfamily **Apinae**
            Genus *Nomada* (cleptoparasitic)
            Genus *Epeolus* (cleptoparasitic)
            Genus *Eucera*
            Genus *Anthophora*
            Genus *Melecta* (cleptoparasitic)
            Genus *Ceratina*
            Genus *Xylocopa*
            Genus *Bombus* (some are social parasites)
            Genus *Apis*

EXPLANATION OF SPECIES ACCOUNTS AND MAPS

Accounts are given for all the 193 species of bee that were found during the survey period (1985-2008) in Surrey, and 29 more that have been recorded at some time prior to 1985, making a total of 222 species. All species accounts follow a similar pattern.

NAME

The heading for each species account is the scientific name of the bee, valid throughout the world, together with the author of the name and date of its publication. The author and date are in brackets if the specific name has subsequently been transferred to another genus. English names are not given, except for three species. The names are based on those used in the Checklist prepared by G.R. Else et al. and published in BWARS Members' Handbook, 2004; if the scientific name has changed from that used in the Checklist then the alternative name is given as a synonym.

The order of genera follows that of the Checklist. Some genera have been divided by taxonomists into subgenera, for example the genera *Hylaeus, Andrena* and *Bombus*. In the genus *Andrena* there are no less than 22 subgenera for the British species and many of them contain only one species. A few subgenera can be useful in grouping together similar species, for instance the subgenus *Micrandrena* is composed of all the very small black *Andrena*. But with so much division it becomes hard to find species in a list in the larger genera. I have therefore decided for simplicity's sake to list all species in a genus alphabetically and not to mention subgenera, except in the genus *Bombus* where the parasitic species are listed alphabetically under the subgenus *Psithyrus*; until very recently these species were included in their own genus *Psithyrus*. Another large genus, *Lasioglossum*, has been subdivided by some taxonomists into three or four genera rather than subgenera, but here again I have disregarded such divisions and all species in the original genus *Lasioglossum* are listed alphabetically.

DISTRIBUTION MAP

Each dot, or cross, represents a record from a 2-kilometre square, known as a tetrad. It shows the distribution of each species, divided into the following date classes:

    1985 to 2008, represented by solid black dots.

    1951 to 1984, represented by grey-filled dots.

    1903 to 1950, represented by open dots.

    Pre-1903 (including those in the VCH), represented by a cross.

NATIONAL STATUS

A rarity status across the whole of Britain has been assigned to most insects and other organisms. The most recent provisional statuses for bees were published in Falk (1991). These are now out of date and it is hoped that a new list of statuses will be published in the near future. Falk's statuses are:

RDB1 Endangered Species in danger of extinction

RDB2 Vulnerable Declining or in vulnerable habitat and likely to become endangered in the near future

RDB3 Rare Very restricted by area or by habitat, or with thinly scattered populations, occurring in no more than 15 10km squares

RDBK Insufficiently known Status information insufficiently known

Nationally Scarce Na **(Formerly Notable A)** Uncommon and estimated to occur in the range of 16 to 30 10km squares

Nationally Scarce Nb **(Formerly Notable B)** Uncommon and estimated to occur in the range of 31 to 100 10km squares

Because Falk's statuses for many species are now misleading, due to the remarkable changes in distribution over the last 20 years, Archer (2007) has devised a new list of statuses for the solitary bees, based on the numbers of 10km squares in which each species occurs in the BWARS provisional distribution maps, from 1970 onwards. These statuses apply to England, Wales and Scotland but not to Ireland or the Channel Islands. His six statuses are defined as follows;

Very rare 1 to 15 10km squares

Rare 16 to 30 10km squares

Scarce 31 to 70 10km squares

Restricted Restricted to about half of England, including East Anglia, southern England and the south-western and southern coasts.

Widespread Extending beyond the restricted area to about three-quarters of England, including the Midland lowlands and nearby coasts, lowland Wales and south-west Scotland, but excluding Northumbria.

Universal Extending also to the rest of England, and further parts of Wales and Scotland.

Under National Status, I first give Archer's status and then Falk's, where applicable.

SURREY STATUS

Following the example of Roger Hawkins in his *Shieldbugs of Surrey* I have assigned a status to each species in Surrey.

Ubiquitous	Found almost everywhere
Common	Found in at least 60 tetrads
Local	Found in fewer than 60 tetrads
Very local	Found in no more than 24 tetrads
Rare	Found in no more than 12 tetrads
Very rare	Found in no more than 6 tetrads
Extinct	Not recorded during the survey period (1985-2008) and now presumed extinct within the county

These statuses are qualified in some way for a few of the species.

There are approximately 550 tetrads wholly or partly in Surrey.

VCH STATUS

This is the status of each species given by Saunders in his account of the bees of Surrey in *The Victoria County History of Surrey*, published in 1902. In this account he either described them as being "Generally distributed", by which I take him to have meant widespread and common, or he gave localities where they had been found, with the name of the collector in brackets. If he gave only one or two localities I have assumed that the species was rare or very rare, but if he gave three to six localities then I have assumed that the species was scarce or local. If he gave no records for Surrey then I state "No records", but if the species had not been published or was not known in Britain at that date then I state "Unknown". If the species was known by a different specific name at that time, I give that specific name in brackets. Surrey is lucky to have such detailed information on the bees at that period, and from such an eminent hymenopterist as E. Saunders, who knew the north-west of the county so well; most other counties only had a bare list of species. With this information it is possible to compare the status of most species of bees in 1900 with their status over one hundred years later, in 2008. At the end of each species account I have therefore stated whether I consider the species has increased, decreased or remained the same since 1900.

TEXT

A brief account is given of each genus, with a note of the number of species in the genus, in Britain and in Surrey. Each species account usually starts with a very brief description of the bee (because of the almost total lack of any books published in Britain on bees), its distribution nationally, its flight period and main forage plant and its nesting habits, if known. This is followed by its distribution in Surrey, with some localities given for the scarcer species and all localities for the rare ones, with dates; the recorder's initials are given in brackets after most localities, and a list of recorders with initials is given above. Any other information relevant to Surrey is given, including notes on parasites and hosts, and on flower visits, although I have not given exhaustive lists of flowers visited as these are, or will be, available in other books. In any case it is difficult to say, without close observation, whether a female is foraging or taking nectar from a flower. NHML stands for The Natural History Museum, London.

SPECIES ACCOUNTS

FAMILY APIDAE

All the bees belong to this one family which is, at present, divided into six subfamilies. Some species are highly social but there are species in some subfamilies which are primitively social; the majority are solitary. The females build and provision in a variety of situations, either below or above ground. Subterranean nesters may have specific requirements for their nest sites, for example vertical banks, sloping or flat ground. Friable soil, often found in sandy soils but also in dry clay or calcareous soils, is usually essential. The nest may consist of one or several cells. The cell walls are often of the surrounding material, e.g. soil or plant stems, but may be lined with collected plant material, resin, mud or glandular secretions which harden. The larval food consists of nectar and pollen, sometimes with plant oils, and the cells are mass-provisioned. The pollen, often moistened with nectar, is normally carried on specialised hairs on the propodeum, underneath the abdomen or on the hind legs, but sometimes in the crop of the female. Nectar is always carried in the crop. A few species collect pollen from a single plant species (monolectic bees), some species from a limited number of related plant species (oligolectic bees), whereas others collect pollen from many plant species (polylectic bees). When each cell is fully provisioned, an egg is laid and the cell sealed. There may be one or more generations each year. Several species are cleptoparasites on other species of solitary bees.

SUBFAMILY COLLETINAE

The bees in this subfamily have a short bilobed tongue which they use to line their cells with a mixture of liquid chemicals secreted by their Dufour's gland in the stomach or salivary glands. This mixture dries to form a cellophane-like membrane which is waterproof and fungus-resistant.

Genus *Colletes* Latreille, 1802

These are medium-sized, hairy, solitary bees with short, blunt bilobed tongues and often with conspicuous, pale, wide hair bands, consisting of dense, short adpressed hairs, on the abdomen. Females carry pollen on the hairs on their hind legs and nest in soil, soft mortar of walls and vertical soft sandstone, sometimes in large aggregations. Nest cells are lined and waterproofed with cellophane-like material and provisioned with a semi-liquid mixture of pollen and nectar; the egg is attached to the upper cell wall. Females of *C. succinctus* forage mainly from heathers and those of *C. hederae* from ivy, but the others forage mainly from plants in the daisy family, especially yellow-flowered ones. There is only one generation a year. Bees in the genus *Epeolus* are cleptoparasites of *Colletes*.

Nationally 9 species, with 6 (1 doubtful or extinct) in Surrey.

Colletes daviesanus Smith, 1846

National Status: Universal
Surrey Status: Local
VCH: Generally distributed

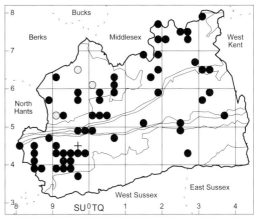

This and *C. similis* have an early flight period, being on the wing by mid-June. It is widespread and common in England but very scarce in Scotland and Ireland and tends to be rather darker than the other species.

In Surrey it is widespread, but scarce on the clay, occurring in almost any habitat, including gardens and urban localities, e.g. Wandsworth Common (DWB) and Wandsworth Park (RKAM). Nests are made in vertical surfaces such as sandy banks, root-plates of trees, sandpits and soft mortar joints of brickwork, where it can cause damage to walls. Females find tansy very attractive but they are normally seen foraging on larger-flowered yellow composites such as common ragwort. They have been seen in numbers foraging on scentless mayweed at Ashtead Common in 2002 (RDH), and at Kew Gardens in 2002 with *C. similis* (DWB), and a male has been recorded on yarrow (RDH).

The bee *Epeolus variegatus* is a cleptoparasite of this species.

Its status is probably unchanged since 1900.

Colletes fodiens (Geoffroy, 1785)   PLATE 9

National Status: Widespread
Surrey Status: Local
VCH: Ripley, Godalming

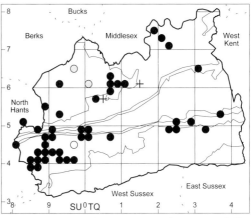

Widespread on sandy habitats in England, Wales and southern Scotland.

In Surrey it is confined to the western heaths, the greensand ridge in the east and the dry acid grassland in the north, e.g. Richmond Park, Wimbledon Common and Brooklands. It is normally found coming to the flowers of common ragwort but has been seen in abundance at Canadian goldenrod on Wimbledon Common in 2001, and, like most *Colletes* species, favours tansy and *Eryngium*. It flies from the end of June till September.

The bee *Epeolus variegatus* is a cleptoparasite of this species. Its status is probably unchanged since 1900.

Colletes hederae Schmidt & Westrich, 1993   PLATE 3

National Status: Very rare

Surrey Status: Very rare

VCH: Unknown

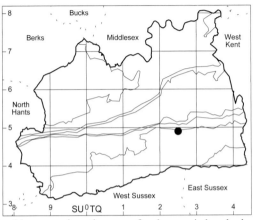

First found in Britain as recently as 2000 on the Dorset coast, this bee since then has spread dramatically along the whole of the south coast and has just started to move inland. It is almost identical in appearance to the heather specialist *Colletes succinctus*, which flies rather earlier. It flies later than all other bees, emerging in late September and continuing till the end of October. Females forage only from ivy blossom, where they can often be seen in hundreds, and nest, sometimes in enormous aggregations, in bare ground.

The first and only Surrey record came from a disused sandpit near Priory Park, Reigate, where J.P. Early watched and photographed a female at her nest in a small sand cliff on 19 October 2007, just in time for entry in this book. It was later captured for positive identification, the very slight differences in the galea and clypeus between this species and *C. succinctus* being visible only under a microscope.

Colletes marginatus Smith, 1846

National Status: Scarce; Na

Surrey Status: Extinct

VCH: Weybridge

In Britain this is a local species confined to sand dunes on the coasts of England and Wales, except for an inland population in the sandy grass-heaths of the East Anglian Brecks. There is a record for Surrey in the VCH from Weybridge by T.A. Marshall in 1890. No voucher specimen is known and the record would seem to be very dubious were it not for the fact that Saunders himself included it in his 1896 book and in his list in the VCH and he probably therefore saw the specimen. It is distinguished by the sharp ridge around the back of the eyes. If the record is correct it may have been a vagrant from the Thames estuary but there is a vague possibility that it was breeding on the dry acid grassland of Brooklands, Weybridge, as the habitat here closely resembles that of the Breck grass-heaths.

Colletes similis Schenck, 1853

National Status: Widespread
Surrey Status: Local
VCH: (as *picistigma*) No records

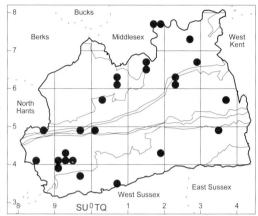

Widespread in southern Britain and Ireland but rarely numerous, this is one of the early species, being on the wing from mid-June, and is not restricted to sandy localities.

Although widespread in Surrey this bee is local, occurring on sandy soils at Frensham and Witley Commons as well as on the Chalk, e.g. Hogs Back, Howell Hill and Priest Hill at Ewell (all DWB) and Worms Heath (GAC), dry acid grassland at Kew Gardens and Brooklands (DWB) and even on London Clay at Wandsworth Common (DWB). Surprisingly, this bee was never found in Surrey in Victorian or Edwardian times, being first recorded as recently as 8 July 1996 on the Hogs Back (DWB). Saunders (1882) gives only a few localities in southern England but says "I expect that this is a common species, but overlooked". It is most surprising that he and others failed to find it or recognise it, especially as he described it as new to Britain. In July 2001 many females were seen on a small patch of waste ground at Kew Gardens, foraging on mayweed with *C. daviesanus* (DWB), but it also comes to tansy.

It nests in level soil and the bee *Epeolus variegatus* is a cleptoparasite of this species.

It was probably overlooked by Saunders and others, but, if not, has increased since 1900.

Colletes succinctus (Linnaeus, 1758)   PLATE 10

National Status: Universal
Surrey Status: Locally common
VCH: Generally distributed

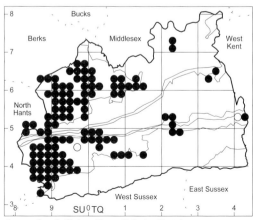

This larger and more brightly-coloured species is one of only three heather-specialist bees in Britain, the others being *Andrena fuscipes* and *Lasioglossum prasinum*. Although foraging almost exclusively from heather (*Calluna vulgaris*) and *Erica* species, it has also been observed collecting pollen from ragwort and a few other plants. It is widespread throughout the British Isles on dry heathland and moorland, flying from July to October.

In Surrey it is also very widespread, occurring wherever heather flourishes and being common on all the heaths, from Farnham in the west to Limpsfield Chart in the east and from Woolmer Hill near Haslemere in the south to Wimbledon Common in the north. Its distribution map is very similar to that of its cleptoparasite *Epeolus cruciger*, as well as those of other heather specialists such as *A. fuscipes* and its cleptoparasite *Nomada rufipes*. It has been recorded on gorse as well as ragwort in Surrey.

Its status is unchanged since 1900.

Genus *Hylaeus* Fabricius, 1793

These are solitary, small, black, almost hairless bees with a short, blunt tongue, bilobed at the tip. They have limited yellow or white markings, usually on the head (with distinctive patterns on the face), thorax and legs. Because of this they are sometimes called 'yellow-faced bees'. They have no hairs for carrying pollen, which is carried with the nectar in the crop. They nest mainly in dead stems (especially bramble) but also in crevices such as in holes in wood, stones or walls. The cells are made in a line and are waterproofed by a cellophane-like material. The egg is laid on a semi-liquid food store of pollen and nectar. There is only one generation a year, usually overwintering as a prepupa. The females are mainly polylectic for their pollen sources.

Nationally 12 species, of which 10, and one doubtful, have been recorded in Surrey.

Hylaeus annularis (Kirby, 1802)

National Status: Restricted

Surrey Status: Local

VCH: (as *dilatata*) Woking

This small species is probably the easiest to identify in Surrey because the female has a distinctive pair of small, almost round, yellow markings on the face while the male has extensive yellow face markings with enormously protruding black and yellow scapes to the antennae and very yellow legs. It is known to nest in dead stems, such as dock, bramble and wild rose, and in holes in wood.

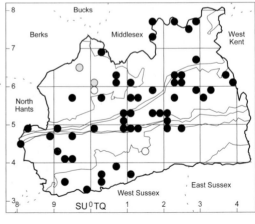

This bee is widespread but local in Surrey, being probably commonest on the Chalk. It is interesting to note that Saunders knew of only one locality a century ago. It has been seen on wild carrot and angelica flowers.

Because it is a bee that is unlikely to be overlooked, it has presumably increased and expanded its range since 1900.

Hylaeus brevicornis Nylander, 1852

National Status: Widespread
Surrey Status: Locally common
VCH: Charlwood, Woking, Wisley

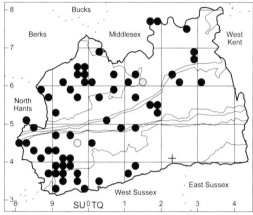

This very small species is reasonably common, both in southern Britain and in Surrey, but it may be overlooked on account of its size. It is similar to the much rarer *H. pictipes*, but the yellow face markings of the female are different and the male has black markings all round the middle of the yellow mid and hind tibiae. It has a long season, being found from late May to mid-September, and may possibly have two generations.

In Surrey this bee is reasonably common and can be found in almost any type of habitat by searching flower heads, especially those of angelica. It is apparently absent from the southeast of the county. I have reared specimens from a dead bramble stem.

It may be commoner now than in 1900.

Hylaeus communis Nylander, 1852

National Status: Widespread
Surrey Status: Ubiquitous
VCH: Generally distributed

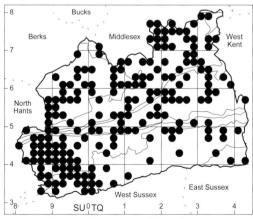

As its name suggests and the map shows, this is the commonest bee in the genus, being very widely distributed throughout England and Wales and Surrey.

It is found from May to August, being most abundant in July, and is often seen at flowers of white umbellifers. It is very similar to others in the group but the female has distinctive striations at the very tip of the clypeus while the male has characteristic yellow face markings that curl around the top of the antennal sockets. This bee visits many different flowers but is often abundant

125

on hogweed, scentless mayweed, Canadian goldenrod, thistles, *Eryngium* and bramble. It has been reared from dead bramble stems from gardens at Milford and South Croydon (DWB and GAC).

Its status is unchanged since 1900.

Hylaeus confusus Nylander, 1852

National Status: Universal
Surrey Status: Local
VCH: Charlwood, Chobham, Woking, Ottershaw, Ripley

Superficially similar to others in the group, this species needs careful examination under the microscope in order to find the subtle differences in punctation and sculpturing of various parts. It is said to favour woodland and nests in dead stems and holes in dead wood. It is widespread in southern Britain, flying from May to September.

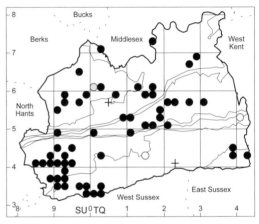

In Surrey this bee is quite local and has a distinctive western bias, being rare in the east. It is particularly common in the south-western, Weald Clay woods such as Sidney Wood and Chiddingfold Forest, where it often comes to angelica. I reared a series of 20 specimens from a wooden trap-nest, drilled with small holes, at Brookwood Cemetery.

Its status is unchanged since 1900.

Hylaeus cornutus Curtis, 1831

National Status: Scarce; Na
Surrey Status: Local
VCH: Godalming, Reigate, Woking, Shere

This species is the only one with an entirely black face, with no yellow markings, in both sexes. The female is also unique in having a prong on each side of the lower clypeus and a swelling just above the clypeus, together forming a depression. The male has a protruding face and very wide yellow scapes to the antennae. It is

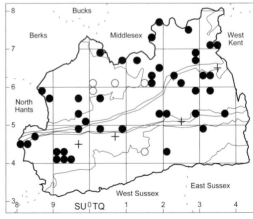

known to nest in dead plant stems. This is a very scarce bee of south-east England although it may have increased recently; it is found in many habitats but mainly on calcareous grassland.

It seems to have become commoner in Surrey also in recent years and is now widespread and not uncommon, especially on chalk and sand, but appears to be absent from the clay. It has been recorded from wild carrot and angelica flowers.

It is probably commoner and more widespread than in 1900.

Hylaeus gibbus Saunders, S.S., 1850

National Status: Rare; RDB3
Surrey Status: Rare
VCH: No records

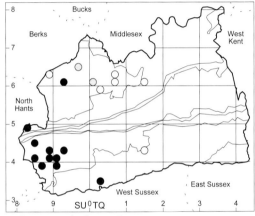

This rare species has always been restricted to the south-central and south-east counties of England and is usually found at woodland edges on heathland, where it nests in beetle and other holes in dead wood. It is one of the larger species in the group; the female has a large amount of yellow on the face but the male is more difficult to identify by differences in punctation, sculpture of the head, etc. It flies from June to early September.

This bee was first found in Surrey at Horsell Common on 2 August 1906 by Nevinson (his specimen is in the NHML). It was next taken in June 1911 by Mortimer at Weybridge, where he collected one on nightshade, followed later by four males and eight females on bramble flowers. On 10 July 1912 Morice was surprised to find a male on bramble flower in the sandpit on Horsell Common. Writing in the *Entomologist's Monthly Magazine* he thought "it rather curious that the existence of *Prosopis genalis* [as it was then known] so near our own doors should never have been discovered nor suspected, either by myself or by my next-door neighbour, the late Mr. Saunders, who himself first introduced the species to the British List (from near Hastings) so long ago as 1879. His captures and those of Mr. Mortimer are the only ones that I have ever heard of in this country." Mortimer found it again at Byfleet in 1912. Between then and 1984 there are about 15 records, with many specimens in the NHML, mainly from the well-worked heaths of Chobham Common and Oxshott Heath.

Since 1985 there have been 15 records, all, except one, coming from the south-western heaths and these are as follows: Hankley Common in 1996 and 1997; Bagmoor Common in 1999; Bourne Wood, Tilford, two in 2000; Bricksbury Hill, Upper Hale in 2000 (all DWB); Frensham Common in 1986 (MEA) and 1995 (ME); Thursley Common in 1992 (ME), in Malaise trap in 1996 (GAC), in 2000 (DWB) and four on thistles in 2008 (JPE); Brentmoor Heath on creeping thistle in 2006 (GAC); Thundry Meadows in 2008 (DWB).

Nearly all heathland species require nectar and pollen sources other than heather. The only record away from the western heaths is of a female taken on 10 June 1997 in Sidney Wood, Dunsfold, a Forest Enterprise wood on Weald Clay with patches of heather (DWB). Clearly Surrey is one of the most favoured counties for this rarity due to the large areas of heaths surrounded by woods.

It was possibly overlooked by Saunders and others until 1906, so its status may be unchanged since 1900.

Hylaeus hyalinatus Smith, 1842

National Status: Widespread
Surrey Status: Local
VCH: Generally distributed

This species is superficially similar to other common species in the group but it does have two distinctive characters that are easily recognisable under the microscope. It nests in sandy soil and has a long flight season like the other commoner species.

This bee is widespread in Surrey, as it is in Britain, but is never very common. It has been recorded on ragwort, Canadian goldenrod, *Eryngium*, angelica and sheep's-bit.

Its status remains the same as in 1900.

Hylaeus pectoralis Förster, 1871

National Status: Rare
Surrey Status: Very rare
VCH: No records

This is one of the very few bees associated with wetland, being found only in or near reedbeds. Until quite recently it was mainly known from the East Anglian fens but is now recorded more widely, especially at coastal sites in south Hampshire and Dorset. It is one of the largest species in the group and flies from June to September, the females probably collecting pollen from various flowers.

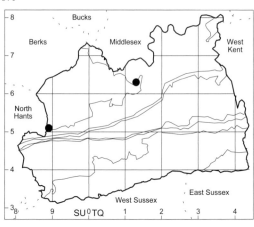

It was first found in Surrey at Black Pond on Esher Common as recently as 27 August 1967 (KMG) and it is still found there regularly (DWB, GAC). The only other reedbed where it has been recorded is at Lakeside Park, Ash (JSD, 1999).

The female generally nests in the empty, used galls of a fly, *Lipara lucens*, which are formed on the flower stems of common reed. These galls are spindle-shaped and very distinctive, and the bee's cells, from one to eight, are constructed in a row within the gall; the nest is sealed with a plug of compacted leaf fragments.

This bee is most easily found by searching the drier edges of reedbeds for the spindle galls (also called cigar galls) and rearing the larva through at home. It can also be netted when flying round the reeds in the summer. There are few reedbeds in Surrey and most of these have been searched for the *Lipara* galls, but the only two places, apart from Esher Common and Ash, where they have been found are Colony Bog on Pirbright Common and a reedbed at Leatherhead. At Colony Bog there were scattered, stunted reeds growing in wettish bog and a high proportion of these had *Lipara* galls, but, of those examined, none contained *Hylaeus* nests (GAC and DWB, 2004).

It has probably spread to Surrey since 1900, but it may have been overlooked by early recorders.

Hylaeus pictipes Nylander, 1852   PLATE 26

National Status: Scarce; Na
Surrey Status: Rare
VCH: Reigate, Chobham, Ripley
This very small species occurs in a variety of habitats, including gardens, and has declined nationally in recent years so that it is now only rarely found away from the south-east corner of England, and even there it is very infrequently recorded. It is similar in size to the common *H. brevicornis* but the female has two distinctive diagonal yellow bars on the face and the male

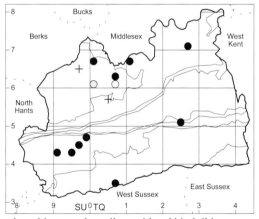

has characteristic black saddle-shaped markings on the yellow mid and hind tibiae.

It has always been a great rarity in Surrey with only 15 records in the last 120 years. Apart from the VCH records, it was taken at Byfleet in 1911 and 1912 (Mortimer) and at Horsell Common in August 1968 (KMG). There are only ten modern records: Walton-on-Thames in a garden on 10 August 1996 (RWJU); the Lammas Lands, Godalming on 23 July 2001 (JSD); a male on hemlock water-dropwort at Brooklands, Weybridge on 7 June 2004; a female on sheep's-bit at Elstead Cemetery on 31August 2005; one at Lyne, near Chertsey, on 24 July 2007; a male at Milford in June 2008 on wild mignonette (all DWB); a male on bramble flower at Colliers Wood on 1 June 2008, which was photographed by D. Element (see Plate 26); a female on Reigate Heath on 30 June 2008 (JPE); one near Shalford on

29 June 2008 (J. Porter). It was also common on 23 and 28 June 2005 on a small patch of just three plants of weld at Cranleigh Brickworks, on Weald Clay, where it was flying in company with *H. communis, H. hyalinatus* and *H. signatus*.

Its status seems unchanged since 1900.

Hylaeus punctulatissimus Smith, 1842

National Status: Extinct
Surrey Status: Doubtful
VCH: No records

There are only two fully authenticated British specimens; one is a male, from Chelsea, Middlesex, in 1827, in the Hope Collection, Oxford University Museum, and the other is a female in the F. Smith Collection, also at Oxford, labelled 'Ham' but with no date. R.C.L. Perkins in 1917 suggested that Ham might be an abbreviation for Hampstead Heath, a locality which Smith visited frequently, but there seems no reason why it should not refer to Ham in Surrey, especially as Smith also visited localities in south London.

Hylaeus signatus (Panzer, 1798)   PLATE 26

National Status: Scarce; Nb
Surrey Status: Local
VCH: Reigate, Chobham, Woking

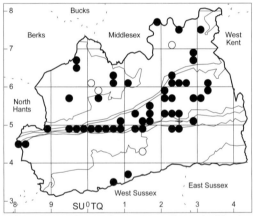

This is the largest bee of the genus in Britain and is locally distributed in southern England where it is closely associated with the flowers of weld and wild mignonette. It is a robust bee with white hair patches on the first tergite of the abdomen that are clearly visible to the naked eye, both sexes being strongly punctate, the male having extensive off-white markings on the face. It flies from June to September and nests in vertical banks, where it may use old nests of *Colletes*, as well as in cavities and burrows in dead stems.

As will be seen from the map this bee is widespread and reasonably frequent in Surrey, especially on the Chalk where wild mignonette is common. It even occurs commonly in Kew Gardens where the non-native white mignonette is grown annually in the Order Beds. Off the Chalk it can usually be found wherever weld is numerous in waste places and on roadsides. I even recorded it at old claypits near Ewhurst and Cranleigh on very small patches of weld, miles from the nearest other known sites. It is easily found by searching clumps of these two plants.

It seems to have become considerably commoner and more widespread since 1900.

SUBFAMILY ANDRENINAE

All members of this group nest in the ground and are strictly solitary, although females of many species nest in dense aggregations and a few species have communal nest entrances.

Genus *Andrena* Fabricius, 1775

This is a very large genus of solitary bees with short pointed tongues; they nest in the ground and are commonly known as 'mining bees'. The cuticle is black, except for males of a few species with a white or yellow face, and some species, in both sexes, with red markings on the abdomen. The hair is white, grey, brown, golden, yellow or black; some species have white or cream hair-bands on the abdomen. Pollen-carrying hairs are present on the sides of the propodeum and on the hind coxa, trochanter, femur and tibia. Nests may be isolated or close together in aggregations. Generally the nest entrance leads to the main burrow with shorter lateral burrows, each ending in a cell or cluster of cells, but females of *A. bucephala*, *A. carantonica* and *A. ferox* may nest communally, with several females sharing a common entrance although it is presumed each has its own discrete nest burrow. The cells are lined with a wax-like substance and the pollen balls are smooth and more or less spherical. Most species have a single generation a year but some have two when the two broods may differ in appearance. Spring species overwinter as adults within their burrows, but summer species overwinter as prepupae. Males emerge a few days earlier than females. Most species are polylectic but some are oligolectic.

Nationally 67 species, of which 56 have been recorded in Surrey although five are now extinct.

Andrena alfkenella Perkins, R.C.L., 1914

National Status: Very rare; RDB3
Surrey Status: Very rare
VCH: Unknown

This is a small black bee, difficult to separate from other similar species (being first described as a new species in 1914), and is rare and very local in southern England. It is double-brooded, flying in late spring and again from July to September, foraging from various plants.

There are only four Surrey records. The first was collected on 5 Sep-

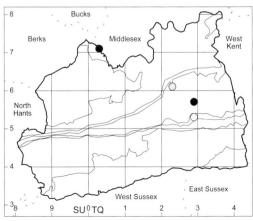

tember 1948 on hawkweed at Merstham by F.D. Lawton, a friend of Baker; the specimen is now in the D.B. Baker Collection at University of Kansas, USA. The second was taken on 19 April 1957 on smallholdings at North Looe Farm, Ewell by Baker, and this specimen is also now in his collection at Kansas. The third was collected on chalk grassland at Farthing Downs, Coulsdon on 30 April 1996 (RDH). This was a male of the rare spring brood and it was on dandelion flowers on the west side of the Downs.The fourth specimen, a female, was taken at Thorpe Hay Meadow as recently as 21 July 2001 (ME). It is probably still very local and under-recorded in Surrey and most likely to be found on the North Downs in the spring or late summer.

Its status is possibly unchanged since 1900, as it was undescribed at that time.

Andrena angustior (Kirby, 1802)

National Status: Widespread
Surrey Status: Local
VCH: Six localities

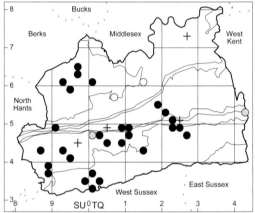

This small, insignificant *Andrena*, distinguished in both sexes by the long marginal area on the second tergite, is widespread in southern Britain but is always local and uncommon. It flies from late April to mid-June in most open types of habitat, the females foraging from various flowers. *Nomada fabriciana* is probably a cleptoparasite of this bee.

In Surrey it is fairly widespread, occurring on heathland, chalk and clay, but is distinctly local. It has not been found in the east of the county nor in or around London.

Saunders cited six localities in the VCH of 1902, all of these being his own records from the 1890s, except that of Latter from Godalming in 1892, whose specimen is in the Haslemere Museum. Saunders' sites were Reigate, Clandon, Wandsworth Common, Chobham Common and Horsell Common. After these comes a specimen in the RHS Wisley Collection, collected by G. Fox Wilson at Wisley in 1920, followed by a record from Abinger by Baker in 1952. The first record during the survey period was from Chobham Common in 1985 (SRM). Since then there have been about 30 records of this bee, mostly from heathlands in the west, the Lower Greensand ridge south of the Chalk and a few from the Chalk itself and from the clay woodlands around Chiddingfold and Dunsfold. A female collected on *Ceanothus* in my garden at Milford in May 2008 had a female *Stylops* sticking out of the abdomen, and from this *Stylops* were emerging dozens of minute and very active larvae, known as triungulins; a male *A. angustior* was also there, on buttercup.

Its status is probably unchanged since 1900.

Andrena apicata Smith, 1847

National Status: Scarce; Nb
Surrey Status: Very rare
VCH: No records

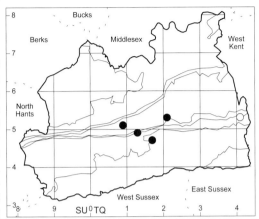

This bee is very similar to the more common *A. praecox* but the males and females are slightly larger, the males having a more pointed tooth on the mandibles than in *A. praecox* and the females having brownish-black hairs on the margin of tergite 4, rather than pale golden as in *A. praecox*. The males behave similarly to *A. praecox*, flying up sunlit tree trunks and poles in a zigzag fashion. It is a very early bee, foraging on sallow blossom from early March to April, and is parasitised by the bee *Nomada leucophthalma*. It is very local but widely distributed in southern Britain.

It was not recorded by the Victorians in Surrey and was only found in the county as late as 1937 at Limpsfield Common (KMG). There are only seven county records in all, but it may well be under-recorded because of its very early flight time, before most hymenopterists are out in the field. Apart from three records at Limpsfield Common in 1937, 1938 and 1945, the only four recent reports are from central Surrey as follows: Headley Heath on 26 April 1996 (ME); White Downs on 8 March 1998 (GAC); North Holmwood Claypit on 19 March 1998 (GAC); Sheepleas, two males on 31 March 1999 (DWB).

It would appear to have increased since 1900, but it was doubtless overlooked by early recorders.

Andrena argentata Smith, 1844   PLATE 15

National Status: Rare; Na
Surrey Status: Locally very
    common
VCH: Chobham, Frensham,
    Ripley

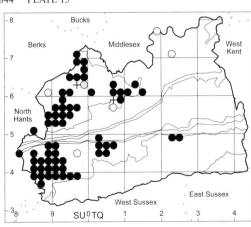

This small bee is restricted to the sandy heathlands of south-east England but it can be abundant where it occurs. Both sexes have a shiny black, punctate abdomen with pure white hair bands. It is single-brooded, flying from June to late August, and collects pollen from heather.

In Surrey this bee is one of the most abundant bees on all the western dry heathlands, as far north as Windsor Great Park and as far east as Oxshott Heath with an outlier at Reigate which was only found in July 2008; it was recorded in 1918 from Wimbledon Common and Kew Gardens but has never been seen there since. It is normally considered to be a heather specialist but it sometimes nests in numbers on dry acid grassland, well away from any heather, such as at Brooklands, Wrecclesham sandpit and an old sandpit at Seale. It normally frequents the hottest and driest areas of loose white sand, where males can often be seen in tens of thousands flying low over the ground searching for virgin females emerging from the sand. These are immediately pounced upon by one, or sometimes up to four or five males. After mating the females can be seen flying low, searching for their nests, presumably by scent, and then diving immediately into the loose sand; the nest burrow is actually made in the compacted sand underneath the loose sand. The nationally scarce bee *Nomada baccata* is a cleptoparasite of this species and is also abundant at almost all its host's sites. In August 2004 I saw both the host and parasite swarming in enormous numbers along 500 metres of wide, loose sandy tracks on Hankley Common, and estimated that there were at least 25,000 pairs of *A. argentata* and a similar number of *N. baccata*.

It has increased and expanded its range since 1900.

Andrena barbilabris (Kirby, 1802)

National Status: Universal
Surrey Status: Locally common
VCH: (as *albicrus*) Generally distributed

Occurring commonly throughout Britain, this bee is usually found in sandy places, nesting in open level paths.

In Surrey it is equally widespread but restricted to sandy areas, such as the western heaths, the acid grasslands around London and the Lower Greensand ridges; it does not occur on the Weald Clay. The

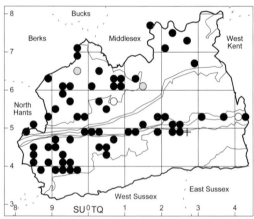

greyish males can often be seen in large numbers, flying low over sunny paths in the spring searching for emerging females. The females almost always nest in well-compacted sandy footpaths. The nests are attacked by the cuckoo bee *Sphecodes pellucidus* which is usually very common at the nesting aggregations of the host. Although this species is considered to be single-brooded, flying from April till June or even July, there are two records for August, which may represent a second brood.

Its status is unchanged since 1900.

Andrena bicolor Fabricius, 1775   PLATE 21

National Status: Universal
Surrey Status: Ubiquitous
VCH: (as *gwynana*) Generally
    distributed

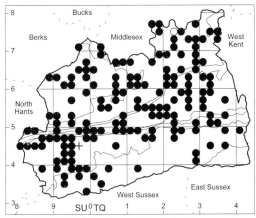

This smallish, dark bee, distinguished in both sexes by having black hairs on the face and on the underside of the middle femur, is common in most of Britain. It flies in two broods, the abundant spring brood from early March to May or June, and the apparently rather scarcer second brood from June to late August. It occurs in almost every kind of habitat and the females forage from various flowers but little is known about their nests. *Nomada fabriciana* is a cleptoparasite of this bee.

In Surrey the map shows that this bee is common over most of the county, including London, but scarce on clay. There are very few old records, presumably because no-one bothered to record common species, but Saunders described it as widespread in 1902. During the survey females of the spring brood have been recorded at the flowers of gorse, alder buckthorn, dandelion, greater stitchwort, forget-me-not and cabbages, and those of the summer brood particularly at bramble but also at creeping thistle, heather, white bryony and *Campanula persicifolia* amongst others. Its cleptoparasite *Nomada fabriciana* is also common in Surrey, but it also attacks other *Andrena* species. The only nest recorded was in a rootplate.

It was probably just as common and widespread in 1900 as it is now.

Andrena bimaculata (Kirby, 1802)   PLATE 11

National Status: Scarce; Nb
Surrey Status: Local
VCH: Woking, Chobham,
    Shirley, Ripley, Worplesdon

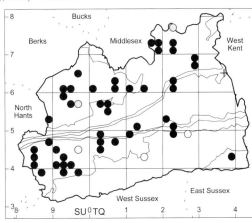

This large, dark bee is very local in southern England, being restricted to sandy soils where it nests in banks. It is double-brooded, flying in the spring and again in July and August. The spring females, with black hairs on the clypeus, forage mainly from gorse, while the summer ones, with golden clypeal hairs, rely on ragwort. Although it is local in Surrey it is widespread on sandy soils, being quite common in the south-west and on the dry acid grasslands around London such as Richmond Park and Wimbledon Common. It is absent from the clay and chalk. Some Surrey females have red markings on the abdomen, which is unknown on females from the south-west and further north in the country. Summer females have been seen on rape and wild parsnip. Nests have been observed in a bank at Milford and at Ripley Green, where there was a nesting aggregation of at least ten nests in a south-facing, sparsely vegetated bank (DWB). The cuckoo bee *Nomada fulvicornis* is a cleptoparasite of this species and in Surrey is not uncommon.

Its status is probably the same now as in 1900.

Andrena bucephala Stephens, 1846

National Status: Scarce; Na
Surrey Status: Very local
VCH: Chobham, Box Hill

This medium-sized, dark bee is widespread in southern England but is scarce and very local. It is mainly found on chalk downland and in woods, flying from mid-April to late May. The rare bee *Nomada hirtipes* is a cleptoparasite of this species.

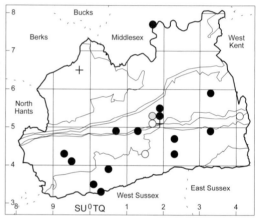

In Surrey it is also scarce and local, being found mainly on chalk, e.g. Westcott Downs, Box Hill, Netley near Shere, Riddlesdown Quarry, Headley Warren and Kenley, but also in the woods on the Weald Clay, e.g. Sidney Wood near Dunsfold, Leigh and Edolphs Copse. It also occurs at Kew Gardens and I once found a singleton in my garden at Milford and another at nearby Bagmoor Common on alder buckthorn. Where it is found it can often occur in large numbers. The females share entrance burrows although it is presumed they have discrete nests within the burrow; a nesting aggregation is usually sited on a south-facing slope. The females can often be seen jostling around the entrance trying to get in. They frequently occur in large numbers at these aggregations and there are often many *Nomada hirtipes* flying and crawling around the burrow entrances.

Its status is similar to that in 1900.

Andrena carantonica Pérez, 1902 (= *scotica* Perkins, R.C.L.)

National Status: Universal

Surrey Status: Ubiquitous

VCH: (as *rosae*) Generally distributed

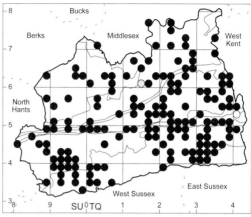

This dark, medium-sized bee, with few distinguishing characters, is common and widespread over most of Britain, flying from the end of March to mid-July. The females forage from many species of flowers and sometimes nest in large aggregations. *Nomada marshamella* and *N. flava* are cleptoparasites of this bee.

It is equally common and widespread in Surrey, being one of the commonest spring bees which can be found in almost any habitat. Females are often found foraging on willow, blackthorn and hawthorn but have also been seen on field maple and white bryony.

It is difficult to say what its status was in 1900 as it was confused with *A. trimmerana* and *A. rosae* but it is likely to have been the same as today.

Andrena chrysosceles (Kirby, 1802)   PLATE 23

National Status: Widespread

Surrey Status: Ubiquitous

VCH: Reigate, Charlwood, Chobham, Ockham

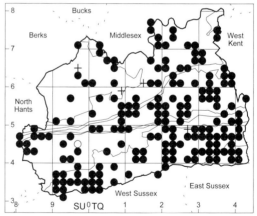

Widespread and common in England and Wales, this rather small, shiny black bee has characteristic orange legs in the female, and the male is one of the very few bees with a white clypeus. It flies from the end of March to the end of June.

This bee is very common and widespread throughout Surrey, regardless of soil type, but is particularly fond of woodlands and woodland edge. It is very catholic in its choice of forage plants, but is often found at hawthorn, cow parsley and buttercups; other flower visits include blackthorn, forget-me-not, dandelion, wood spurge, hemlock water-dropwort, ground-elder, germander speedwell, wood avens, lesser stitchwort and bramble. Little is known about its nesting habits.

It may have increased since 1900.

Andrena cineraria (Linnaeus, 1758)   PLATE 18

National Status: Widespread
Surrey Status: Local
VCH: Wandsworth

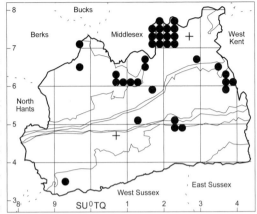

This is one of the most beautiful and distinctive species of all the *Andrena*, with its blue-black body and pale ashy grey hairs on the front and back of the thorax, giving it a ruffed look (the males have an all-grey thorax). It is widespread in southern Britain, but only recently so in the south-east; it flies mainly in April, the females foraging from various flowers and nesting in large or small aggregations in barely vegetated or bare soil, mainly on sand but, in the south, also on chalk. *Nomada lathburiana* is the well-known cleptoparasite of this bee.

In Surrey it was known only from Wandsworth 100 years ago but it started to expand its range southward and westward in the 1980s and is now fairly widespread in the north of the county, being especially common around the Richmond Park area. Saunders mentions in his book (1896) that although it was very widely distributed in Britain "yet I have never taken it at either Woking or Chobham". In the VCH (1902) he gives Wandsworth (where he lived till 1857) as the only Surrey site. The next record was from Wimbledon Common in 1944 (C.O. Hammond) but there were no more until 1986 when it was found on the Chalk at Addington, well south and east of Wimbledon (GBC). Since then there has been a mass of records from numerous sites. In the 1990s it was found at Kew railway station, Barnes Common, Putney Heath, Mitcham Common, Ham Common, Wimbledon Common again, Richmond Park, and even as far west as Chobham Common. In 2000 it was recorded even further west at Windsor Great Park and in 2001 as far south as Reigate Heath. In 2002 it was seen at Ranmore Common on the North Downs west of Dorking, where it was nesting in acid clay, and at Ditton Common near Esher, as well as in Kew Gardens and in 2005 at Oxshott Heath.

At many of these sites this bee nests in large aggregations, usually in bare or sparsely vegetated ground under or near low branches of oak trees, the burrow entrance often being under dead oak leaves; its cleptoparasite *Nomada lathburiana* is nearly always present with it in good numbers. At Ham Common on 8 May 2001 the ground was black with males and females over many square metres and I estimated there were about 10,000 bees, with about 5,000 *Nomada lathburiana*. But where this enormous number forage for pollen is a mystery, because the nesting site is in a small clearing in a wood, with very few flowers in the immediate neighbourhood. It has been recorded on flowers of brassica and spurges at Kew Gardens, and on hawthorn and hemlock water-dropwort elsewhere.

It has increased and expanded its range dramatically since 1900.

Andrena clarkella (Kirby, 1802)   PLATE 13

National Status: Universal

Surrey Status: Widespread but local

VCH: Generally distributed

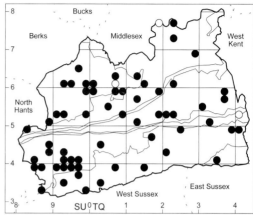

This is another very early bee associated with sallow blossom, sometimes appearing as early as mid-February. The females are easily recognised, being very robust and hairy, with a black head and abdomen, a dull brown thorax and brown pollen hairs on the hind legs. Like the previous species the males zigzag up sunny tree trunks and the nests are parasitised by *Nomada leucophthalma*. It is widely distributed throughout Britain but is local.

In Surrey it is also very widespread but always local, being found on heaths and in open woodland as well as at old sandpits and claypits. It occurs in London at Barnes Common and Wimbledon Common. Because of its size, and being so distinctive, it is probably not overlooked in spite of its very early flight time. It nests in large aggregations, especially in rootplates (Bagmoor Common, DWB) and on bare banks in open woodland, e.g. in my garden at Milford, and in banks of old sandpits, e.g. Horsell Common and Reigate. The earliest flight date is 11 February 2008 in a sandpit at Reigate (JPE).

Its status is unchanged since 1900.

Andrena coitana (Kirby, 1802)

National Status: Universal

Surrey Status: Very rare

VCH: Woking, Chobham

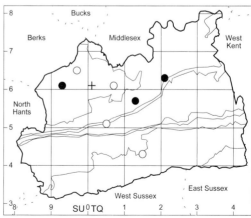

This small bee, the female black and shiny and the male with a yellow face, is widespread throughout Britain and Ireland but is rare in the south-east.

It has always been rare and local in Surrey and has only been recorded from three localities in modern times. After the Victorian records, and a few more in Edwardian times, it was first rediscovered on 13 August 1972 at Bookham Common (PJC), where it was found again on 23 August 2000

(AJH) and in July 2007 (GAC). The only other modern records are from Brentmoor Heath on 21 August 1998 (AJH), and from rough ground along the Hogsmill River at West Ewell, where Baker reported finding it regularly in 1990. It is a rather unobtrusive bee and may possibly be overlooked. Saunders found it commonly on thistles in August 1884. The rare *Nomada obtusifrons* is a parasite of this species, but it has been found only once in Surrey, in 1913.

It may have declined since 1900 but it has always been scarce and elusive.

Andrena congruens Schmiedeknecht, 1883

National Status: Rare; Na

Surrey Status: Very rare

VCH: Unknown

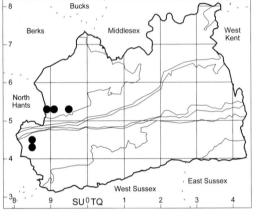

A very scarce bee of southern England which is also very local but can be abundant where found, especially in old sandpits. It is double-brooded, flying from mid-May to mid-June and from July to mid-August. The males are very similar to the common *A. bicolor*.

It is rare in Surrey, having been found in only two areas, both in the extreme west. Surprisingly it was only first recorded in the county as recently as 1997, when males were found in early April, flying low and fast in some numbers over a sunny south-facing sandy bank at Wyke Common on Ash Ranges. In April and May 2000 males were seen again, flying low in large numbers over sandy banks at Ash Common and Furze Hill at the western edge of Ash Ranges, about a mile or two from the original site. In April 2002 large numbers of males and females were seen flying low over a bank where they were nesting at Cobbett Hill, next to Ash Ranges (all DWB). The only site away from Ash Ranges is at Tilford Woods, where a large aggregation, of males and females, was found in April 2002 (ME, DWB), again on a sunny, south-facing sandy bank. So far no specimens of the second brood have been seen. It was not mentioned in Saunders (1896) nor in the VCH, as it was then confused with *A. bicolor*. However, it has apparently increased and spread in England in the last century and therefore it may well be a recent arrival in Surrey.

It has probably increased since 1900.

Andrena denticulata (Kirby, 1802)

National Status: Universal

Surrey Status: Widespread but local

VCH: Chobham, Woking, Godalming

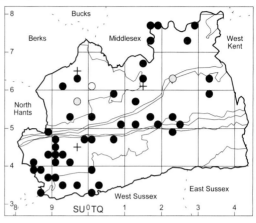

This late summer, medium-sized bee, flying from July to September, is very hairy in the female, with distinctive wide, pale hair bands; the male has a characteristic ridge behind the eye. It forages on yellow composites and is widespread throughout the British Isles but is never common and usually local, being found mainly on sand.

In Surrey it also local and never found in numbers. It frequents mainly open grassland with plenty of yellow composites, such as the dry acid grasslands around London, e.g. Richmond Park and Kew Gardens, the Lower Greensand, where this is not too acid for the composites, the Chalk and even on dry clay woodland rides. Females have been recorded at sheep's-bit and ragwort, and a nest was found in bare ground at Westcott Downs.The cuckoo bee *Nomada rufipes* is a cleptoparasite of this species.

It probably has the same status now as it had in 1900, although it may have increased.

Andrena dorsata (Kirby, 1802)   PLATE 22

National Status: Widespread

Surrey Status: Ubiquitous

VCH: Woking, Chobham, Cobham

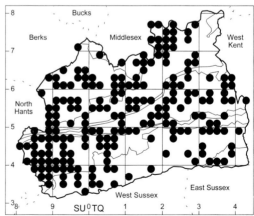

Widespread and frequent in southern Britain, this medium-sized bee flies in two broods, in the spring and then again from July to September. The females forage from a variety of plants.

This is possibly the commonest *Andrena* in Surrey and is very widely distributed on all types of soil. It occurs in most sorts of habitat, including scrub, road verges and gardens. Female flower visits include tormentil, trailing tormentil, hogweed, bramble, creeping thistle, angelica and *Ceanothus*.

It probably has the same status as it had in 1900, but it may have increased.

Andrena falsifica Perkins, R.C.L., 1915

National Status: Rare; Na

Surrey Status: Very rare

VCH: Unknown

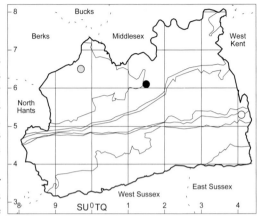

Another rare, small bee that is probably overlooked in Britain as it is never numerous and occurs only in southern England. It is black and similar to other species in the group, and was described as a new species in 1915; little is known about its habits.

There are only four records for Surrey and just one of these is modern. It was first recorded in June 1908 by Saunders at Chobham Common, where it was found again in June 1968 by Guichard, who also found it at Limpsfield Common in May 1939. All three specimens are at the NHML. The sole modern record is of one taken on Oxshott Heath on 24 July 2004 (ME). It may be overlooked by modern recorders due its small size and similarity to other small black bees.

Its status is unchanged since 1900.

Andrena ferox Smith, 1847   PLATE 2

National Status: Very rare; RDB1

Surrey Status: Very rare

VCH: No records

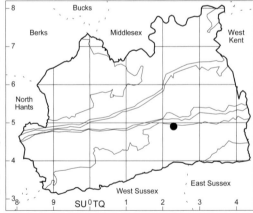

This bee has always been an extremely rare species in Britain, with only very few recent records from Kent, Hampshire (the New Forest) and Surrey.

The only record for Surrey is of a single female taken on the golf course at Reigate Heath on 11 May 1998 (RDH). Various searches have been made for it at this locality since then, but so far without success, although it is assumed that there is a breeding population somewhere in the vicinity. The female, which has distinctive, translucent yellow, hind tibiae clothed with pale golden hairs, apparently collects pollen only from oak trees and the flight season therefore has to coincide with the brief flowering of the oaks in May. Because the females spend most of their time foraging high in the canopy, they are likely to be found only at their nesting aggregations in short turf, where they share a communal entrance to the nest burrows. Some males are distinguished by their very large heads, from which they derive their specific name. However, both sexes have been found taking nectar from hawthorn flowers in the New Forest, locally in abundance, and it would be worth searching these at the right time in Surrey.

It is not possible to say whether it has increased since 1900.

Andrena flavipes Panzer, 1799   PLATE 14

National Status: Restricted
Surrey Status: Ubiquitous
VCH: (as *fulvicrus*) Generally distributed

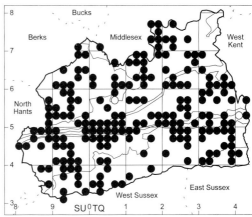

This large bee, with distinctive orange-yellow pollen hairs on the hind tibia and wide pale hair bands on the abdomen, has expanded its range recently, being now found throughout southern England and Wales. It is double-brooded, flying in the spring and again from July to September, and forages from a wide range of plants.

This bee is widespread and very common in Surrey, being just as frequent on the clay as on the sand, and has increased dramatically in the last 20 years. It sometimes occurs in vast nesting aggregations of thousands of nests, especially at old sandpits and claypits, such as Papercourt Gravelpits, Hambledon Claypit, Wrecclesham Sandpit and North Holmwood Claypit. Female flower visits include Canadian goldenrod, dandelion, forget-me-not, buttercup, common knapweed, ragwort, charlock, beaked hawk's-beard, *Eryngium* and creeping thistle.The cuckoo bee *Nomada fucata* is a cleptoparasite of this species, being present at almost all nest sites of its host, and sometimes being seen in thousands at these large nesting aggregations.

It has probably increased since 1900.

Andrena florea Fabricius, 1793   PLATE 5

National Status: Scarce; RDB3
Surrey Status: Locally very
  common
VCH: Woking, Chobham,
  Weybridge

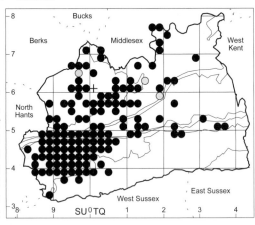

This striking medium-sized shiny black bee is conspicuous by the wide red band on the abdomen of both sexes. It has a very restricted distribution in south-east England where it occurs in Hampshire, West Sussex, Surrey, Middlesex and Essex. It is the only British *Andrena* that is restricted to a single plant species for pollen, namely white bryony.

In Surrey this bee is widespread and locally common, being found, sometimes in large numbers, at almost every flowering plant of white bryony. The plant and the bee are abundant on the Bargate Sands around Godalming, and common on the western Chalk as well as on the Greensand and Bagshot Sands, but both are absent from the Clay and from very dry acid heaths. Both plant and bee also occur sporadically on the dry acid grassland commons around southwest London, such as Barnes Common, Richmond Park and Kew Gardens. From the map the bee seems to peter out in the east of the county but this may be due to lack of recording, as the plant does occur there. It was possibly as common and widespread in Victorian times but there is no doubt that the centre of distribution in this country is west Surrey.

Because the bee is restricted to white bryony it is one of the easiest bees to find; go to a flowering plant and there it will be, identifiable at once by its red band, although many other *Andrena* species and honey bees will also be found there. Both males and females fly to white bryony for nectar but swarms of males have been observed flying round patches of gromwell at Sheepleas and Westcott Downs (DWB), these possibly being mating areas.

The nest burrows are usually found in hard sandy paths, sometimes in large aggregations. This bee is single-brooded and flies from late May to early July, but it has been observed nesting as late as 4 August 1998 at Burrowhill Green and even 10 August 1998 at Compton (DWB); the latest date it was seen, but not nesting, was at Albury Heath on 13 August 1998 (GAC).

It has probably increased and expanded its range since 1900.

Andrena fucata Smith, 1847

National Status: Universal
Surrey Status: Local
VCH: Chobham, Oxshott, Ockham

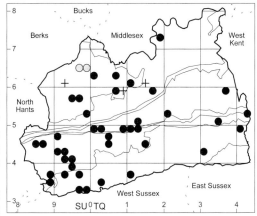

A medium-sized *Andrena*, but rather nondescript in both sexes, this species flies from mid-May to mid-July and occurs locally throughout Britain. It collects pollen from various flowers and is probably parasitised by *Nomada panzeri*.

It is widespread in Surrey but not common and is never numerous where found. It occurs in open woodland and on heaths and is said to nest solitarily but no nests have been found. A female taken at Fairmile Common on 5 April 2002 was stylopised. It probably has the same status now as it had in 1900.

Andrena fulva (Müller, 1766)   PLATE 19

National Status: Universal
Surrey Status: Common
VCH: Generally distributed

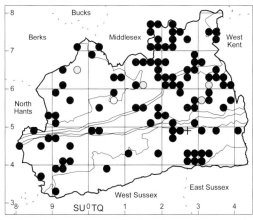

The female of this widespread and common species is by far the most beautiful of all *Andrena*, the abdomen being covered in dense, bright golden-orange hairs, with rather darker reddish-brown hairs on the thorax. The male is clad in golden-brown hairs.

In Surrey it is widespread, being common in and around London but less so in the west, as the map clearly shows. The reason for this London bias may be that the females prefer to nest in level open ground with short, sparse grass, especially where there are bare patches. The dry acid grasslands of Richmond Park, Wimbledon, Barnes and Wandsworth Commons provide prime nesting sites and it is very common at these localities. Garden lawns are often used as nest sites and because of its striking appearance this bee is sometimes reported by non-hymenopterists. It usually nests in aggregations, often at the same site for several cosecutive years, making a mound of excavated earth at the centre of which is the burrow entrance; an aggregation of 70 nests was seen at Richmond Park. It flies from late March to mid-June and collects pollen from numerous sorts of herbs, bushes and trees, and is an important pollinator of fruit crops such as plum and currants; records of flower visits include blackthorn, field and Norway maple, and *Ceanothus*. The locally common *Nomada panzeri* and the very rare *N. signata* are cleptoparasites of this bee. The latter has been seen at *A. fulva* nesting sites at three different localities in recent years: at Headley Heath, Reigate Heath and a garden in Reigate.

Its status is unchanged since 1900.

Andrena fulvago (Christ, 1791)

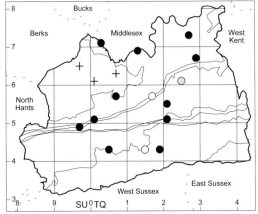

National Status: Rare; Na

Surrey Status: Rare

VCH: Chobham, Woking, Weybridge

A very local, smallish bee of southern England, the female is distinguished by its bright orange, hairy hind legs and orange tip to the abdomen. It has a long flight period from mid-May to July. The females forage from yellow composites.

There are only 11 very widespread modern records for this bee in Surrey and only a handful of older ones. It seems to favour sandy and chalky localities. The modern records are: Mitcham Common, 21 June 1991 and 6 July 1991; Molesey, 21 May 1995 (all RKAM); Thorpe Hay Meadow, 3 June 2001 (ME); Wisley, by the A3, 19 June 2001; Winterfold, on ragwort on 25 July 2001 (both DWB); Betchworth Sandpit, 19 June 2001 (GAC); Strawberry Grove, Guildford, 17 June 2006 (AJH); Stoke Park, Guildford, on beaked hawk's-beard on 22 May 2007 (RDH); Wandsworth Common, two females on a hawk's-beard on 10 June 2007 (DWB); Great Hurst Wood, Headley, 18 May 2008 (GAC); Newdigate, 11 June 2008 (RDH).

Its status is unchanged since 1900.

Andrena fuscipes (Kirby, 1802)   PLATE 12

National Status: Universal
Surrey Status: Locally common
VCH: Chobham, Woking, Ripley, Holmwood

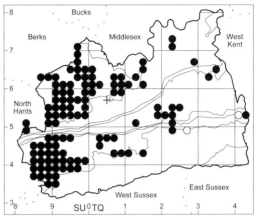

One of the very few heather specialist bees, this medium-sized species is dull black with distinct pale hair bands on the abdomen, the female having brown hairs on the thorax and the male being much smaller. It flies in late summer, foraging almost entirely on heather and nesting in bare sand amongst the heather. It is distributed throughout the British Isles but is restricted to heaths and moors.

In Surrey this bee is usually abundant on all the heaths, including the high hills of Hindhead and Leith Hill, and it even occurs on small remnant patches of heather such as at Ranmore and Ditton Commons, Nower Wood, Croham Hurst and Addington Hills. Its distribution map shows almost the exact distribution of heather in Surrey. The small silvery-grey males can often be seen flying fast around a clump of heather or small gorse bush. The cuckoo bee *Nomada rufipes* is a cleptoparasite of this species, and is also abundant in late summer. Its status has probably not changed since 1900.

Andrena haemorrhoa (Fabricius, 1781)   PLATE 21

National Status: Universal
Surrey Status: Ubiquitous
VCH: (as *albicans*) Generally distributed

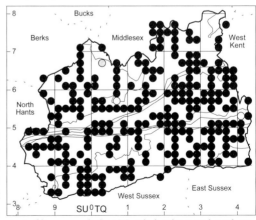

This is one of the commonest spring bees, distributed throughout the British Isles and occurring in almost all types of habitat. The medium-sized female has foxy-red hairs on the thorax and at the tip of the shiny black abdomen, and has orange hind legs; the smaller male has similar, but duller, colouring. It forages from a wide range of plants, being found mainly on willow at the start of its season in late March, but later on hawthorn, blackthorn and apple. Little is known about its habits.

It is equally abundant and widespread in Surrey, being found at woodland edges, hedgerows, gardens, meadows and scrub where females visit blackthorn, hawthorn and apple, as well as dandelion, rape, hogweed, buttercup and *Ceanothus*. The cuckoo bee *Nomada ruficornis* is a cleptoparasite of this species.

Its status is unchanged since 1900.

Andrena hattorfiana (Fabricius, 1775)   PLATE 6

National Status: Scarce; RDB3
Surrey Status: Very rare
VCH: No records

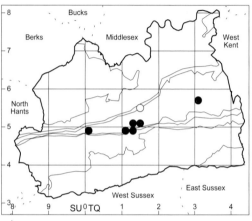

This large and very distinctive bee is widespread in southern England but has declined substantially in the last 50 years, due probably to agricultural improvement, and is now very local. Its main pollen source is field scabious *Knautia arvensis* but it is sometimes seen at small scabious. It is a large and spectacular black bee, occasionally having red bands on the abdomen, and flies from late June to mid-August.

In Surrey it has been found at six sites along the North Downs, the first record being that on 17 July 1949 by Baker at Happy Valley, Coulsdon where it was found again in 1999 (PJH). Baker found it on two dates in July 1950 at Bookham, and in 1960 it was taken at Westcott Downs near Dorking and at White Downs, just to the west, by S.F. Imber. In 1998 it was refound at Westcott and White Downs in good numbers by various recorders and in the same year it was also seen in numbers at Pewley Down, Guildford, where it was refound in 2005 (DWB). In view of its size it is surprising that it was not recorded by earlier collectors in Surrey, although they rarely visited the North Downs. The vast majority of specimens seen are females visiting flowers of field scabious, conspicuous by their salmon-pink pollen-loads, but the occasional male, with its distinctive white face, is sometimes seen flying extremely fast from one flower to another, searching for females. The red colour form has been seen only once in Surrey, at Westcott Downs. The extremely rare *Nomada armata* is a cleptoparasite of this species and was recorded by F. Smith at Woking in about 1850, although the host has never been found in that area.

It was no doubt present on the North Downs in 1900, but overlooked, and its status is probably unchanged.

Andrena helvola (Linnaeus, 1758)

National Status: Widespread

Surrey Status: Local

VCH: Esher, Reigate, Stoke d'Abernon

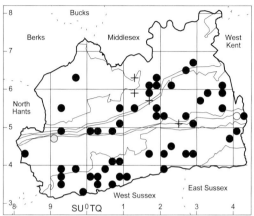

This rather dull, nondescript bee is similar to others in the genus and is widespread in southern Britain, becoming scarce in the north. This is mainly a woodland bee, flying from late April to the end of June and nesting solitarily.

In Surrey it is fairly widespread but always local and never seen in numbers. As the map shows, it is commoner on chalk and clay than on the sand. Although females collect pollen from many plants, they have a definite preference for wood spurge, a plant which is most abundant in the woodlands on the Weald Clay in the very south of the county. Most records therefore come from these clay woodlands, especially the Forestry Commission ones, such as Botany Bay, Sidney Wood and Holmens Grove, which are clear-felled in rotation, thus encouraging mass flowering of wood spurge.

Its status is unchanged since 1900.

Andrena humilis Imhoff, 1832   PLATE 17

National Status: Scarce; Nb

Surrey Status: Very local

VCH: Reigate, Chobham, Woking, Oxshott

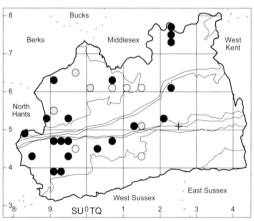

A very local bee of sandy soils in southern England and Wales, this is one of the few species of *Andrena* in which the male has a white face; the medium-sized female is a dull black with dull yellow hairs on the hind legs and tip of the abdomen. It flies from mid-May to late June and forages from yellow composites.

It is also very local in Surrey, being restricted to the sandy western commons and the Lower Greensand ridges to the east, acid grassland on top of the North Downs at Ranmore Common, as well as a few of the acid grassland commons around London, e.g. Barnes and Wimbledon Commons. It is usually found at flowers of dandelion. It sometimes nests in large aggregations on flat, almost bare ground, such as at Puttenham Common and Ranmore Common. The rare cuckoo bee

Nomada integra is a cleptoparasite of this species, and has been recorded with it at Puttenham Common, Cobbett Hill Common, Ranmore Common and Headley Heath. Its status is probably unchanged since 1900.

Andrena labialis (Kirby, 1802)   PLATE 16

National Status: Widespread
Surrey Status: Local
VCH: Generally distributed

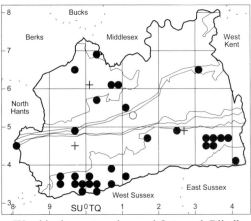

The females of this large bee have shiny, very punctate, black abdomens with pale hair bands, and the males have very distinctive large yellow areas on the face. It is locally common in southern Britain, flying from May to July and foraging on various plants, mainly clovers.

It is very local in Surrey, being mainly found on the Weald Clay in the forestry rides of Chiddingfold Forest, Sidney Wood and Somersbury Wood in the west, and around Outwood, Blindley Heath and Dormansland in the east. Away from clay it is extremely local, being found at Wrecclesham Sandpit (where Gault Clay is present), Chobham Common, Thorpe Quarry and Beddington Sewage Farm, near Mitcham. The scarce cuckoo bee *Sphecodes rubicundus* is a cleptoparasite of this species, one of the few of its genus to parasitise an *Andrena* species, and can be found commonly at most of the host's nest sites on the Weald Clay. Its status is probably unchanged since 1900.

Andrena labiata Fabricius, 1781   PLATE 23

National Status: Restricted; Na
Surrey Status: Common
VCH: (as *cingulata*) Chobham, Woking, Holmwood

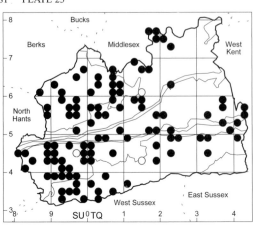

This small bee is easily identified because it is the only *Andrena* species with a mainly red abdomen in both sexes, the male also having a white face. However it could possibly be overlooked or mis-identified as a *Sphecodes* species. It is very local over southern England, being mainly confined to sandy areas.

It is common and widespread in Surrey, although it decreases in the east before reappearing near the Kent border. It occurs wherever its main forage plant, germander speedwell, is found, and can be seen on the Weald Clay as well as on the acid grassland commons around London. It is particularly fond of germander speedwell but also visits other small herbaceous plants such as forget-me-not, greater stitchwort, chickweed, sheep's-bit, beaked hawk's-beard, brassica and star-of-Bethlehem. It has increased dramatically in recent years.

The endangered RDB1 bee *Nomada guttulata* is a cleptoparasite of this bee but it has been recorded with it on only two occasions, at Richmond Park in 2003 (DWB) and just north of Horsell Common in 2004 (AJH).

It has probably increased since 1900.

Andrena lapponica Zetterstedt, 1838   PLATE 24

National Status: Universal
Surrey Status: Local
VCH: No records

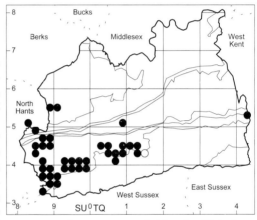

Widespread in the British Isles and often common, but only where its main forage plant, bilberry, occurs, this medium-sized bee has bright orange-brown hairs on the thorax. Although it is considered to be very scarce in south-east England this bee has very recently been found to be common along the bilberry-covered greensand ridges of south Surrey, and in a few places on the Bagshot Sands ridges where bilberry occurs. It was unrecorded by the Victorians, presumably because they never ventured into the southern parts of the county, and was first discovered in 1906 at Leith Hill (probably by Mortimer), where it was found again in 1921 (Mortimer). After that it was not recorded again until 5 May 1989 when it was found at Friday Street in the same general area, where bilberry is abundant (RKAM). From 1996 onwards it was found in numerous localities wherever bilberry was present but particularly in the Leith Hill area, around Hindhead, Witley and Farnham (all DWB), with outliers at Limpsfield Chart (GAC) and Mountain Wood, West Horsley, where it was recorded in 1997 (DWB), and on Bagshot Sands at Ash Ranges (DWB).

The males, which are much slimmer and duller than the females, fly fast and low over the bilberry bushes but the females fly slowly amongst the bushes collecting pollen and are not easily seen in spite of the conspicuous white pollen loads on their hind legs. *Nomada panzeri* is a cleptoparasite of this species and it can often be seen flying around bilberry bushes where the bee occurs.

Its status is probably unchanged since 1900, having been overlooked by early recorders.

Andrena marginata Fabricius, 1776   PLATE 25

National Status: Scarce; Na

Surrey Status: Very local

VCH: (as *cetii*) Chobham, Woking, Clandon, Croydon

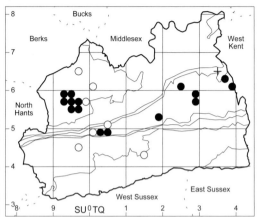

This medium-sized bee is very distinctive because the female has three different colour forms: an entirely orange abdomen, apart from the black basal segment, or an entirely black abdomen like the male, or an intermediate form of a banded orange and black abdomen. The male is conspicuous by its white clypeus. It is local and uncommon, mainly in southern Britain, on calcareous grassland and heaths, and seems to be declining. It is strongly associated with small scabious and field scabious on the calcareous grassland, and with devil's-bit scabious on heaths. Little is known about its nesting habits, but it may nest gregariously.

In Surrey this bee is widely distributed but very local. It is found at various places on the Chalk along the North Downs, where it is associated with small and field scabious, and flies from mid-July to August. It is also common, and sometimes abundant, in a small area around Pirbright where it is associated with devil's-bit scabious on grass heath at Brookwood Cemetery and Bisley Ranges. Here it flies rather later, from August to late September, to coincide with the later flowering devil's-bit scabious. Here, also, it is commonly parasitised by the very rare bee *Nomada argentata* that is unknown from the Chalk. A female was seen entering its nest site in bare earth, but under a plantain leaf, at the side of a track in Brookwood Cemetery (DWB). All three colour forms of the female seem to be equally common in Surrey.

Its status is unchanged since 1900.

The plates are not arranged in taxonomic order. First come a few national rarities, Surrey specialities and Surrey rarities, followed by various bees with their cuckoo bees, mostly *Andrena* with *Nomada*. After that come other bees roughly in taxonomic order, some with both sexes to show how different they can be, and bumblebees with their cuckoos. Plate 44 shows some bee mimics, Plate 45 shows predators and parasites, Plate 46 shows a bee box and some nests and Plates 47 and 48 show nesting sites.

Photographer credits are given in brackets at the end of each caption; DE is David Element, GAC is Graham Collins and JE is Jeremy Early.

Nomada flava, female. A cuckoo bee of various mining bees. (DE)

PLATE 1

National and Surrey rarity
1. *Andrena ferox* on hawthorn. Male, showing large head and red bands on abdomen. (GAC)
2. *Andrena ferox*, female, showing yellow hind tibia with golden hairs. (GAC)

PLATE 2

Surrey rarities
1. ***Colletes hederae***, female, at her nest in a Reigate sandpit. The only Surrey specimen. (JE)
2. ***Bombus hypnorum***, worker, at the same sandpit. A recent national and Surrey colonist. (JE)

PLATE 3

1

2

National and Surrey rarities

1. *Andrena niveata*, female, showing continuous white hair band on tergite 4 of abdomen. Only ever found at Ewell. (GAC)
2. *Dufourea minuta*, female. Note two submarginal cells on forewing. Thought to be extinct in Britain until rediscovered in 2007. (GAC)

PLATE 4

Surrey specialities

1. *Andrena florea*, male on white bryony, showing red bands on abdomen. (JE)
2. *Andrena florea*, female, showing less red on abdomen. (JE)
3. Small carpenter bee *Ceratina cyanea*, male, showing white facial marking. (GAC)
4. *Ceratina cyanea*, female, flying to nest in bramble stem. (JE)

PLATE 5

Surrey rarity

1. The large *Andrena hattorfiana* on field scabious. The normal dark female, with salmon-pink pollen on her pollen hairs. (DE)
2. *Andrena hattorfiana*, the uncommon red form of the female. (DE)
3. *Andrena hattorfiana*, the smaller male (white facial marking not visible). (DE)

PLATE 6

Surrey rarities

1. *Hoplitis claviventris*, female. (JE)
2. Her rare cuckoo bee *Stelis ornatula*, female, showing white abdominal markings. (JE)
3. The small and rare *Heriades truncorum*, female on ragwort, showing pollen brush below abdomen. A Surrey speciality. (JE)
4. Her even rarer cuckoo bee *Stelis breviuscula*, female, with no pollen brush. A Surrey speciality. (JE)

PLATE 7

Surrey rarities
1. *Eucera longicornis*, the long-horned bee. Male, showing yellow face. (JE)
2. *Eucera longicornis*, male. (JE)
3. *Megachile dorsalis*, female. Very small and known only from Wrecclesham Sandpit. (JE)

PLATE 8

1. *Colletes fodiens*, female on ragwort, its usual forage plant. (JE)
2. Her cuckoo bee *Epeolus variegatus*, female at the nest site. (JE)

PLATE 9

1. *Colletes succinctus*, female,
   foraging from heather. (JE)
2. Her cuckoo bee *Epeolus
   cruciger*, female. (JE)

PLATE 10

1. *Andrena bimaculata*, female on gorse, showing red patches on side of abdomen. (JE)
2. Her cuckoo bee *Nomada fulvicornis*, female. Note orange facial pattern running up sides of eyes. (JE)

PLATE 11

1. *Andrena fuscipes*, male, on heather. (DE)
2. Its cuckoo bee *Nomada rufipes*, female, showing yellow patch on back of thorax and reddish legs. (DE)

PLATE 12

1. *Andrena clarkella*, a pollen-laden female. (JE)
2. Her cuckoo bee *Nomada leucophthalma*, female, showing two small red dots at back of thorax and orange band at front of abdomen. (JE)

PLATE 13

1. *Andrena flavipes*, female, with conspicuous pale hair bands. (DE)
2. *Andrena flavipes*, male, also with pale hair bands. (DE)
3. Their cuckoo bee *Nomada fucata*, female, showing yellow marking on
   back of thorax and orange band at front of abdomen. (JE)

PLATE 14

1. *Andrena argentata*, a mating pair. Note brown hair on female's thorax. (JE)
2. Their cuckoo bee *Nomada baccata*, male, with white face. (JE)
3. *Nomada baccata*, female. (JE)

PLATE 15

1. *Andrena labialis*, male, with cream facial markings. (JE)
2. *Andrena labialis*, female. (JE)
3. Their cuckoo bee *Sphecodes rubicundus*, female, at nest site. Note almost entirely red abdomen. (JE)

PLATE 16

1. ***Andrena humilis***, female. Note conspicuous yellowish hair band at end of abdomen and yellowish pollen hairs on hind tibia. (JE)
2. Her cuckoo bee ***Nomada integra***, female. Note red abdomen with few black markings. (JE)

PLATE 17

1. The beautiful *Andrena cineraria*, female. (GAC)
2. Her cuckoo bee *Nomada lathburiana*, female, investigating her host's nest. (JE)

PLATE 18

1. The very striking ***Andrena fulva***, female. A common spring mining bee. (JE)
2. Her very rare cuckoo bee ***Nomada signata***, female, inspecting a nest hole at Reigate Heath. Note conspicuous yellow markings on back of thorax and completely clear and wide yellow bands on abdomen. (JE)

PLATE 19

1. *Anthophora plumipes*, male, at yellow archangel. (DE)
2. *Anthophora plumipes*, male, showing cream facial markings. (JE)
3. *Anthophora plumipes*, male. (DE) (1, 2 and 3 show hair pattern on mid tibiae.)
4. *Anthophora plumipes*, female, all black with orange hairs on hind tibia. (JE)
5. Their cuckoo bee *Melecta albifrons*, male, showing white hair patches on mid
   and hind tibiae and on abdomen. (JE)

PLATE 20

1. *Andrena bicolor*, pair mating. Note black hairs on face and size difference between sexes. (JE)
2. *Andrena haemorrhoa*, female. Note reddish hair on thorax. Red hairs at end of abdomen are just visible. (DE)
3. *Andrena nitida*, female. (JE)

PLATE 21

1. *Andrena wilkella*, female, showing interrupted white hair bands and orange hind tibiae. (JE)
2. *Andrena dorsata*, female. (JE)
3. *Andrena trimmerana*, male, showing red patches on abdomen. (JE)

PLATE 22

1. *Andrena labiata*, male, with white facial markings. (JE)
2. *Andrena labiata*, female. The only *Andrena* with almost entirely red abdomen. (JE)
3. *Andrena chrysosceles*, female, showing red legs. (DE)

PLATE 23

1. *Andrena lapponica*, female on bilberry, showing white hairs on hind tibia. (GAC)
2. *Andrena synadelpha*, female, showing brown hairs on abdomen. (JE)

PLATE 24

1. *Andrena marginata* on devil's-bit scabious at Brookwood Cemetery. Female, orange form, with white pollen load. (JE)
2. *Andrena marginata*, female, dark form. (JE)
3. *Andrena marginata*, male, with white clypeus. (JE)
4. Their rare cuckoo bee *Nomada argentata*, female, showing silvery hair patches on side of abdomen. (JE)

PLATE 25

1. ***Panurgus calcaratus***, male. (JE)
2. ***Panurgus banksianus***, male, much larger than *P. calcaratus*. (JE)
3. ***Hylaeus signatus***, male, on wild mignonette, showing white face and conspicuous white hair band on abdomen. This is the largest of the *Hylaeus*. (JE)
4. ***Hylaeus pictipes***, male, on bramble flower. A very small and rare bee with large white facial markings and diagnostic saddle-shaped black markings on mid and hind tibiae. (DE)

PLATE 26

1. *Lasioglossum morio*, female, showing blue/green tinge. (JE)
2. *Lasioglossum prasinum*, female, showing very wide hair bands. A heather specialist. (JE)
3. *Lasioglossum calceatum*, male, with red markings. (JE)
4. *Lasioglossum calceatum*, female. (DE) (3 and 4 show sexual dimorphism.)
5. *Sphecodes geoffrellus*, a cuckoo bee of *Lasioglossum* species. Male, showing more black on abdomen than female. (JE)
6. *Sphecodes geoffrellus*, female. (JE)

PLATE 27

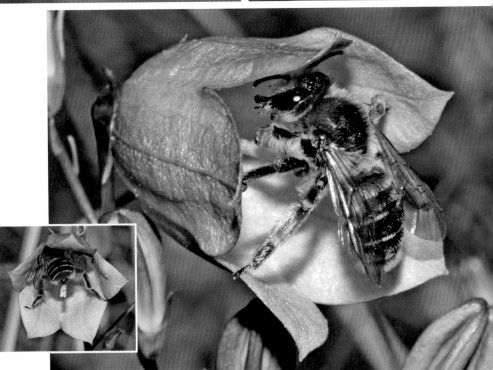

1. *Macropis europaea*, male, with yellow clypeus, on yellow loosestrife. Note the wide, black hind tibia and tarsus. (JE)
2. *Macropis europaea*, female. Note the contrasting white-haired hind tibia and black-haired tarsus. (JE)
3. *Melitta haemorrhoidalis*, female foraging at harebell, with inset showing red posterior. (JE)

PLATE 28

1. ***Dasypoda hirtipes***, male, on yarrow. (JE)
2. ***Dasypoda hirtipes***, female, showing very long-haired hind tibia. (DE) (1 and 2 show sexual dimorphism.)
3. ***Dasypoda hirtipes***, female with pollen-laden hind tibiae at her nest on Frensham Common. (JE)

PLATE 29

1. *Anthidium manicatum*, the wool-carder bee. Male showing facial pattern and silvery hairs on tarsi. (JE)
2. *Anthidium manicatum*, female, showing gold markings on abdomen, surrounded by shaved plant hairs. (DE)

PLATE 30

1. *Chelostoma campanularum*, female. (JE)
2. The larger *Chelostoma florisomne*, female. (JE)
3. *Osmia spinulosa*, female, asleep in scabious. (DE)
4. *Osmia spinulosa*, female, on yellow composite flower. (DE)
5. Shell-nest of *Osmia spinulosa*, sealed with mastic of chewed plant material. (DE)

PLATE 31

1. ***Osmia aurulenta***, pair mating, showing sexual difference. The female is reddish-brown on thorax and abdomen. (DE)
2. ***Osmia aurulenta***, female, at shell-nest. (DE)
3. ***Osmia aurulenta***, male, showing white hairs on sides of thorax. (DE)

PLATE 32

1. *Osmia bicolor*, female, showing striking contrast between black head and thorax, and red abdomen. (DE)
2. *Osmia bicolor*, female, placing dead grass-stem over nest. (DE)
3. *Osmia bicolor*, female, entering shell-nest. (DE)

PLATE 33

1. ***Osmia caerulescens***, male, with brown hairs. (JE)
2. ***Osmia caerulescens***, bluish female. (JE)
3. ***Osmia leaiana***, female, with yellowish-red pollen brush beneath abdomen. (JE)

PLATE 34

1. *Osmia rufa*, female, showing prongs on face below antennae. (JE)
2. *Osmia rufa*, female flying to her nest, showing reddish pollen brush beneath abdomen. (JE)

PLATE 35

Cuckoo bees
1. ***Coelioxys elongata***, female showing pointed tip of abdomen. (JE)
2. ***Coelioxys inermis***, male, showing spiked tip of abdomen. (JE)
3. ***Stelis punctulatissima***, female, with cream bands on abdomen. (JE)

PLATE 36

Leaf-cutter bees

1. *Megachile versicolor*, male. (GAC)
2. *Megachile versicolor*, female, with cut leaf. (JE)
3. *Megachile centuncularis*, male. (JE)
4. *Megachile centuncularis*, female, with cut leaf. She
   is covered in brick dust from her nest in a wall. (JE)
5. *Megachile willughbiella*, male, covered in white
   pollen; note wide, white front tarsus. (JE)
6. *Megachile willughbiella*, female, at pea flower. (DE)

PLATE 37

Nomada, cuckoo bees of _Andrena_ and _Lasioglossum_ species
1. **_Nomada marshamella_**, female. (JE)
2. **_Nomada goodeniana_**, female searching for nest of its _Andrena_ host. (JE)
3. **_Nomada fabriciana_**, female, with diagnostic red and black antennae. (JE)
4. **_Nomada flava_** or **_panzeri_**, male; males are indistinguishable. (JE)
5. **_Nomada ruficornis_**, female. (JE)
6. **_Nomada flavoguttata_**, female; a small species. (JE)
7. **_Nomada sheppardana_**, female; very small and a cuckoo bee of small
   Lasioglossum species. (JE)

PLATE 38

Anthophora
1. ***Anthophora bimaculata***, female, showing green eyes. (JE)
2. ***Anthophora bimaculata***, female, showing facial pattern. (JE)
3. ***Anthophora furcata***, male. (JE)

PLATE 39

Bumblebees
1. *Bombus jonellus*, female, a heather specialist. (JE)
2. *Bombus pascuorum*, female in flight, showing pollen load. (DE)
3. *Bombus pascuorum*, very bright female, newly emerged. (JE)
4. *Bombus pratorum*, female. (GAC)

PLATE 40

Bumblebees

1. *Bombus lapidarius*, male, with yellow collar. (JE)
2. *Bombus lapidarius*, female. (DE)
3. *Bombus lapidarius*, female, with pollen load. (JE)
4. *Bombus rupestris*, female, cuckoo bumblebee of *Bombus lapidarius*. (JE)
5. *Bombus rupestris*, female, showing black wings. (JE)

PLATE 41

Bumblebees and their cuckoos

1. *Bombus lucorum*, queen, with white tail. (JE)
2. *Bombus sylvestris*, her cuckoo, female. (JE)
3. *Bombus terrestris*, queen, with buff tail. (DE)
4. *Bombus vestalis*, her cuckoo, female. (JE)
5. *Bombus vestalis*, female, showing yellow hairs on
   white tip of abdomen. (DE)

PLATE 42

1. Violet carpenter bee, ***Xylocopa violacea***, male, a new colonist to Britain (DE). Inset of small carpenter bee, ***Ceratina cyanea***, is to scale, showing the size difference. (GAC)
2. Honey bee, ***Apis mellifera***, worker at ivy. (DE)
3. Honey bee, ***Apis mellifera***, worker in flight. (DE)
4. Honey bee swarm on back of car; the queen had gone up the exhaust pipe. (Isobel Girvan)

PLATE 43

Bee mimics

1. ***Criorhina floccosa***, a hoverfly mimicking *Bombus pascuorum*. (JE)
2. ***Criorhina ranunculi***, a hoverfly mimicking a white-tailed bumblebee. (JE)
3. ***Merodon equestris***, a hoverfly, female form mimicking a red-tailed bumblebee. (DE)
4. ***Merodon equestris***, form with tawny hair and whitish tail, mimicking *Bombus humilis*. (DE)
5. ***Bombylius major***, a bee-fly mimicking *Bombus pascuorum*. (JE)
6. ***Eristalis arbustorum***, a hoverfly mimicking a honey bee. (DE)

PLATE 44

Predators and parasites

1. The bee-wolf, ***Philanthus triangulum***, a solitary wasp that preys upon honey bees. (JE)
2. A female bee-fly, ***Bombylius major***, laying eggs at the entrance to a bee's nest. (JE)
3. A female parasitic wasp, ***Gasteruption jaculator***, using its long ovipositor to lay an egg in the cell of a mining bee. (JE)
4. A crab-spider, ***Misumena vatia***, with its bumblebee prey. (JE)
5. A jewel-wasp, ***Chrysura radians***, a parasitoid of dead-wood-nesting mason bees. (JE)
6. A conopid fly, ***Conops quadrifasciatus***, mimicking a wasp but a parasitoid of bumblebees. (JE)
7. Another conopid fly, ***Physocephala rufipes***, also a parasitoid of bumblebees. (JE)
8. Wingless female mutillid wasp, ***Smicromyrme rufipes***. It is an ant mimic but a parasitoid of ground-nesting bees. (JE)
9. *Andrena* species parasitised by *Stylops*. Note female parasite sticking out between last two segments of bee's abdomen. (GAC)

PLATE 45

Bee nests

1. *Ceratina cyanea*. Dead bramble-stem split open reveals female in her nest. (GAC)
2. Egg of leaf-cutter bee in its cell. (Kim Taylor)
3. Cigar-like nest of *Megachile versicolor* in opened-up dead wood. (GAC)
4. *Osmia rufa* nest in glass tube of bee box. Female laying egg on pollen mound, with half-constructed cell partition and previously completed cells. Inset shows whole bee box. (Kim Taylor)

PLATE 46

Favoured nest sites

1. Dry lowland heath at Brookwood Cemetery. (JE)
2. South-facing root plates. (JE)
3. Slipping clay cliff at Hambledon Brickworks, nest site of the rare *Eucera longicornis*. (JE)
4. Sandy track on heathland, favoured by many species of mining bees. (JE)
5. Sand cliff on Frensham Common, nest site of various *Colletes* species. (JE)

PLATE 47

Dead-wood nest sites

1. Old log-pile at Mare Hill Common, with many types of wood in varying stages of decay. (JE)
2. Dead tree-trunk with old beetle holes. (JE)
3. Old beetle-ridden logs set up in a garden to attract bees. (JE)

PLATE 48

Andrena minutula (Kirby, 1802)

National Status: Universal
Surrey Status: Ubiquitous
VCH: Generally distributed

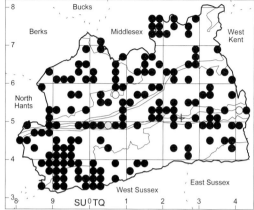

This is by far the commonest species in its group, both in Britain and in Surrey, and occurs very commonly in all types of habitat. It visits many different flowers for pollen but little is known about its nesting habits. It is double-brooded, the first brood flying from mid-March to late May, and the second brood from early June to late September. The males of the first brood have black hairs on the face whereas those of the second brood have white ones.

In Surrey it is widespread and common. Female flower visits include blackthorn, forget-me-not, dandelion, cow parsley, hogweed, sheep's-bit, willowherb, bell heather and bramble. Its cleptoparasite is *Nomada flavoguttata*.

Its staus is unchanged since 1900.

Andrena minutuloides Perkins, R.C.L., 1914

National Status: Rare; Na
Surrey Status: Local
VCH: Unknown

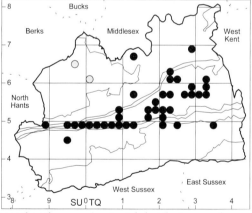

Very similar to and difficult to separate from the preceding species, but very much scarcer and confined to southern England, this small black bee occurs mainly on calcareous grassland in the east and on sandy sites in the far west. It is also double-brooded but the first brood flies slightly later than *A. minutula* and the second brood is much more numerous than the first. The hair bands on the female are sparser than those on *A. minutula* but the two species are difficult to separate, especially when specimens are worn, and some records may not be reliable. This species also is probably parasitised by *Nomada flavoguttata*.

In Surrey it is widespread along the North Downs from the western end of the Hogs Back to Coulsdon and Riddlesdown in the east, and can often be found in large numbers, especially on short downland turf. It is perhaps more common here than anywhere else in England.

Off the Chalk it has only been recorded on Bargate sand at Shackleford (DWB) and on Thames Basin gravels at Molesey (GAC) and Mitcham Common (RKAM). It is often seen on flowers of wild carrot, angelica and hogweed in late summer. It was separated from *A. minutula* in 1914 so it was unknown to the early recorders.

It was no doubt present along the North Downs in 1900, but not recognised, and its status is probably unchanged.

Andrena nana (Kirby, 1802)

National Status: Endangered RDB1
Surrey Status: Extinct
VCH: No records

There are only five confirmed records for Britain, none since 1930, and it is presumed to be extinct.

In Surrey one was taken on Oxshott Heath in July 1915 by an unknown collector, and this specimen, determined by R.C.L. Perkins, is in Oxford University Museum. A specimen standing under the name *nana* in the RHS Wisley Collection, collected by G. Fox Wilson at Wisley in May 1919, has been shown to be only *A. minutula* (DBB).

Andrena nigriceps (Kirby, 1802)

National Status: Scarce; Nb
Surrey Status: Very rare
VCH: No records

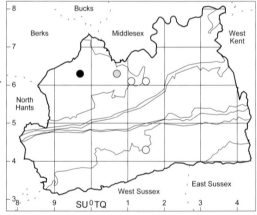

Another late summer bee, this species is rare and very local in Britain, foraging at a variety of plants, including knapweed, bramble and thistles. It is very similar to *A. simillima*, which has never been recorded in Surrey, and may even be the same species.

There are very few records for Surrey and it was not mentioned by Saunders. The first record is from Cobham in 1907 by Nevinson, followed by two from the Holmwood area in 1928 and 1930 by Mortimer. Guichard found it at Oxshott Heath in 1942 and at Weybridge in 1947. Most of these records are supported by specimens in the NHML. The only modern record is by A.S. Davidson in 1994 at Burrowhill Green near Chobham.

Its status is possibly unchanged since 1900 as it was probably overlooked by early recorders.

Andrena nigroaenea (Kirby, 1802)

National Status: Universal

Surrey Status: Common

VCH: Generally distributed

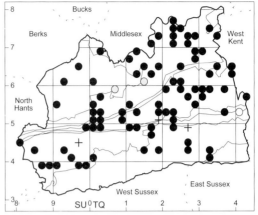

This large brown bee, with orange pollen hairs on the hind tibia of females, is very common through-out most of Britain, flying from late March to the end of May or June and foraging from a large variety of flowers. *Nomada goodeniana* is the cleptoparasite of this bee.

It is also widespread and common in Surrey, except that, like *A. nitida*, it appears to be very scarce on the western heaths, and it is also rather scarce on the clay. Female flower visits include forget-me-not, dandelion, cherry laurel and *Pyracantha*.

Its status is unchanged since 1900.

Andrena nigrospina Thomson, 1872

National Status: Rare

Surrey Status: Very rare

VCH: (as *pilipes*) Woodham, Chobham, Godalming, Shirley

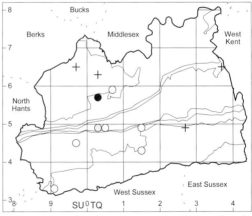

This striking, large, entirely black bee is now extremely rare, being known from only half a dozen widely scattered localities in England, of which two are coastal and the others are inland in Staffordshire, Worcestershire and at Papercourt Gravelpits near Send, Surrey. Although it has been reported from various places in Surrey since it was first found in about 1860, there is only one current locality.

Until recently this bee was recorded as *A. pilipes,* a species that was convincingly shown by Baker (1994) to consist of two very similar species: *A. pilipes* which has two broods and is entirely coastal, and *A. nigrospina* which is single-brooded and occurs inland as well as at the coast. *A. nigrospina* had been described as a separate species by some European authors since at least 1966, but it had been confused or misidentified by British authors until Baker published his paper in 1994. At the moment only males can be reliably identified, by comparing the genitalia and relative lengths of antennal segments, and by the presence of pale hairs on the thorax of *A. nigrospina*.

Most of the Surrey records are supported by specimens in museums or collections, and all those that have been checked appear to be *A. nigrospina*. Because of the extreme rarity of *A. nigrospina* in this country and because of the difficulty in separating the two species, a full list of Surrey records, in chronological order, is given below, with the sex of the specimen, if known, the locality, the name of the collector and where the specimen is, or if no specimen, the journal in which the record was published.

c 1860		Shirley nr Croydon	F. Smith	VCH
1881		Longcross, Chobham Common	E. Saunders	EMM
1890		Woodham nr Woking	F.D. Morice	VCH
1890		Godalming	O.H. Latter	VCH
1900	m+f	Redhill Common	F.D. Morice	NHML
26.5.1916	mm	Godalming	O.H. Latter	Haslemere Mus.
5.1920	m	Wisley	G. Fox Wilson	RHS Wisley Coll.
6.1922	f	Holmwood nr Dorking	C.H. Mortimer	NHML
11.6.1922	f	Haslemere	J.E.H. Roberts	NHML
23.5.1924		Wisley	G. Fox Wilson	RHS Wisley Coll.
17.6.1924	f	Wisley	G. Fox Wilson	RHS Wisley Coll.
7.1930	m	Holmwood nr Dorking	C.H. Mortimer	NHML
14.6.1936	m	Clandon Downs nr Guildford	D.O. Boyd	NHML
30.6.1935	m	Westcott nr Dorking	W.E. China	NHML
30.5.1937	m	Clandon Downs nr Guildford	D.O. Boyd	NHML
12.6.1964	f	Newlands Corner nr Guildford	S.F. Imber	S.F.Imber Coll.
17.6.2000-06		Papercourt Gravelpits, Send	A.S. Davidson	

Apart from the single Haslemere specimen, all the records since 1920 are from just three areas: first Wisley, in the 1920s, which is only a mile or so from the present-day locality of Papercourt, secondly the North Downs near Dorking (Mortimer's Holmwood labels often refer to the North Downs, two miles north of his home) and thirdly Clandon Downs, which is the same locality as Newlands Corner. All the dates, May and June and one in July, are correct for *A. nigrospina*.

After a gap of nearly 40 years it was rediscovered by A.S. Davidson on 17 June 2000 at Papercourt Gravelpits, Send. Here it was foraging on a large yellow-flowered crucifer, which was eventually identified as hoary mustard, *Hirschfeldia incana,* an introduced plant of roadsides and waste ground that was first recorded in Surrey in 1970. Since then this bee has been seen regularly by various recorders at this site in June, sometimes in good numbers, but no nest site has yet been found. It was only seen at hoary mustard here until this plant became very scarce locally in 2005, and it was then seen visiting rape and ground elder in 2006. It was not seen at all in 2007 or 2008 and it is feared that it may have become extinct at this site. In Staffordshire it forages at cow parsley, upright hedge-parsley, hogweed and other white umbellifers.

Its status is probably unchanged since 1900.

Andrena nitida (Müller, 1776)   PLATE 21

National Status: Widespread
Surrey Status: Ubiquitous
VCH: Wandsworth, Woking, Godalming, Cobham, Ottershaw

This large and distinctive, late spring *Andrena* has bright brown hairs on the thorax and, in the female, white hairs on the sides of the front three segments of the black, shining abdomen. It is common in southern Britain and flies from April to June, nesting in open, short grasslands and foraging

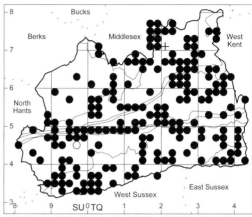

on a variety of flowers. It may be parasitised by *Nomada goodeniana*.

The map clearly shows that this bee is common and widespread in Surrey, right into London, but it appears to be absent from a small area of heathland in the west, where its close relative *A. thoracica* occurs. It is distinctly scarce on all the dry heathland areas and it may be that, because of lack of competition, *A. thoracica* can survive on these heaths. Apart from the dry heaths it can be found in almost any type of habitat and at most flowers, but especially hawthorn. It was abundant on spurges at Kew Gardens and has been recorded at hogweed, cow parsley, lesser stitchwort and germander speedwell.

It may be commoner and more widespread now than in 1900.

Andrena nitidiuscula Schenck, 1853

National Status: Scarce; RDB3
Surrey Status: Extinct
VCH: (as *lucens*) Chobham, Woking, Box Hill

Always rare and confined to southern England, this bee is now almost entirely restricted to coastal sites.

Saunders (1896) considered it rare but in July and August 1882 at Burrow Hill Green, Chobham he took "a male flying about over the heather and a female at bramble flowers in a hedge close by". It was

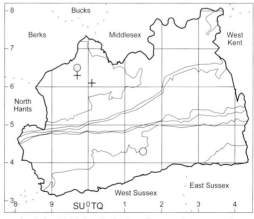

collected again at Chobham Common in July 1918 by R.C. Bradley and as recently as 3 August 1974 by Guichard. Saunders (1902) also mentions a record by Ramsden from

Box Hill, but there is no mention of a specimen and this must remain doubtful. However, Mortimer recorded it in August 1906 and July 1908 from the Holmwood area, which could have included Box Hill; it often occurs on short downland turf. Since it has not been seen for over 40 years this bee is presumably extinct in Surrey.

It has declined to extinction since 1900, but it was always rare.

Andrena niveata Friese, 1887   PLATE 4

National Status: Very rare; RDB2
Surrey Status: Very rare
VCH: No records

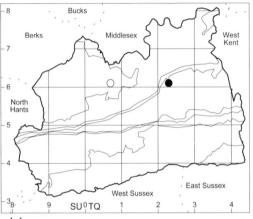

A very rare and decreasing small bee of southern Engand, now mainly confined to the coast although the only records outside Surrey since 1970 have been from the Maidstone area of Kent and the East Sussex Downs. It flies in May and June and is normally seen around brassicas. It differs from other small black *Andrena* species by having a conspicuous, complete hair band on the fourth tergite of the abdomen.

It was first discovered in Surrey at Byfleet by Mortimer in May 1913, having been added to the British List in 1899 by Saunders. There were no further records until 2 June 1957 when Baker found it flying, not uncommonly, around flowering cabbages on smallholdings at North Looe Farm, Ewell. He found it there again in 1959. In 2001 Baker told me exactly where he had found it and I visited the site on 4 June 2001. All except one smallholding had gone but on the remaining one were three flowering brassica cultivars, purple sprouting broccoli. To my amazement there were quite a number of very small black bees flying round and collecting pollen from these brassicas. Some of these had obvious white hair bands and were clearly not *A. minutula*. I netted a few of these bees and on examination at home found that I had four female *A. niveata* with a few *A. minutuloides*, *A. minutula* and *Lasioglossum minutissimum*. This incident shows how a rare species of bee can persist for a very long time at the smallest of sites so long as the habitat, in this case bare ground, and the right forage plant, are still present. Unfortunately the smallholding was grassed over in 2002 and there are now no more cabbages there. Luckily however, when I was there in 2001, the owner of the adjoining property, a Croatian lady, showed great interest in the bees, which she had observed for many years and told me where they nested. She is now growing cabbages in her garden, which she deliberately allows to go to seed each year, so *A. niveata* may not yet be extinct in Surrey.

Its status is probably unchanged since 1900.

Andrena ovatula (Kirby, 1802)

National Status: Widespread
Surrey Status: Local
VCH: (as *afzeliella*) Generally distributed

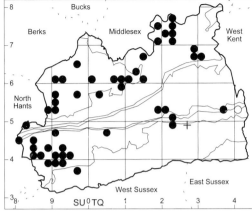

A medium-sized bee which is fairly common locally in southern Britain, flying in two broods, one in the spring and another from June to September. It forages from various plants and is found on heaths, acid grassland and the coast. It is very similar in appearance to its close relative *A. wilkella*, both having orange hind tibiae and black abdomens with white hair bands.

In Surrey this bee is fairly common on acid soils but is absent from the Chalk and clay. It occurs on all the heaths, as well as on the dry acid grasslands around London, such as Richmond Park, Wimbledon and Mitcham Commons, and also along the Lower Greensand ridge to the south of the North Downs. Its very similar relative *A. wilkella* mainly avoids the acid soils but occurs on the Chalk and clay.

It is as common now as it was in 1900.

Andrena praecox (Scopoli, 1763)

National Status: Widespread
Surrey Status: Local
VCH: Chobham, Woking, Weybridge, Godalming

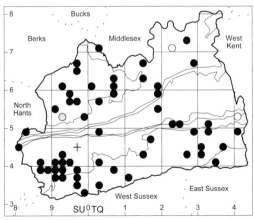

This bee is very similar to its close relative *A. apicata*, and difficult to separate from that species. It is widespread in southern Britain, being commonest in the south-east, but is always local, albeit sometimes common where found. This is one of the first solitary bees of the year, flying from early March to the end of April on heathland and open woodland, wherever there is plenty of willow. The females forage only from willow catkins of various species. The rare *Nomada ferruginata* parasitises this bee.

In Surrey it is also widely distributed but it is a local bee although sometimes common in certain places. At Papercourt Marsh, Send, where there are acres of willows, it nests in very large numbers in the bare sand. The males, like most of its close relatives, can best be found when they zigzag up sunlit tree trunks and telegraph poles, presumably looking for females which sometimes settle on these trunks. These males also fly around willow catkins although they never seem to take nectar. The larger females are best found as they fly round the willows foraging for pollen. This bee occurs most commonly on the clay and damp heaths, where willows are numerous, and is rare on the drier chalk, where there are few willows.

The RDB1 cleptoparasitic bee *Nomada ferruginata* has been found only once in Surrey, at Thorpe Hay Meadow, where *A. praecox* is common.

It is probably as common and widespread now as it was in 1900.

Andrena proxima (Kirby, 1802)

National Status: Scarce; RDB3
Surrey Status: Very local
VCH: Weybridge

This, the largest of the *Andrena minutula* group, is a rare bee of southern England and is distinguished by the very coarse sculpture of the clypeus and of the back of the thorax.

It was a very rare bee in Surrey, with only one record in about 1880 by Saunders, until it was rediscovered on the Chalk at Fetcham in June 1989 (RKAM). It was found again

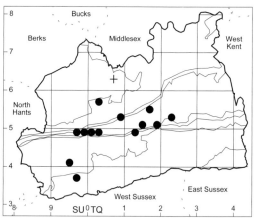

in 1999, this time at Westcott Downs (DWB), and since then it has turned up more and more frequently, mostly from mid-May to late June at white umbellifers such as cow parsley at various sites on the chalk, such as Sheepleas, Buckland Hills, Box Hill, Guildown on the Hogs Back near Guildford, where about 50 females were foraging on a white umbellifer, and allotments at Pewley Down in Guildford, where females were on flowering cabbages, carrots and parsnips. But it is not restricted to the Chalk, as it has occurred on the sand at Papercourt Gravelpits near Send, coming to ground elder, and in my garden at Milford on hemlock water-dropwort, and on the clay at Strawberry Grove, Guildford and Hambledon Claypit, where males and females were flying round cypress spurge and speedwells. Its cleptoparasite is *Nomada conjungens* which was discovered for the first time in Surrey at Westcott Downs in June 2007 (GAC).

It has increased dramatically since 1900.

Andrena rosae Panzer, 1801

National Status: Very rare; RDB2
Surrey Status: Extinct
VCH Status: No records

Until recently this red-marked bee was considered to be double-brooded, although in the spring brood the males had a strong spine on the cheek and the females foraged from various plants, whereas in the summer brood the males had no spine and the females foraged only from umbellifers. These two broods are now considered to be two separate species, the spring bees now known as *A. stragulata*. *A. rosae* has always been a rare bee of southern England but it has declined recently to the point of near extinction, being now found only very occasionally in Cornwall. Saunders considered *A. rosae*, *A. carantonica* and *A. trimmerana* to be one species, which he called *A. rosae* in his book.

There have only ever been three records of this bee in Surrey, the last being in 1913. G.A.J. Rothney first reported it in the EMM from Shirley in 1881 and this record is quoted in Saunders, 1896, although it is possible that it referred to one of the other two common species. There are two specimens in the NHML: one taken by Mortimer in July 1913 at Byfleet and the other taken by him in July 1924 in the Holmwood area.

It is not possible to be sure whether its status has changed since 1900, but it has probably declined to extinction.

Andrena semilaevis Pérez, 1903

National Status: Universal
Surrey Status: Common
VCH: (as *nana*) Generally distributed

This is a common small, black bee, occurring in various types of habitat over most of the British Isles, flying from May to August, probably in two broods. Little is known about its habits but it seems to favour white umbellifers for pollen.

It is reasonably common and widespread in Surrey but it seems to avoid the dry acid heaths in the

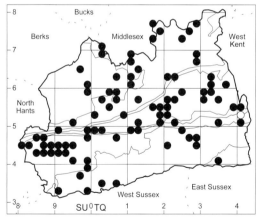

west, possibly because of a lack of forage plants. Records of flower visits include hogweed, hemlock water-dropwort, fool's water-cress, sheep's-bit and speedwells. The small red-bodied cuckoo bee *Nomada flavoguttata* is a cleptoparasite of this species.

Its status is unchanged since 1900.

Andrena similis Smith, 1849

National Status: Widespread; Nb
Surrey Status: Extinct
VCH: Wandsworth, Woking, Chobham, Bisley, Oxshott

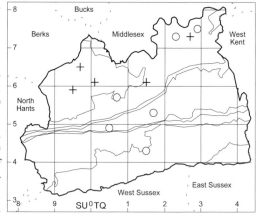

This bee is still widespread in Britain but has become very scarce, especially inland, in the last 50 years.

In Surrey it appears to have been frequent and widespread from 1880 to 1920, judging by the number of specimens in the NHML; for instance it occurred at Wimbledon and Wandsworth Commons and was taken regularly near Horsley from 1901 to 1918. It was taken at RHS Wisley in 1919 and 1920, with three specimens in the Fox Wilson Collection. But after 1920 the only other specimen was one taken by Guichard at Clapham Common on 6 May 1937, which is now in the NHML. The reason for its decline is not clear as it is a bee of varied habitats, and it collects pollen from numerous plants.

It has declined to extinction since 1900.

Andrena stragulata Illiger, 1806

National Status: Very rare
Surrey Status: Extinct
VCH: Unknown

Only recently separated from *A. rosae*, this spring bee has always been a great rarity of southern England and may now be extinct.

There is just one Surrey specimen known; this is in the NHML and was taken on Chobham Common in April 1896 by Saunders.

Andrena subopaca Nylander, 1848

National Status: Universal
Surrey Status: Ubiquitous
VCH: Unknown

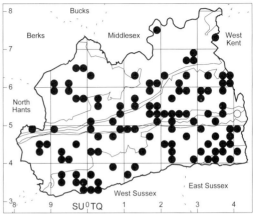

Another common, small, black bee, widespread in Britain, which flies from April to August in two broods. Little is known about its habits, but it seems to prefer woodlands and forages from various plants.

It is fairly common and widespread in Surrey. Records of flower visits by females include oxeye daisy, shepherd's purse, germander speedwell, lesser stitchwort and small-flowered crane's-bill. It was unknown to Saunders as it had not yet been separated from other similar small black species of *Andrena*. The small cuckoo bee *Nomada flavoguttata* is a cleptoparasite of this species.

Its status is presumably the same as in 1900.

Andrena synadelpha Perkins, R.C.L., 1914   PLATE 24

National Status: Widespread
Surrey Status: Local
VCH: (as *ambigua*) No records

This rather small bee is mainly dark but the female has light brown hairs on the thorax and long pale hairs on the abdomen. It is difficult to identify but the extremely long marginal areas are diagnostic. It is a local bee of southern England, flying from mid-April to mid-June and foraging on many different flowers.

In Surrey it is also local but scattered over most of the county. As the map shows, it seems to be particularly plentiful in and around London, where it occurs at Kew Gardens, Richmond Park, Barnes and Wimbledon Commons. It also occurs elsewhere on chalk and clay, but apparently not on sand. It was first described as new to science (as *Andrena ambigua*) by R.C.L. Perkins in 1895 and it therefore appears only in the Supplement to Saunders' famous book, published in 1896. In this supplement just three sites are mentioned, none of them in Surrey. Clearly this bee had been misidentified or overlooked before that and Saunders does not mention it in the VCH, published in 1902. However, there is in the NHML a specimen collected by Saunders in April 1896 at Horsell Common; presumably he had misidentified this specimen and it was later renamed. Morice found it the following year at Stoke d'Abernon and over the next few years it was found at Oxshott, Cobham and Byfleet by Nevinson, Mortimer and Le Marchant. Guichard found it at various sites from 1939 to 1972, and Baker from around Ewell in the 1950s. During the survey it has been recorded at numerous sites and seems to be less rare than previously. It is a difficult bee to locate but it can and does turn up almost anywhere, perhaps especially along hedges. A stylopised female was found at Kew Gardens on 8 May 2001 and a stylopised male at Glovers Wood, Charlwood on 28 April 2001.

It may have increased and expanded its distribution since 1900.

Andrena tarsata Nylander, 1848

National Status: Universal
Surrey Status: Very rare
VCH: (as *analis*) Chobham, Woking, Weybridge

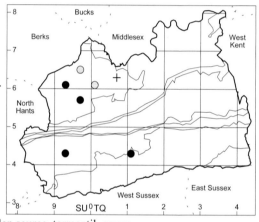

The male of this small black bee is one of the few British species of *Andrena* to have a yellow clypeus and the female is the only one to have a three-toothed mandible. Although widespread in the British Isles, it is commoner in the north; it is nearly always a scarce species and may well be declining. It is found on moorland, heathland and in open woods, where its main pollen source, tormentil, grows.

Always a rarity in Surrey, this bee has only been recorded at four localities during the survey period. One was taken at Holmbury Hill on 23 July 1994 (RKAM). It was seen regularly from 1997 to 2001 at Brookwood Cemetery, where tormentil is abundant (DWB), and also at Bagmoor Common in 1998 and 1999 on a path covered in tormentil (ME, DWB, GAC). More recently it was found at Folly Bog, Pirbright Common on 7 July 2007 (GAC). It has been found on various occasions at Chobham Common in recent times but not since 1984, although it could still survive there. There are plenty of sites in west Surrey where tormentil is abundant and it should be searched for in these places as it is possibly under-recorded.

It has probably declined since 1900.

Andrena thoracica (Fabricius, 1775)

National Status: Widespread
Surrey Status: Very local
VCH: Generally distributed

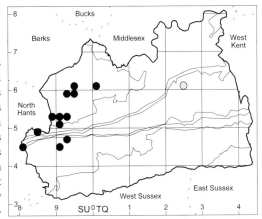

This large and attractive bee has bright brown hairs on the thorax and a shiny black abdomen, and is similar to *A. nitida* except that it is entirely black on the underside in both sexes, whereas *A. nitida* has various patches of white hairs underneath. It is locally common in coastal sites in southern Britain but it also occurs more scarcely in a few inland heathy sites. It is double-brooded, flying from March to May and from July to August, and females forage from many different flowers. It nests in sandy cliffs or level sandy areas and is parasitised by *Nomada goodeniana*.

In Surrey it is very local, occurring on a few of the western heaths. According to Guichard it was found at Horsell Common in 1897, but he does not mention the collector. It may have been Saunders, who describes it as widespread in the VCH; it was refound at Horsell Common in 2001 (DWB). The next record was from Cheam in 1960 (DBB), but it has not been found since in that area. During the survey it has been recorded at eight sites in the west: Ash Common on Ash Ranges in 1987 (SRM); Brentmoor Heath in 1994 (ASD); Puttenham Common, by the lake and the upper car park, in 1996 and 1998 (DWB); Wyke Common on Ash Ranges in 1997 (DWB); Rowhill Local Nature Reserve, Farnham in 1998 (JSD); Horsell Common in 2001 on forget-me-not (DWB); Henley Park Range on Ash Ranges in 2005, 2006 and as a second brood in 2007 (GAC); Wrecclesham Sandpit in 2005, which is the only modern site off heathland (DWB). Except for Henley Park all these records were in the spring, and the only other second-brood sites where it has been recorded are at two separate localities on Century Range at Bisley Ranges (29 July 2005, DWB). It has not yet been found on the Thursley, Hankley, Frensham Common complex. At the Puttenham Common upper car park, several nests were located in a bare sandy bank.

It is difficult to say whether there has been any decline in this species since 1900 although this is possible.

Andrena tibialis (Kirby, 1802)

National Status: Scarce; Na
Surrey Status: Local
VCH: Generally distributed

This scarce, large bee, with distinctive yellow hind tibiae, is confined to southern England, flying from March to the end of May, and little is known about its biology. It forages from a variety of plants and occurs in most types of habitat, including gardens.

It is local in Surrey, being found mainly on the sand, and is absent from the Weald Clay. It is most

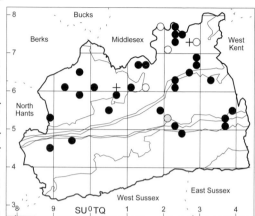

frequent around London, where it occurs at Wandsworth, Barnes, Wimbledon and Mitcham Commons, and Nonsuch Park. At Tandridge a female was seen going into a hole, presumably a nest burrow, at the base of a bank on 31 May 2004 (RDH). The only record of a flower visit is on sallow. The rare cuckoo bee *Nomada fulvicornis* is a cleptoparasite of this species.

Its status is probably unchanged since 1900.

Andrena trimmerana (Kirby, 1802) PLATE 22

National Status: Scarce; Nb
Surrey Status: Local
VCH: Confused with
  carantonica

This dark, medium-sized bee is widely distributed in southern Britain but is very local, flying in two broods, in spring from mid-March to the end of April, and again in summer from July to late September. It is found at the coast and inland on heaths and commons. Both sexes have a reddish band of varying width on the second tergite

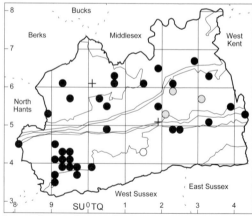

and the males of the spring brood have a long spine on the lower gena but not in the summer brood. This species was confused with *A. carantonica* and *A. rosae* by Saunders. *Nomada marshamella* is probably a cleptoparasite of this bee.

In Surrey it is locally frequent, especially on sandy heaths in the south-west, e.g. Witley, Mare Hill, Hambledon, Puttenham and Thursley Commons. It also occurs less frequently on heathland further north, such as Ash Ranges, Oxshott Heath and Brentmoor Heath, and on sandy sites, such as Brooklands near Weybridge, Papercourt Marsh near Send, Mitcham and Limpsfield Commons, Headley Heath and Gravel Hill Wood near Bletchingley. The only records from the Chalk are from Newlands Corner near Abinger, Headley Heath and South Croydon, and from the clay only at Holmens Grove near Brook. In the spring females are most often seen on gorse and in the summer on hogweed. With the confusion in names it is impossible to know the status of this species 100 years ago. However, there is in the NHML a specimen collected by Saunders in March 1894 from Horsell Common and another collected by Mortimer in May 1922 from Holmwood area, so it was clearly present and probably scarce. A female at Holmens Grove, Grayswood on 15 May 2005 was stylopised. It may have increased since 1900.

Andrena varians (Kirby, 1802)

National Status: Scarce; Nb
Surrey Status: Rare
VCH: Wandsworth, Woking, Clandon

This bee is similar to others in the same group but the female is more robust and darker than most, being black with dark brown hairs on the thorax. It is widespread in southern England but is scarce and very local, flying from April to June. The females forage from many different flowers. *Nomada panzeri* is a cleptoparasite of this bee.

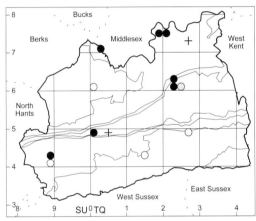

In Surrey it is a rare bee and has been recorded only from six sites during the survey. It was reported from a scatter of sites a century ago, including the first county record by Saunders in March 1882 from Wandsworth Common, and 50 years later by Baker on various occasions around Ewell and Banstead in the 1950s, including one in his own garden. The modern records are: Pewley Down, a female on a hedge at blackthorn blossom on 4 April 1997 (DWB); Thundry Meadows, Elstead on 4 May 1998 (ME); Thorpe Hay Meadow, three females on a hedge at blackthorn blossom on 3 May 2001 (DWB); Priest Hill, Ewell, one female and two males on dandelion flowers on 2 April and 4 May 2001 (DWB); Howell Hill, East Ewell, two females on 21 April 2001 (ME) and a female on 8 May 2001 (GAC); Richmond Park, a female at Sheen Gate on 27 May 2002 and another in a Malaise trap behind Holly Lodge on 15 May 2004 (both DWB). The area around Ewell seems to be the best place to find this elusive bee and flowering blackthorn hedges the best habitat to search. However, it is one of those bees that can turn up anywhere and it may be under-recorded.

Its status is probably the same as in 1900.

Andrena wilkella (Kirby, 1802)   PLATE 22

National Status: Universal
Surrey Status: Local
VCH: Generally distributed

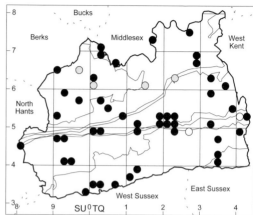

This medium-sized bee differs from its close relative *A. ovatula* in being single-brooded, flying from April to June, and in favouring chalk grassland and clay. It is widespread, being found in most of Britain. It forages from a variety of plants, especially vetches and clovers.

This bee is rather local in Surrey but can be found at various places along the North Downs, in the Weald Clay woodlands, at a few places on London Clay and at some places on neutral soils. Females have been recorded visiting flowers of buttercup, smooth tare, dyer's greenweed and wood spurge.

Its status is probably the same as it was in 1900.

Genus *Panurgus* Panzer, 1806

These are solitary, medium-sized, black, mining bees with short tongues. Pollen-carrying hairs are on the hind tibia. Females nest in loose aggregations in bare or sparsely vegetated soil. The nest entrance leads to a main burrow with lateral burrows, each ending in a terminal cell. The cells are lined with a wax-like material. The pollen balls are smooth and almost round. They overwinter as diapausing prepupae. Females forage for pollen mainly from yellow composites.

Nationally two species, both of which occur in Surrey.

Panurgus banksianus (Kirby, 1802)   PLATE 26

National Status: Widespread

Surrey Status: Local

VCH: (as *ursinus*) Godalming, Woking, Chobham

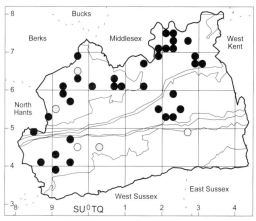

This, the larger of the two species, is a very hairy black bee restricted to southern Britain, being locally common in the southern counties but very scarce further north. It flies from June to August in a single brood and forages from yellow composites, nesting in sandy soils. This bee is local in Surrey, being found mainly on sand, very locally on chalk and absent from clay. It is commonest on the dry acid grasslands around London, where it is found at Richmond Park, Ham, Barnes, Wimbledon, Wandsworth, Ditton and Mitcham Commons; all these sites are rich in yellow composites. It occurs less commonly on the western heaths and commons, wherever yellow composites flourish.

Its status is probably unchanged since 1900.

Panurgus calcaratus (Scopoli, 1763)   PLATE 26

National Status: Restricted

Surrey Status: Locally common

VCH: Godalming, Woking, Chobham

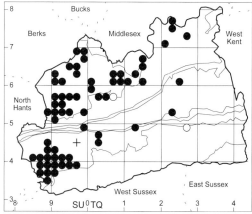

This smaller bee, with much shorter hairs in the female and with a tooth, or spur (from which it is named), under the hind femur in the male, is much commoner than *P. banksianus* but has a very similar distribution. It is rare on the Chalk, being recorded only at Westcott Downs and Banstead Downs, and absent from the clay. In contrast to *P. banksianus* it seems to prefer the dry western heaths, and here it can be very common wherever yellow composites grow. However, it also occurs on the dry acid grasslands but it is not so common there.

Its status is the same as in 1900.

SUBFAMILY HALICTINAE

These are ground-nesting species with short, pointed tongues, and may be solitary or social. In the solitary species the female establishes a nest in the spring and the males and new females emerge in the summer; after mating the males die and the females overwinter as diapausing adults. In the social species the overwintered female, or queen, rears a small brood of workers which then help her rear the subsequent brood of males and new queens.

Genus *Halictus* Latreille, 1804

Small to large bees. The cuticle in some species e.g. *H. rubicundus* is black but in others e.g. *H. tumulorum* metallic bronzy-green. The abdominal tergites often have posterior white hair bands. The pollen hairs are on the hind femur and tibia. Females nest in aggregations. *H. rubicundus* and H. *tumulorum* may be solitary or social.

Nationally six species (two extinct), four in Surrey (one extinct).

Halictus confusus Smith, 1853

National Status: Rare; RDB3

Surrey Status: Very local

VCH: No records

This is a rare bee, restricted to the sandy heaths of south-east England. It is very similar, especially in the female, to the common and widespread *H. tumulorum* and identification requires some expertise. The male has entirely yellow trochanters on the second and third legs when viewed from below, but the genitalia are the best character for certain identification from *H. tumulorum*.

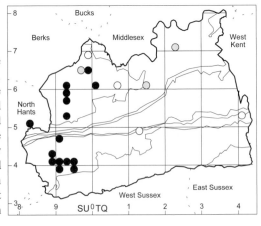

It was still unrecognised as a British species in Saunders' time but the earliest Surrey specimen is one in the NHML collected by him in 1880 on Chobham Common. There are a few specimens in the Museum collected over the next 90 years by several Surrey hymenopterists, Mortimer, Richards and Guichard, from their usual haunts of Byfleet, Oxshott Heath, Horsell, Chobham and Limpsfield Commons and even from London, at Wimbledon Common. Since 1985 there have been 18 records, all from the western heaths i.e. Hankley, Thursley, Puttenham, Horsell, Chobham, Hambledon and Mare Hill Commons, Pirbright Ranges and Brentmoor Heath. I collected both males and females visiting flowers of shrubby cinquefoil in my garden at Milford in June 1996 and 1997, but this almost adjoins the heathland of Witley Common.

It is impossible to know what its status was in 1900.

Halictus maculatus Smith, 1848

National Status: Endangered RDB1
Surrey Status: Extinct
VCH: Weybridge

Not recorded in Britain for 75 years and now probably extinct. There were only ever about five singletons found, apart from two breeding aggregations in Devon in the 1920s.

In Surrey there is only one very old record, in 1844, when F. Smith found a female at Weybridge.

Halictus rubicundus (Christ, 1791)

National Status: Universal
Surrey Status: Common
VCH: Generally distributed

This attractive bee, with bright orange-yellow hind legs in both sexes and with distinctive white hair bands in the female, is common and widespread in Britain. Being mainly social, it has a long flight period, the queens emerging in April and the few workers being present from May, with the new males and females flying from July to early October.

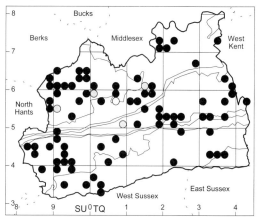

It is a fairly common and widespread bee in Surrey but not as common as the much smaller *H. tumulorum*. It is frequently found on the sand and chalk but only rarely on the clay. Flowers visited include forget-me-not, hogweed and angelica. The two red-and-black cuckoo bees *Sphecodes gibbus* and *S. monilicornis* attack the nests of this bee.

Its status is unchanged since 1900.

Halictus tumulorum (Linnaeus, 1758)

National Status: Universal

Surrey Status: Ubiquitous

VCH: Generally distributed

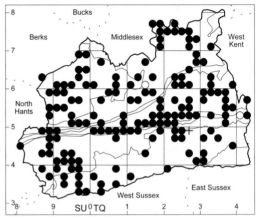

This is a very common and widespread small bee; the female has a very characteristic metallic bronzy-green tinge on the head and thorax, and broad pale hair bands on the abdomen; the male has yellow legs. It flies in one brood from April to October and is found in almost any habitat, visiting various plants, including forget-me-not, water-pepper, oxeye daisy, common fleabane, red clover, lesser stitchwort, bramble and a *Geranium* sp.

It is also very common and widespread in Surrey, in all types of habitat.

Its status is unchanged since 1900.

Genus *Lasioglossum* Curtis, 1833

This is a large genus of small to medium-sized, usually black bees, although many males have yellow or white markings on the clypeus and legs, and a few have red markings on the abdomen. A few species have a bronzy-green or metallic-blue cuticle. Many species have anterior white hair patches or hair bands on the abdominal segments. Some species are solitary and others social. All species are probably polylectic for pollen sources.

Nationally 32 species, with 28 in Surrey (one extinct).

Lasioglossum albipes (Fabricius, 1781)

National Status: Universal
Surrey Status: Common
VCH: Generally distributed

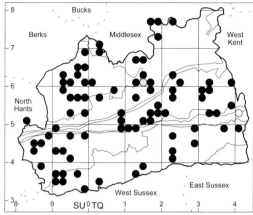

This is common and widespread in Britain, flying from March to October and foraging from numerous plants. It is very similar in appearance to *L. calceatum*.

It is also widespread in Surrey but nowhere near as common as its close relative *L. calceatum*. It is most often found at yellow composites, including ragwort, but has also been recorded on angelica and dandelion. The common cuckoo bee *Sphecodes monilicornis* is a cleptoparasite of this species.

Its status is unchanged since 1900.

Lasioglossum brevicorne (Schenck, 1870)

National Status: Scarce; RDB3
Surrey Status: Locally common
VCH: No records (but confused with *pauperatum*)

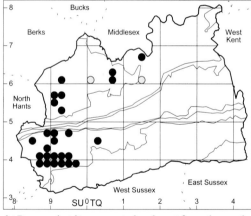

This small species is very local, being restricted to light sandy soils in south-east England, although it has become more common and has increased its range in the last few years. The female flies from May to late July and forages from yellow composites.

In Surrey it is reasonably common on almost all the south-west heaths and on Ash Ranges as well as Pirbright Ranges, but it appears to be absent from the north-west heathlands. There is also an outlying site at Blackheath near Albury. At these sites it is found on yellow composites, mainly cat's-ear, growing on almost bare sandy areas, usually at the edges of the heaths. It also occurs on dry acid grassland at Brooklands near Weybridge and at Ditton Common in the north of the county. Here it occurs where there are plenty of yellow composites growing on hot, sparsely vegetated ground. There is no doubt that it has increased considerably over the last ten years. Saunders did not know it because it was then confused with *L. pauperatum* (as *L. breviceps*) and there are no records of it until 1966 when Guichard found it at Horsell Common. He and Baker then found it in the 1970s there again and at Oxshott Heath. There were a few records in the 1980s and 1990s but since 2000 there have been over 30; this high number is partly due to improved fieldcraft and knowing exactly where to find it.

It is almost certainly more common and widespread than it was in 1900.

Lasioglossum calceatum (Scopoli, 1763)   PLATE 27

National Status: Universal

Surrey Status: Ubiquitous

VCH: (as *cylindricus*) Generally distributed

This is very widespread and possibly the commonest *Lasioglossum* in Britain. It flies in a single brood from April to October and is found in a variety of open habitats where it forages from many different plants.

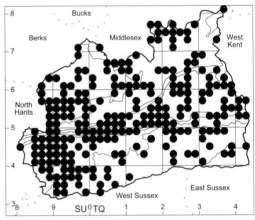

It is by far the commonest *Lasioglossum* in Surrey and is also found everywhere, on the sand, chalk and clay. It forages from a great variety of flowers but is most often found at ragwort in mid summer; other flowers include thistles, buttercups, common fleabane, lesser burdock, sheep's-bit, red campion, chickweed and rough hawkbit. The very common cuckoo bee *Sphecodes monilicornis* is a cleptoparasite of this species, and *S. ephippius* may also be. Its status is unchanged since 1900.

Lasioglossum cupromicans (Pérez, 1903)

National Status: Universal

Surrey Status: Very rare

VCH: Unknown

This medium-sized metallic green species mainly replaces the very similar *L. smeathmanellum* in the north and west of Britain, but there are a few recent records from south-east England. The females fly from late April to late October and forage from various flowers.

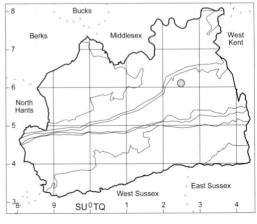

The only Surrey record is from Banstead Downs, near Belmont station, where Baker collected a male on 4 August 1975. This bee may be particularly associated with rosebay willowherb in lowland Britain according to P.R. Harvey.

It is a newcomer to Surrey since 1900.

Lasioglossum fratellum (Pérez, 1903)

National Status: Universal
Surrey Status: Very local
VCH: Confused with
  fulvicorne

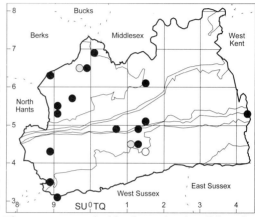

This medium-sized species is widespread throughout Britain but is commoner in the north where it is especially found on moors. In the south it is local, being found mainly on lowland heaths. Females fly from early April to September and forage from a variety of flowers. They are social and the queen often guards the nest entrance while the daughters do most of the foraging. The nests are attacked by the cuckoo bee *Sphecodes hyalinatus* and possibly *S. ferruginatus*.

In Surrey it is distinctly local, being found mainly on heathland, especially near woods, but it has been found on the Chalk at Westcott Downs near Dorking. Many of the sites where it has been recorded are heathery areas at high elevations of nearly 1,000 ft above sea level, resembling moors rather than lowland heaths, e.g. Hindhead Common, Blackdown, Holmbury Hill, Leith Hill and Limpsfield Chart. It was not recorded by Saunders in 1900, partly because it was then confused (as *subfasciatus*) with *L. fulvicorne*, and partly because none of the collectors at that time visited the localities in the south where it it has now been found, and the first county record appears to be that of Mortimer in August 1906 when he took it near Holmwood (probably Leith Hill). The next record was not until 1952 when Baker recorded it at Holmbury Hill. The only other sites, not mentioned above, where it has been found during the survey period are Chobham Common, Bagshot Heath, Egham, Ash Ranges, Oxshott Heath and Hankley Common.

It possibly has the same status as it had in 1900.

Lasioglossum fulvicorne (Kirby, 1802)

National Status: Widespread
Surrey Status: Locally common
VCH: (as *subfasciatus*) Reigate, Shere, Clandon, Box Hill, Holmwood

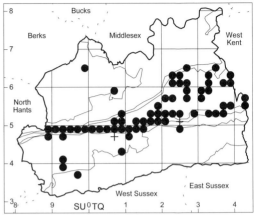

This medium-sized species is common and widespread in England and Wales but is mainly found on calcareous grassland. The females have a long flight period from mid-March to late September and forage from various flowers. Little is known about its life history but it is a solitary nester and the nests are parasitised by the cuckoo bees *Sphecodes hyalinatus* and *S. ferruginatus*.

In Surrey it is almost entirely restricted to the chalk downs, where it is widespread and extremely common, but it also occurs very locally at a few sites on the sand, such as Mare Hill Common near Witley, Seale old sandpit, Chobham Common, RHS Wisley and even on the Weald Clay at Hambledon Claypit. Females have been seen on ground-ivy. Saunders' records in VCH are probably of this species, as most are from the Chalk, but in his time it was confused with *L. fratellum*.

It probably has the same status now as in 1900.

Lasioglossum laevigatum (Kirby, 1802)

National Status: Restricted
Surrey Status: Locally common
VCH: Reigate, Clandon, Shere, Cobham

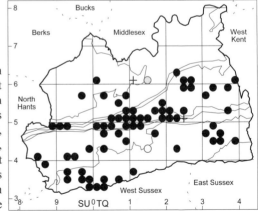

This bee is confined to southern Britain where it is local but occasionally common, mainly on calcareous grassland. The female is robust with prominent hair bands, some of the hairs being very long, a character which distinguishes it from other species. The females have a very long flight period from mid-April to September and forage from various flowers in several different families.

In Surrey it can be common on the Chalk from Farnham to the Kent border but it also occurs frequently in woodland rides and clearings on the Weald Clay. It is distinctly uncommon on sand. Females have been recorded visiting germander speedwell, meadow buttercup, greater stitchwort, pignut, angelica and oxeye daisy.

Saunders also knew it mainly from the Chalk, and its status is probably much the same now as it was then.

Lasioglossum lativentre (Schenck, 1853)

National Status: Widespread
Surrey Status: Fairly common
VCH: Confused with
    quadrinotatum

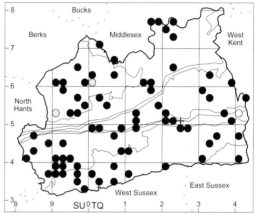

A common and widespread small bee in Britain which flies from March to October. It is said to be parasitised by the small cuckoo bee *Sphecodes ephippius* and possibly also by *S. puncticeps.*

It is very widespread but never all that common in Surrey. It occurs in all types of habitat and visits a variety of plants including red clover, buttercups, creeping cinquefoil and cat's-ear. A nest was found in bare ground near Godstone and a female seen collecting pollen from dandelion.

Its status is no doubt unchanged since 1900.

Lasioglossum leucopus (Kirby, 1802)

National Status: Universal
Surrey Status: Locally common
VCH: Chobham, Woking, Shere,
    Godalming

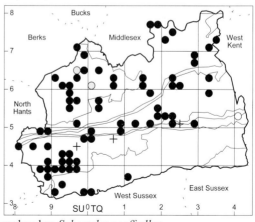

This small metallic blue-green species is very similar to the abundant *L. morio*, but is distinguished in the female by the round face and in the male by the yellow hind tibia. It is found over most of Britain in a variety of habitats but little is known about its life history or nesting habits in spite of it being a common species. Its nests are thought to be attacked by the small cuckoo bee *Sphecodes geoffrellus.*

It is reasonably common and widespread in Surrey, occurring mainly on the sand and chalk but also occasionally on the clay, but it is nowhere near as common as *L. morio*. Females have been recorded on wild carrot and ragwort.

Its status is probably unchanged since 1900.

Lasioglossum leucozonium (Schrank, 1781)

National Status: Widespread
Surrey Status: Ubiquitous
VCH: Generally distributed

This is common and widespread in Britain and is said to be parasitised by the cuckoo bee *Sphecodes pellucidus* and possibly also by *S. ephippius*.

It is very common and widespread in Surrey, although it is scarce on the Weald Clay. Females have been recorded visiting flowers of common fleabane, angelica, ragwort and smooth hawk's-beard, and a nest was found on the side of a ditch.

Its status is unchanged since 1900.

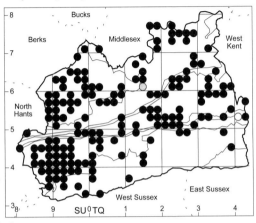

Lasioglossum malachurum (Kirby, 1802)

National Status: Restricted; Nb
Surrey Status: Ubiquitous
VCH: Chobham

This fairly large species, easily recognised by its rectangular-shaped shoulders on the front of the thorax, is now widespread and common to abundant in south-eastern England. It was formerly a scarce bee but it has increased its range dramatically and is now found in a wide variety of open habitats. The females fly from early April to October and forage from numerous flowers. The nests are attacked by the cuckoo bee *Sphecodes monilicornis*. It is a well-known social species.

In Surrey it is widespread and very common, and often even abundant; it sometimes nests in large aggregations in well-trodden paths, in many different habitats, but particularly on clay soils. An aggregation of nests in clay and flints lying on top of the North Downs at

Ranmore Common was studied by Jeremy Field in 2003 in connection with his investigations into sociality amongst *Lasioglossum* species. Females have been recorded visiting rape, dandelion, germander speedwell, bulbous buttercup, angelica and hedge bindweed. In Saunders' time it was clearly very scarce as he knew only of Smith's record from Wandsworth Common in about 1860, as well as his own record from the same site in 1890. J.F. Perkins found it on the London Clay at Claygate in 1939 and 1953 and Guichard collected it on various occasions between 1971 and 1978 at Chobham Common, Oxshott Heath and Horsell Common. It was still scarce until 1985 but since then it has been recorded at numerous sites in every part of the county. No explanation has been put forward for this extraordinary increase in the last 20 years but it could be caused by climatic change.

It has increased dramatically and expanded its range since 1900.

Lasioglossum minutissimum (Kirby, 1802)

National Status: Widespread

Surrey Status: Common

VCH: Generally distributed

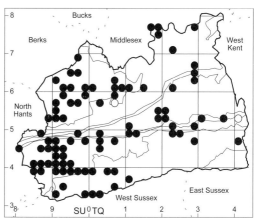

This very small species is one of the smallest of all British bees and is distributed widely over much of southern Britain.

It is common and widespread in Surrey but apparently far more common in the west than in the east, and on the sand rather than on the Chalk or clay. It is usually found in large nesting aggregations on bare ground and on banks, and females have been seen visiting forget-me-not, rape and sheep's-bit. It is thought to be parasitised by the very small and scarce cuckoo bee *Sphecodes longulus*, which certainly occurs on most of the dry, sandy areas frequented by *L. minutissimum*.

Its status is the same now as in 1900.

Lasioglossum morio (Fabricius, 1793)   PLATE 27

National Status: Widespread
Surrey Status: Ubiquitous
VCH: Generally distributed

This is a very small species with metallic blue-green head and sides of the thorax, and it is very common over much of England and Wales. The females fly from late March to late October and forage from a large variety of flowers.

The nests are attacked by the small cuckoo bee *Sphecodes niger* and possibly also by *S. geoffrellus* and *Nomada sheppardana*.

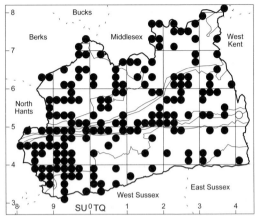

In Surrey it is also very common and widespread, occurring in almost any habitat where there is dry, bare earth in a sunny situation. It is found just as commonly on the Chalk as sand, as well as on the dry acid grasslands around London, including Battersea Park. It is rather less common, but still frequent, on the Weald Clay. Flower visits by females include forget-me-not, ivy, figwort, common fleabane, speedwell, sheep's-bit, ragwort and dog rose. The females nest in large, sometimes very large, aggregations in bare earth and many of these have large numbers of *S. niger* crawling in and out of the burrows. The males of this cuckoo bee are very small and all black, thus resembling their host. I have also seen *Nomada sheppardana* flying around a nesting aggregation on the Chalk at Sheepleas and Westcott Downs. *L. morio* is also attacked by the small black conopid fly *Thecophora atra* which can sometimes be seen flying round nesting sites.

Its status is unchanged since 1900.

Lasioglossum nitidiusculum (Kirby, 1802)

National Status: Universal
Surrey Status: Very rare
VCH: Generally distributed

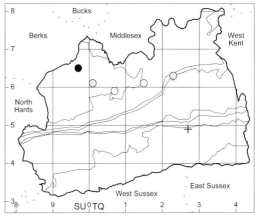

Although it is widely distributed over southern Britain it is very local and has declined significantly in recent years. It flies from April to September, foraging from numerous plants but mainly from yellow composites.

Saunders described it as generally distributed in Surrey in 1902 but it appears to have declined dramatically since then, unless it has been overlooked, and there is only one modern record for the county. As this species is very similar to *L. parvulum*, or even *L. punctatissimum*, it is possible that modern recorders have failed to recognise it. The first Surrey record appears to be a specimen in the BENHS Collection, collected by Frisby at Redhill Common on 20 May 1900. The next record was by Fox Wilson at Wisley in 1924. Guichard collected three specimens at Oxshott Heath between 1937 and 1939 and two specimens at Horsell Common sandpit in 1965 and 1968. Baker collected one in his garden at Ewell on 25 April 1973 and the only modern record, and the last for Surrey, is of a singleton taken in a Malaise trap on Chobham Common on 10 July 1993 (JPB, det. ME).

Its status has clearly changed from being common in 1900 to extremely rare now.

Lasioglossum parvulum (Schenck, 1853)

National Status: Widespread
Surrey Status: Common
VCH: (as *minutus*) Woking,
   Chobham, Clandon, Shere

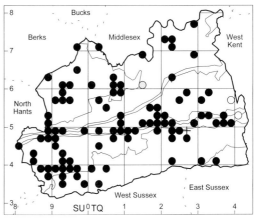

Widespread and common in southern Britain, this small bee forages from various plants in many different types of habitat, flying from March to September.

It is fairly common and widespread in Surrey, with no obvious preference for any type of habitat. Females have been seen at flowers of angelica and red campion and nests have been found in a root-plate and on a bank. The very small and dark cuckoo bee

Nomada sheppardana is a cleptoparasite of this species; *Sphecodes geoffrellus* may also parasitise it. A female of *L. parvulum* was found on the very early date of 11 February 2008 at a sandpit in Reigate (JPE).

Its status is probably unchanged since 1900.

Lasioglossum pauperatum (Brullé, 1832)

National Status: Very rare; RDB3
Surrey Status: Very rare
VCH: (as *breviceps*) Woking, Chobham, Clandon, Guildford

This small, rare and very localised species is restricted to southern England, being found mainly on light soils such as heathlands and gravel and chalk pits. Little is known about its life history or its habits.

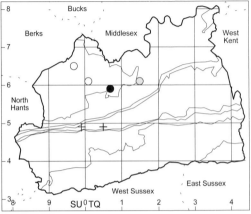

This is a very rare bee in Surrey where it has been recorded on only 16 occasions and at just five sites, with only one record during the survey period. The first records, quoted in the VCH, were from Horsell Common in 1888 and Chobham Common in 1890, both the specimens collected by Saunders, and then two by Morice in 1896, possibly from the Chalk, at Clandon and Guildford; however, at that time *L. pauperatum* was confused with *L. brevicorne* (as *L. breviceps*), so it is not certain to which species he was referring. There are also three Saunders specimens in the NHML, from Horsell Common in September 1902, from Chobham Common in June 1902 and from Horsell Common again in September 1907. There is also a specimen in the BENHS Collection from Horsell Common in May 1888, collector unknown.

Apart from one record by P.F. Yeo on 27 August 1949 at Chobham Common, all the remaining records are by Baker from 1937 to 1988. His first record was on 18 April 1937 from Oxshott Heath, where he subsequently collected four further specimens in the summer of 1972. He also recorded one on 2 May 1937 at Wisley Common and another there on 7 August 1988, this being the last record for Surrey. It is difficult to make a targeted search for this species because in the field it looks like any other small black species of *Lasioglossum*; it apparently has no specific habitat preferences nor is it associated with any particular flowers and it never occurs in any numbers at a site.

It has become much rarer since 1900.

Lasioglossum pauxillum (Schenck, 1853)

National Status: Restricted; Na

Surrey Status: Common

VCH: Charlwood, Shere

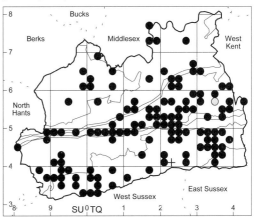

The female of this small species can be recognised immediately under a microscope because the inner spur of the hind tibia has broad round lobes, quite unlike those of most other species of *Lasioglossum,* excepting only *L. lativentre,* which all have pointed teeth. Until recently this was a scarce bee of south-east England, but it has increased in recent years and has extended its range northwards and westwards. The females fly from mid-April to late September, foraging from many different flowers and nesting in many different open habitats.

It is now common and widespread in Surrey, being especially numerous on the Weald Clay and on the Chalk but uncommon and local on the sand. In Saunders' time it was clearly very scarce as in 1896 he knew only of his own record from Charlwood on the clay and that of E. Capron from Shere. Mortimer found it at Holmwood on the clay in 1905 and Saunders took it at Horsell Common in 1908. Between then and 1995 there are only three records but since 1995 there have been over 250. It seems to have increased dramatically in the last few years in the same way as *L. malachurum.* The nests are excavated in almost bare, level soil and the burrow entrances have very characteristic turrets of soil. These nests are often in large aggregations and the species is social. Females have been recorded at flowers of rape, hogweed, rosebay willowherb, creeping buttercup, spurge, lesser hawkbit, thistle and dandelion.

It has clearly increased enormously since 1900.

Lasioglossum prasinum (Smith, 1848)   PLATE 27

National Status: Scarce; Na
Surrey Status: Locally common
VCH: Chobham, Woking, Ripley

This distinctive bee is very localised in southern Britain, being almost entirely restricted to the lowland heaths of Surrey, Hampshire and Dorset. It is a large species, the male having a diagnostic red tip to the abdomen and the female having diagnostic dense hair patches on the front shoulders of the abdomen. The female, being continuously brooded, has a very long flight period, from May to October, and forages mainly from heather.

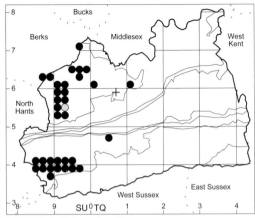

In Surrey it has been found on most of the western heaths, occurring as far east as Fairmile Common near Esher and as far north as Windsor Great Park, and can be common. Saunders collected the first county specimen in 1878 at Chobham Common and the second in 1893 at Horsell Common. F.D. Morice found it on Wisley Common in 1900 and stated that it was parasitised by the very scarce cuckoo bee *Sphecodes reticulatus,* which currently occurs quite commonly on most of the heaths where *L. prasinum* is present. There were no further records for over 70 years until Guichard refound it at Chobham and Horsell Commons in 1972. S.R. Miles then found it at various sites on Ash Ranges in the early 1980s. Since 1985 there have been well over 100 records from all the well-worked heathland sites but it never occurs in any numbers. In 2006 it was found nesting in the sandy bank of an erosion channel on Hindhead Common, at a height of about 800 ft above sea level. The females forage from bell heather in the summer and then from heather (*Calluna vulgaris*) later in the year, the latest date being 4 November, at Frensham Common in 2007 (DWB). It may well be commoner now than in 1900.

Lasioglossum punctatissimum (Schenck, 1853)

National Status: Widespread
Surrey Status: Common
VCH: Reigate, Chobham,
Woking, Wandsworth

This small bee is common and widespread, flying from April to September and foraging from various plants in most types of habitat.

It is widespread in Surrey but appears to be absent from the Chalk and is uncommon in the eastern half of the county. In the western half it is very common on the sandy

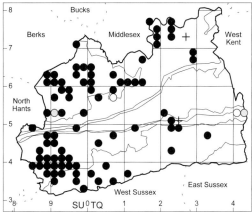

heaths and rather less common in the clay woodlands; it also occurs frequently on the dry acid grasslands around London. Female flower visits include forget-me-not, dandelion and common vetch.

It is possibly commoner now than in 1900.

Lasioglossum puncticolle (Morawitz, F., 1872)

National Status: Restricted; Nb
Surrey Status: Very local
VCH: Coombe Wood?

This is a fairly large species for a *Lasioglossum* and is found very scarcely in only the southernmost counties of England. The female is distinguished from those of all other species by having very strong, deep and shining striations on the underside of the head. It is normally found on clay at coastal soft rock cliffs, claypits and in open woodland. Little is known about its

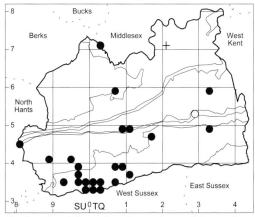

life history or habits but the females fly from late May to late September and forage from various plants, preferring composites, especially common fleabane. It is thought to have declined recently, especially in many inland areas.

It is fairly widespread but very local in Surrey, being found most frequently in the woodland rides and clearings on the Wealden Clay in the south-west and also in old claypits there. Apart from a very dubious record by Brunetti cited in the VCH from Coombe Wood (a site that may be in Kent or near Richmond Park), the first county record appears to be as recent as 1948, when F. Lawton found it at Merstham. There were no further records until 1995 when it was found at Botany Bay, Chiddingfold. Since then it has been found regularly, but never in numbers, in most of the Weald Clay woods around Cranleigh, Dunsfold, Chiddingfold and Brook. It has also been recorded frequently from old claypits at Hambledon, Cranleigh, Somersbury (near Ewhurst), and North Holmwood; it even occurs in an old sandpit (with some Gault Clay) at Wrecclesham near Farnham. There is only one record from the eastern Weald Clay, at Bransland Wood near Nutfield. Off the Weald Clay it is extremely local, with just two records from the Chalk at Hackhurst Downs near Gomshall and at Riddlesdown Quarry, and two from the sand, at Hankley Common and in my garden at Milford. There is also one record from a semi-wooded area by the River Wey at RHS Wisley. Females have been recorded from flowers of angelica and marsh thistle.

For a species which was only discovered in 1948, but then recorded on 40 occasions at 20 sites in the last ten years, it would not be unreasonable to assume that it had only recently colonised the county and had increased dramatically. However, the truth is that almost none of the older collectors ever visited the Weald Clay and therefore failed to record it. Its status may possibly be the same now as it was in 1900.

Lasioglossum quadrinotatum (Kirby, 1802)

National Status: Rare; Na
Surrey Status: Rare
VCH: Confused with *lativentre*

This very local species is widespread but very scarce in England where it is found in various habitats but mainly on dry sandy soils, especially heathlands. Females fly from April to late September and visit a wide range of flowers.

In Surrey it has been recorded on 13 occasions and at 11 sites since 1985, all of them in the west of the county but in a variety of habitats.

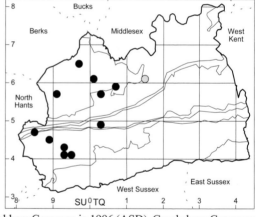

From heathland the records are: Chobham Common in 1996 (ASD), Crooksbury Common on 10 July 1997, Bagmoor Common on 8 June 1999, Gapemouth Plantation at Ash Ranges on 21 August 2001, and Mare Hill Common in Malaise trap on 1 August 2003 (all DWB). It has been found twice in my garden at Milford, on 9 June 1996 and 3 May 1997, and from Papercourt Gravelpits on 8 June 2006 (DWB) and again there on 4 May 2007 (GAC). There is only one record from the Chalk, at Newlands Corner on 29 May 1997 (DWB). The other two records are from a flowery meadow at Bourne Mead near Horsell Common on 13 August 2000 and from an open wooded site by the River Wey at RHS Wisley on 28 July 2003 (both AJH). The most recent record is from Farnham Park on 19 May 2007 (GAC).

It is difficult to know what the status of this species was in Saunders' time because it was treated as one species with the very similar *L. lativentre*, under the name *Halictus quadrinotatus*. For this reason Saunders described *H. quadrinotatus* as widespread in the VCH but no doubt most records would have been of the common *L. lativentre*. However, there are three of Saunders' specimens in the NHML which have now been correctly identified as *L. quadrinotatum*, two from Horsell Common in June 1878 and September 1902, and one from Chobham Common in June 1878. The two species were separated by R.C.L. Perkins in 1913, and from that date until 1984 there are only four more records, by Yeo, Guichard and Baker from Oxshott Heath, Horsell Common and Wisley Common respectively.

Lasioglossum semilucens (Alfken, 1914)

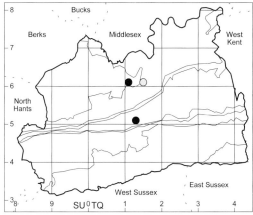

National Status: Very rare; RDB3
Surrey Status: Very rare
VCH: Unknown

This small and very rare species is usually associated with dry sandy areas, sometimes in open woodland, and was first recorded in Britain in 1945. Since then it has been found at several sites, all in the extreme south-east corner of England and mainly in Kent. Little is known of its life history or its habits.

In Surrey it has been found on four occasions, at only three sites, and is either extremely rare or overlooked, because in the field it looks like any other small species of *Lasioglossum*. It was first found on 6 September 1972 at Oxshott by Baker, who found a second male there on 9 September 1973. There must have been a strong nesting aggregation at the site as he had three specimens in his collection and he told me that he had given away other specimens to taxonomists in Europe. A female was collected on the Chalk at Westcott Downs on 10 July 1999 (ME) and another on Thames Terrace gravel at Old Common, Cobham, on 24 June 2002, where it was probably nesting in a sandy bank at the edge of a wood (DWB).

It has increased since 1900, being an apparent newcomer, unless it was overlooked before 1973.

Lasioglossum sexstrigatum (Schenck, 1870)

Just before this book went to press, this widespread European species of sand dunes and sandpits was confirmed as new to Britain. On 5 June 2008 a female was found by R.D. Hawkins in a sandpit near Merstham managed by Surrey Wildlife Trust. The female is a small black bee with rounded shoulders of the propodeum and narrow white hair bands, interrupted centrally, on the margins of tergites 2-4.

Lasioglossum sexnotatum (Kirby, 1802)

National Status: Very rare; RDB1

Surrey Status: Extinct

VCH: Chobham, Woking, Weybridge

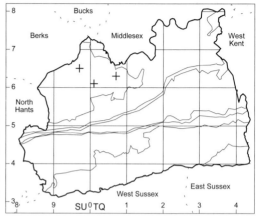

With only about seven very old records, the last being in 1913, this species of dry, sandy heathland was thought to be extinct in Britain until it was refound in 1985 in Breckland and from 2004 onwards on chalk grassland in East Sussex. It is a large species and Saunders describes it as being "very distinct by its ashy grey pubescence".

In Surrey F. Smith found it at Weybridge, probably in about 1850, but it is not known whether it was nesting there. Saunders found it on four occasions and all his specimens are in the NHML. At Woking, probably Horsell Common, he recorded a female in August 1888, on flowers of figwort and bryony, and at Weybridge on bramble; he also found it twice at Chobham Common, a female in June 1876 and another in June 1878. The recent records from Norfolk and Sussex raise hopes that this species could still exist in, or could recolonise, its old haunts in Surrey.

It has decreased to extinction since 1900.

Lasioglossum smeathmanellum (Kirby, 1802)

National Status: Widespread

Surrey Status: Local

VCH: Godalming

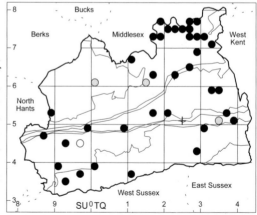

This very handsome metallic green species is distributed over most of England and Wales and was common but appears to have declined recently. The female flies from April to September and nests gregariously in cliffs and walls and visits numerous different flowers.

In Surrey it is widespread but distinctly local, except around London where it is common, possibly because there are plenty of suitable nest sites in walls of buildings there. The females can often be seen nesting in old mortar joints, e.g. Guildford Castle, Richmond Park boundary walls, Kew Gardens and Ham House. They have been recorded at flowers of autumn hawkbit, angelica and Shasta daisy.

It seems odd that Saunders knew of only one Surrey record, that of O.H. Latter from Godalming in about 1890, although there is a specimen collected from Reigate in 1890 in the BENHS Collection. Possibly it was genuinely rare at that time.

It has probably increased since 1900.

Lasioglossum villosulum (Kirby, 1802)

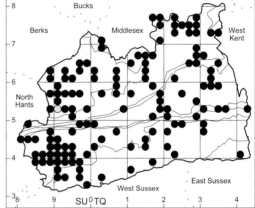

National Status: Universal

Surrey Status: Ubiquitous

VCH: Generally distributed

This small species, which is not easy to distinguish from others in the genus, is common and widespread in Britain, occurring in a variety of habitats. Females fly from early April to October and forage from many flowers, but mainly from yellow composites.

It is equally common and wide-spread in Surrey, occurring on sand, gravel, chalk and clay but it appears to prefer sand and gravel soils for nesting. Females have been seen at flowers of dandelion, cat's-ear, angelica, prickly sow-thistle, ragwort and smooth hawksbeard.

It is no doubt as common now as it was in 1900.

Lasioglossum xanthopus (Kirby, 1802)

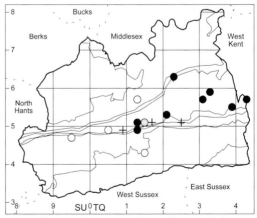

National Status: Scarce; Nb

Surrey Status: Rare

VCH: Shere, Box Hill

This is by far the largest species in the genus and in the field can easily be mistaken for an *Andrena* species. The female is distinctive with her translucent yellow hind tibiae and prominent white hair bands. It is a scarce and local bee of southern Britain, being found mainly on the coast, and inland on calcareous grassland. It appears to have declined significantly in recent years, especially inland. The overwintered females fly from early April onwards but the new generation of males and females emerge in late August; these females are rarely seen but the males are usually found in September or even October. The females forage from a range of flowers but the males seem to prefer purple or blue flowers in the autumn, such as stemless thistle, knapweed and devil's-bit scabious.

This is a rare and very local bee in Surrey, being confined to the chalk grassland of the North Downs. It was first recorded in 1886 by T.R. Billups from Reigate, in 1890 by E. Capron from Colekitchen Down near Shere, and in about 1890 by T. Marshall from Box Hill. There are three specimens in the NHML, one from Newlands Corner in 1918 and two, labelled Holmwood, but probably collected by Mortimer at Box Hill, in 1920 and 1922. Guichard cites a record in 1929 from Puttenham Heath, at the base of the Hogs Back, and Baker collected one in 1950 at Bookham Common, which is just off the Chalk. Two males were found in the collection of S.F. Imber, which he had collected from Westcott Downs near Dorking in September 1963 and 1965.

During the survey period it has been found on ten occasions at seven different sites. It was refound at Westcott Downs on 21 September 1998 when at least ten males were seen on greater knapweed, field scabious, small scabious, and stemless thistle (DWB and GAC), and a female was seen there on dog rose on 17 June 2002 (DWB). The other sites are Riddlesdown Quarry (females flying over clay bank on 9 and 15 April and 2 May 1997, RDH), a female at Dawcombe NR near Betchworth on 13 April 1997 (GAC), a male on the late date of 11 October 1999 at Happy Valley near Coulsdon (RDH), a female at Tatsfield on 28 April 1999 (GAC), another female at Howell Hill NR near Ewell on 21 April 2001 (ME) and two females at Oxted Downs on 15 May 2005 (GAC).

The nests are attacked by the large and very rare cuckoo bee *Sphecodes spinulosus*, which has only been found twice in Surrey, at Coulsdon Common in 1937 (OWR) and at Westcott Downs on 29 May 1998 (GAC).

It probably has the same status as it had in 1900.

Lasioglossum zonulum (Smith, 1848)

National Status: Restricted
Surrey Status: Common
VCH: Holmwood, Chobham, Woking, Weybridge, Ripley

This large species with polished, shining abdominal segments is restricted to the southernmost parts of Britain where it can be common on heathland and in woods. The females fly from early April to October, forage from a variety of flowers and are social.

In Surrey this bee is widespread and common, especially on the sand and on both Weald and London Clay, but is largely absent from the north-east of the county. On the sand it is found commonly on most of the western heaths, and on the Weald Clay it mainly occurs in woodland rides and clearings, as well as in old claypits. The only locality on the Chalk is the Sheepleas. Females have been seen on flowers as diverse as buttercup, germander speedwell, ragged robin, forget-me-not, sheep's-bit, angelica, dandelion and yellow iris. The rare and distinctive cuckoo bee *Sphecodes scabricollis* is a cleptoparasite of this species, and its range in Surrey corresponds with that of the present species, even though it is much scarcer and less widespread.

Its status is probably unchanged since 1900, but it may be commoner now.

Genus *Sphecodes* Latreille, 1804

These are small to medium-sized bees which are cleptoparasites on various species in the genera *Halictus* and *Lasioglossum*, and, in a few cases, in *Andrena*. They are sparsely hairy, black, usually with red markings on the abdomen. The female, which lacks pollen-carrying hairs, enters the cell of its host, destroys the host's egg and lays an egg on the pollen ball; it has even been reported that *S. monilicornis* may kill the female of one of its hosts. Very little investigation has been done on which hosts are parasitised by which species of *Sphecodes*. The males are difficult to identify, apart from their diagnostic genitalia. Another male character is the amount of fine pubescence on the underside of the antennal segments. In all species, except *S. rubicundus* and *S. spinulosus*, only the mated females hibernate, emerging in the spring to raid the nests of their hosts; their progeny emerge in the summer when males and females can be found until September. The other two species hibernate as adult males and females and produce only one brood in the spring.

Nationally 16 species all of which occur in Surrey.

Sphecodes crassus Thomson, 1870

National Status: Scarce; Nb
Surrey Status: Common
VCH: (as *variegatus*) Chobham, Weybridge

A scarce but widespread, small bee in Britain, it flies in two broods from May to September and is found in various types of habitat.

It is a widespread but rather local bee in Surrey, possibly found more often than a century ago due to better understanding of its identity. It has been recorded visiting hogweed for nectar. It is probably a cleptoparasite of *Lasiogossum parvulum*.

It is possibly more common than in 1900.

Sphecodes ephippius (Linnaeus, 1767)

National Status: Widespread
Surrey Status: Ubiquitous
VCH: (as *similis*) Generally distributed

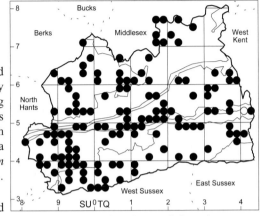

This is a common and widespread bee in Britain, occurring in many different types of habitat and flying from April to September. It varies greatly in size, depending on which host it is parasitising. It is a cleptoparasite of *Lasioglossum leucozonium* and possibly *L. calceatum* and *L. lativentre.*

It is very common and widespread in Surrey, occurring wherever its hosts' nests are to be found, especially at bare sunny banks.

It is probably as common now as in 1900.

Sphecodes ferruginatus Hagens, 1874

National Status: Scarce; Nb
Surrey Status: Rare
VCH: Clandon

Although widespread in England this species is scarce everywhere. Its hosts are thought to be the common *Lasioglossum fulvicorne* of chalk and limestone, its close relative *L. fratellum* and possibly *L. pauxillum.*

In Surrey it is rare and some of the records are dubious, as it is a very difficult species to identify correctly. All the supposed hosts, except *L. fratellum*, are common in Surrey so it is a mystery as to why it is so scarce.

It is most likely that its status is unchanged since 1900.

Sphecodes geoffrellus (Kirby, 1802)   PLATE 27

National Status: Universal

Surrey Status: Common

VCH: (as *affinis*) Generally distributed

A small, common and widespread bee throughout Britain, flying from April to September and found wherever its hosts are nesting. It is considered to be a cleptoparasite of *Lasioglossum nitidiusculum, L. parvulum, L. villosulum, L. cupromicans, L. leucopus* and *L. morio.*

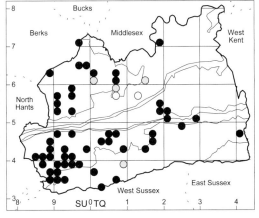

It is common and widespread in Surrey, being found wherever its hosts' nests are located, especially at south-facing banks. Its status is unchanged since 1900.

Sphecodes gibbus (Linnaeus, 1758)

National Status: Widespread

Surrey Status: Local

VCH: Generally distributed

This is one of the largest of the *Sphecodes* and is widespread and common in Britain, flying from April to September, wherever its host *Halictus rubicundus* is nesting.

In Surrey it is common in the west, but appears to be distinctly local and uncommon in the east, although its host is common there.

Its status has probably not changed since 1900.

193

Sphecodes hyalinatus Hagens, 1882

National Status: Widespread
Surrey Status: Local
VCH: Clandon, Box Hill

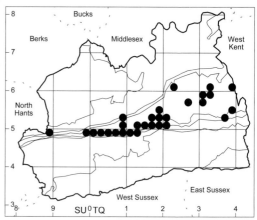

The female of this small species is distinguished by having short, dense, felt-like hairs on the underside of the thorax. It is widespread in Britain but occurs only on chalk or limestone. It flies from May to September and attacks the nests of *Lasioglossum fulvicorne*, an abundant bee of chalk and limestone, and its close relative *L. fratellum*.

In Surrey it is entirely restricted to the chalk of the North Downs, where it is abundant from the Hogs Back at Guildown, near Guildford, in the west, to New Addington on the Kent boundary in the east. Here it is the parasite of the equally abundant *L. fulvicorne*.

Saunders knew of only two sites on the Chalk but as the Victorian and Edwardian collectors rarely visited the North Downs its status is probably unchanged since 1900.

Sphecodes longulus Hagens, 1882

National Status: Rare; Na
Surrey Status: Very local
VCH: Woking, Chobham,
    Weybridge, Wisley,
    Godalming

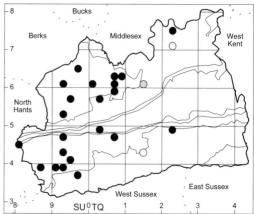

This is the smallest bee in the genus and and also one of the rarest, being recorded very sparingly in sandy habitat only in the south-east of England. It parasitises small species of *Lasioglossum*, such as *L. minutissimum* and possibly *L. morio* and *L. leucopus*.

In Surrey it occurs sparingly on most of the western heaths but it has also been found on dry acid grassland at Brooklands and Barnes Common. It has been recorded at Wrecclesham Sandpit, well away from heathland, and even in a claypit at Hambledon, where there is very dry friable clay on a south-facing cliff. I have even taken it on three occasions on bare sandy soil in my garden at Milford, where both *L. morio* and *L. minutissimum* are common. I have also found it twice coming to wild carrot in flower lures on heathland at Witley and Mare Hill Commons. Saunders knew it from various sites around 1900, including one of the first British records from Chobham Common in 1884 and another from Horsell Common in 1889, and it was recorded from Wimbledon Common in 1909.

It seems that it had the same status in 1900 as it has now.

Sphecodes miniatus Hagens, 1882

National Status: Scarce; Nb
Surrey Status: Very local
VCH: (as *dimidiatus*) Woking, Chobham, Godalming

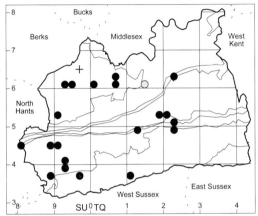

A very small and scarce species of southern Britain, this cuckoo bee is found mainly on sand and occasionally on chalk. Its host is unknown but it has been reported to be associated with *Lasioglossum nitidiusculum*. It is a difficult bee to identify and may therefore be under-recorded as well as mis-identified.

It is very local in Surrey and is found mainly on the western heaths and occasionally on dry acid grasslands (Brooklands, 2004, DWB), a sandpit (Wrecclesham, 2005, DWB), a dry south-facing slope of a claypit (Hambledon, 2004, DWB) and on the Chalk (Headley Heath, chalk area, 1996, ME). As *L. nitidiusculum* is not now found in Surrey, it must have another unknown host.

It seems likely that its status is probably unchanged since 1900.

Sphecodes monilicornis (Kirby, 1802)

National Status: Universal
Surrey Status: Ubiquitous
VCH: (as *subquadratus*) Generally distributed

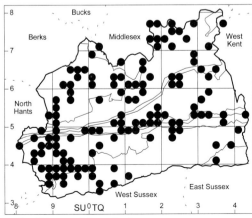

This is probably the most common and widespread species of *Sphecodes* in Britain. Under the microscope, when viewed from above, the female has a distinctively square-shaped head with three or four rows of punctures behind the ocelli. It flies from April to September and is a cleptoparasite of halictines such as *Halictus rubicundus, Lasioglossum calceatum, L. albipes* and *L. malachurum.*

It is also the commonest and most widespread *Sphecodes* in Surrey, being found wherever its hosts are nesting, and is seen most often flying slowly around the nest burrows and crawling in and out of the entrances. It has been recorded coming for nectar to flowers of wild carrot, Canadian goldenrod, common fleabane and creeping thistle. It is frequent on the clay where *H. rubicundus* and *L. malachurum* breed commonly, but in other areas it probably attacks the nests of *L. calceatum.*

Its status has not changed since 1900.

Sphecodes niger Hagens, 1874

National Status: Restricted; RDB3

Surrey Status: Local

VCH: No records

This small dark species is distinguished in both sexes by the smooth and brightly shining area immediately below the wing base, the hypoepimeral area. The male is entirely black and is easily overlooked as a *Lasioglossum* species but the female has red on the abdomen, although rather less than in other species. It is a

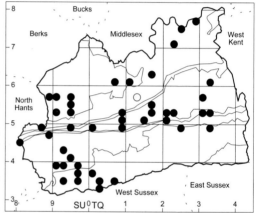

cleptoparasite of the very common *Lasioglossum morio*. It has always been a great rarity of south-east England but in the last few years it has expanded its range westwards and northwards dramatically. It is now found in Somerset and Yorkshire.

In Surrey, since 1996, it has been proved to be not only widespread, with about 40 sites, but also locally common, mainly on chalk but also on clay and sand. It is nearly always found, sometimes in numbers, at nesting aggregations of *L. morio*, where it crawls around and frequently enters the nest burrows. On the North Downs, where it is fairly common, it occurs typically around rabbit burrows and scrapes, whereas on the the Weald Clay it frequents bare sunny banks along woodland rides in the Forestry Commission woods at Botany Bay and Sidney Wood. It also occurs on the London Clay on a sunny bank at Chessington Zoo (DWB). It is widespread on the sand in the south-west, where it again occurs on sunny banks, and even on the Thames Basin gravels in London at Wimbledon Common and Wandsworth. It has been recorded visiting flowers of wild carrot and angelica for nectar.

Before 1996 it had been recorded only twice; the first record was in 1930 on the Chalk at Colekitchen Down, Gomshall by R.C.L. Perkins and the second was in 1950 on London Clay at Bookham Common by Baker. Why is it that such a formerly rare bee is now found to be common and widespread? Has it increased its range and abundance dramatically in the last few years or was it overlooked by earlier collectors, possibly on account of its size and difficulty of identification? One reason may be that it does not apparently occur on the heaths of north-west Surrey, the area most frequented by the early recorders; for instance there are no records for Chobham, Woking, Byfleet or even Oxshott.

It has probably increased dramatically since 1900.

Sphecodes pellucidus Smith, 1845

National Status: Widespread
Surrey Status: Locally common
VCH: (as *pilifrons*) Generally distributed

This is a very common and widespread species in Britain, being found chiefly on sandy soils where its main host, *Andrena barbilabris,* occurs. It may also parasitise nests of *Lasioglossum leucozonium.*

In Surrey it is absent from the clay (as is its main host), very scarce on chalk, but abundant on sand, both on the western heaths and on the

dry acid grasslands around London; it also occurs along the Lower Greensand ridge to the south of the North Downs.

Its status is probably unchanged since 1900.

Sphecodes puncticeps Thomson, 1870

National Status: Widespread
Surrey Status: Fairly common
VCH: Reigate, Woking, Chobham

This small species is widespread and reasonably common in Britain, flying from June to September, and apparently attacking nests of *Lasioglossum lativentre, L. villosulum* and *L. quadrinotatum.*

This is a very widespread species in Surrey, occurring in various types of habitat but most common on sandy soils, both heaths and dry

acid grasslands. It has been seen at flowers of angelica. All three hosts occur in Surrey although *L. quadrinotatum* is rare and restricted to the western heaths.

It may be more widespread and commoner now than in 1900.

Sphecodes reticulatus Thomson, 1870

National Status: Widespread; Na
Surrey Status: Increasingly
common
VCH: Chobham, Woking, Ripley

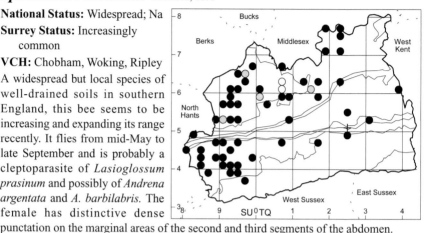

A widespread but local species of well-drained soils in southern England, this bee seems to be increasing and expanding its range recently. It flies from mid-May to late September and is probably a cleptoparasite of *Lasioglossum prasinum* and possibly of *Andrena argentata* and *A. barbilabris*. The female has distinctive dense punctation on the marginal areas of the second and third segments of the abdomen.

In Surrey it is common on the western heaths, where it probably parasitises the heather specialists *L. prasinum* and *A. argentata*, but it also occurs frequently on dry acid grassland around London, such as Richmond Park, Barnes Common and Kew Gardens, where there is no heather and there it may attack *Andrena barbilabris*. It is also found in gardens where it may possibly attack *Andrena dorsata*. It is often found visiting thistle flowers for nectar but can be found on a range of other plants including forget-me-not, mint, yarrow and *Eryngium*.

It seems to be much more common and widespread than it was around 1900.

Sphecodes rubicundus Hagens, 1875   PLATE 16

National Status: Scarce; Na
Surrey Status: Very local
VCH: No records

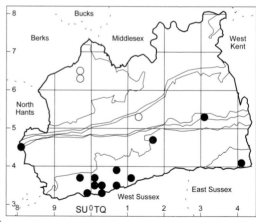

A large, robust and very red species, which occurs very sparingly in southern England and is a clepto-parasite of the scarce mining bee *Andrena labialis*. Unlike other species of *Sphecodes*, except *S. pellucidus* and possibly *S. reticulatus*, it parasitises a species of *Andrena*. It is also unusual in having only one brood, flying between early May and late June, to coincide with the flight time of its host; the adults of both sexes are fully developed by late August but remain in their cells until the next spring.

This species has a rather similar distribution in Surrey to *S. scabricollis*, being found mainly in the Weald Clay woods of the south-west where it can be found on thistles, wood spurge and germander speedwell. It was first recorded in 1902 by F.D. Morice at Chobham Common and Effingham, having first been added to the British List in 1896 by Saunders. It was not found again until 1997 when it was taken in Sidney Wood, Dunsfold and has been seen there in subsequent years quite frequently (DWB). It also occurs fairly commonly in another wood, Sayers Land, north of Dunsfold aerodrome (DWB), and was found in 2007 at Walton Heath and Priory Park, Reigate (JPE). Six of the other localities where it occurs are old claypits: Somersbury Brickworks near Ewhurst (1998 and 2007, DWB), North Holmwood Claypit (1999, RDH), Hambledon Claypit (2001 to 2007, DWB), Cranleigh Brickworks (2005, DWB), Cranleigh Swallow Tiles Claypit (2007, DWB) and Wrecclesham Sandpit, which also has clay (2005, DWB). It was found in the very south-east corner of the county at Dormansland in 2004, on a clay bank by a pond (RDH). Its host *A. labialis* has been found at all these localities.

It seems to have increased considerably since 1900 and has probably expanded its range although the Victorians and Edwardians rarely collected in the southern Weald Clay woodlands where it occurs today.

Sphecodes scabricollis Wesmael, 1835

National Status: Rare; RDB3
Surrey Status: Very local
VCH: Unknown

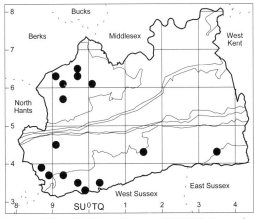

Occurring sparingly in southern England, this bee is a cleptoparasite of the common *Lasioglossum zonulum* and is found mainly in open woodland and at edges of heaths. It is one the larger species in the genus and it can be recognised by the very dense and deep pits of the punctation on the head and thorax, especially in the female.

In Surrey it was first recorded on 29 August 1993 at Chobham Common (RKAM). Recently, from 1997 to 2004, it has been found to be locally frequent in the the open rides of the Forestry Commision woods on the Weald Clay around Dunsfold, Chiddingfold and Brook, where it is usually seen coming to flowers of thistles, e.g. Sidney Wood, Botany Bay, Oaken Wood, Holmens Grove and Boundless Copse (all DWB). It has also been found recently on heathland edge, again at thistle flowers, in the north-west of the county at Chobham Common on 29 August 1993 (RKAM), Horsell Common sandpit on 25 August 1998, Hagthorne Bog on 11 August 2003 and Pirbright Ranges on 25 August 2003 (all DWB). It has been recorded on thistles at heathland edge on Hankley Common (1997, DWB) and below Leith Hill (2006, DWB) and at Somerset Bridge, Elstead (2004, DWB).

The only locality in the east of the county is Newchapel on the Weald Clay (20 August 1994, RKAM). It has also been seen on flowers of yarrow and common fleabane. The earliest flight date is 30 May 1997 at Oaken Wood, but it is not normally seen until July and is most common in August.

It seems that this bee is becoming more common and expanding its range in Surrey; it was unknown in Saunders' time, being added to the British List in 1917. The host bee is fairly common and widespread in the western half of the county and on the Weald Clay in the south-east, and there seems no reason why it should not spread to all these areas.

It may be a recent newcomer to Surrey.

Sphecodes spinulosus Hagens, 1875

National Status: Very rare; RDB2
Surrey Status: Very rare
VCH: No records

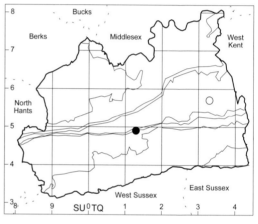

This bee, the largest of the *Sphecodes*, has declined seriously in Britain from being a scarce bee to an extremely rare one and is now confined to only a few sites. It is a cleptoparasite of the scarce mining bee *Lasioglossum xanthopus* and flies from mid-May to late June. It can be recognised by its size and, under a microscope, by the unique and distinct trough at the back of the head in both sexes.

There are only two records for Surrey, one being very recent. The first was by Prof. O.W. Richards from Coulsdon Common on 6 June 1937, not far from where *L. xanthopus* still occurs today. The second was by G.A. Collins who collected a single female at Westcott Downs, Dorking on 29 May 1998, but, in spite of later searches there, no others have been seen since. Males of *L. xanthopus* have however been found to be quite common there in the autumn. It should be searched for wherever its host occurs.

As the early collectors rarely visited the Chalk it is difficult to say whether it has increased since 1900.

Genus *Dufourea* Lepeletier, 1841

These are very small black solitary species, which nest in the soil. The body is covered in greyish hairs and the fore wings have only two submarginal cells.

Nationally two species, but one not seen since 1956; both in Surrey, but neither has been seen here since 1920.

Dufourea halictula (Nylander, 1852)

National Status: Endangered RDB1

Surrey Status: Extinct

VCH: no records

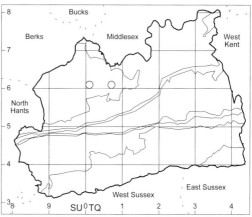

This very small black bee is an extreme rarity and was first discovered in Britain in about 1910 by O.C. Silverlock at Horsell Common, Surrey, and has only ever been found at three other British sites, namely Byfleet, Surrey and Ferndown and Parley, both in Dorset. It was last seen at the Parley site on 30 July 1953 and it may well now be extinct. It is thought to forage only from sheep's-bit in Britain, but it has been recorded from other species of *Campanula* in Poland, especially nettle-leaved bellflower.

Saunders (1910), writing only six weeks before his death, published its discovery "in the large sandpit on Woking Heath (Horsell Common), a locality which has been worked constantly by numerous Hymenopterists. It must be exceedingly rare, as although it is a small insignificant species, it could not have escaped the notice of either Mr. Morice, Mr. Nevinson or myself. It greatly resembles a small *Halictus*, from which its wings with only two submarginal cells will easily distinguish it. The male is particularly like a small *Halictus*, but the structure of its antennae will distinguish it."

Mortimer published his own finding of the second record at Byfleet in June 1913: "In June last I found a male of this species…and afterwards met with this sex in increasing profusion for some days, usually at rest on stones or low-growing plants. Within a week the females appeared in equal abundance. …as nothing is known of its habits it may be well to record that the females were constructing their burrows between stones chiefly on a hard sandy footpath, less frequently in an adjoining sandy moss-covered bank, and provisioning them with pollen collected from *Jasione montana.* The insect is extraordinarily Halictiform and might easily be passed over for *H. minutissimus* (which species, however, looks considerably blacker than *halictula* owing to the much more profuse grey pubescence of the latter), and I am inclined to think that it will prove less rare than has been thought now that its food plant is known." It was indeed found at this site by Nevinson and Bradley until 24 June 1920 but the site is now built-over. There are about 30 specimens from Mortimer and three from Nevinson in the NHML, with a further 21 specimens collected there by these two on 22, 23 and 24 June 1915, with another dated June 1920, in Oxford University Museum.

Being so small and, in the field, difficult to distinguish from small *Lasioglossum* species, it could easily be overlooked. However, sheep's-bit has become much scarcer in Surrey over the last 50 years and large patches of it are now very difficult to find. But any patch of this plant is worth examining for *D. halictula*. In 2003 I heard that there was still a large colony of sheep's-bit at the old Brooklands airfield near Byfleet, and that the dry acid grassland there was sometimes blue with the flowers. This locality is very near to Mortimer's Byfleet site and it seems more than likely that sheep's-bit would have been growing there in Mortimer's time also. Therefore there is a good chance that not only was the bee present at Brooklands then but that it could possibly be surviving there even now. Unfortunately the site was badly damaged by development in 2005 although some plants still survive. I searched the area for the bee in 2003, 2004 and 2007 but have so far failed to refind it.

Dufourea minuta Lepeletier, 1841   PLATE 4

National Status: Endangered RDB1

Surrey Status: Possibly extinct

VCH: (as *vulgaris*) Woking, Chobham

This extremely rare bee has been found at only five sites in Britain, two in Dorset, two in Surrey and one in Essex. It was first recorded in 1879 at Chewton, then in Hampshire but probably now in Dorset. Until 2007 it was thought to be extinct in Britain, having last been seen in 1956 at Holt, Dorset,

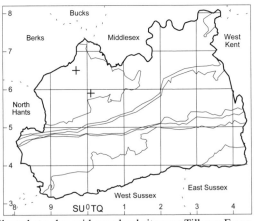

but on 30 June 2007 a male was collected at a dry acid grassland site near Tilbury, Essex (MEA).

T.R. Billups (1881) described the first capture in Surrey in 1881; "While walking along the banks of the Basingstoke Canal at Woking on the 1st of August last, I observed a number of small black Apidae busy at work on the bloom of the Ragwort: to capture some few of them was the work of a very few minutes, and amongst them was one specimen, which when I picked it off the bloom, did not attempt to fly away but appeared very sluggish and lay in the palm of my hand as though feigning death, or as though benumbed with cold. Not knowing this insect I submitted it to Mr. E. Saunders…it is a female and somewhat resembles a small *Panurgus calcaratus* in whose company it was taken; it is rare both on the continent and in this country. Although I have looked carefully several times since in the same locality I have not been again able to meet with it."

Saunders (1891) described the capture of the only other Surrey specimen: "On the 1st of August, 1891 I took a male on a dandelion flower at Chobham. As I have repeatedly looked for this insect about here without success, I think it may be fairly concluded that it is a great rarity. It is so like a small *Halictus* that I have been constantly afraid of passing it over, but the different style of flight of the specimen I have just caught told me at once that I had got something unusual and distinct from *Halictus*. I hope more specimens may be found before the 1st August, 1901." Saunders (1896) noted "Its flight is different, it 'wriggles' into a flower. Although I only saw the male for a second before it settled, I knew by its wriggling flight that I had got something good, and suspected *Dufourea* at once." From his diary note it seems that he was near Burrowhill on that occasion. Both the Saunders and Billups specimens are in the NHML.

It has not been seen since then in Surrey but it is just possible that it still survives, overlooked by recorders as a small *Lasioglossum* or *Panurgus* because of its small size .

SUBFAMILY MELITTINAE

These are solitary, ground-nesting bees with short pointed tongues, similar in appearance to *Andrena*.

Nationally six species in three genera, of which five species in three genera occur in Surrey.

Genus *Melitta* Kirby, 1802

These are medium-sized to large, black solitary bees, with white or tawny hair bands on the abdomen. They are similar to *Colletes* and *Andrena* but distinguinguished from both of these by the thickened claw-segment, a slight difference in wing venation and the obliquely truncated last segment of the antenna. Pollen-carrying hairs are on the hind tibia and basitarsus. Females are oligolectic for pollen sources. The main nest burrow leads to lateral burrows. Winter is passed as a diapausing larva enclosed in a cocoon. They fly from mid to late summer.

Nationally four species, with three in Surrey.

Melitta haemorrhoidalis (Fabricius, 1775)   PLATE 28

National Status: Scarce

Surrey Status: Local

VCH: Godalming, Shirley, Weybridge, Chobham

The female is easily recognised by the bright reddish-gold hairs at the tip of the abdomen but the male is more difficult, having indistinct white hair bands on the abdomen, whereas the other two Surrey species have wide and distinct hair bands.

The female collects pollen only from flowers of the *Campanula* family and nests in the soil, flying from mid-July to late August. Although widely distributed in southern Britain it is only at all common on the chalk soils of south-east England.

In Surrey it is frequent all along the North Downs wherever its favoured pollen source, nettle-leaved bellflower, is present, although it also takes pollen from clustered bellflower and harebell. Off the Chalk it has been found at harebell, e.g. on Bagmoor Common, and at nettle-leaved bellflower where this plant occurs on the Bargate Beds around Godalming, and at the introduced *Campanula persicifolia*. It is probably much less common on the sand now than it was in Victorian times, due to the recent dramatic decline in the harebell. It is abundant at Kew Gardens where it frequents the various species of *Campanula* growing in the Order Beds; it is probably parasitised by *Nomada flavopicta* there as I have taken this cleptoparasite in the Order Beds more than once and its other two hosts have not been recorded at Kew.

Some years ago I scattered some seeds of nettle-leaved bellflower in my garden at Milford and the plant still survives in good numbers; since then this bee has been a very regular and common visitor to my garden. The males fly very fast from one flower to another, looking for females. At Dawcombe NR, where this bee is common, I once observed females sheltering in the flowers of musk mallow whenever the sun went behind a cloud or during a shower. Both sexes also visit these flowers for nectar.

Its status is probably unchanged since 1900.

Melitta leporina (Panzer, 1799)

National Status: Widespread
Surrey Status: Very local
VCH: Woking, Chobham

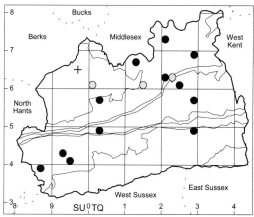

This bee is very similar to *M. tricincta* but it has yellowish hair bands when fresh, rather than white; there are other subtle differences, best looked at under the microscope. However, this species collects pollen only from clovers and vetches whereas *M. tricincta* is found only at red bartsia. It is easily mistaken for an *Andrena* species. Although it is widely distributed in southern Britain it is common only in the south-east. It is becoming scarcer. It is mainly found on open grassland on chalk and sand.

In Surrey it is widespread but very local and much the scarcest of the three species. There are a few records from the Chalk, a few from dry acid grassland on Thames Gravel Terraces e.g. Richmond Park and Molesey, and a few from the sand in the south-west, e.g. Hankley Common, Bagmoor Common and my garden at Milford. In 1986 it was seen in numbers by Baker by the Hogsmill River at West Ewell. In my garden I have seen a female at red clover and another at hare's-foot clover. The cleptoparasitic bee *Nomada flavopicta* probably parasitises this species, but Richmond Park is the only locality where both have been recorded and other species of *Melitta* have not.

Its status is probably unchanged since 1900.

Melitta tricincta Kirby, 1802

National Status: Scarce; Nb

Surrey Status: Locally common

VCH: No records

This bee has distinctive white hair bands in both sexes, and is only ever found around red bartsia, its sole pollen source. It flies from late July to early September, to coincide with the flowering of red bartsia. It is restricted to southern England but can be locally abundant.

In Surrey it is common along the Chalk from Pewley Down, Guildford, to the Kent border, and

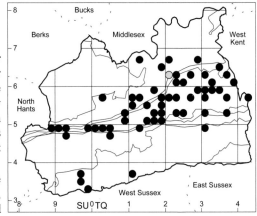

is usually abundant wherever there is a good growth of red bartsia. This plant also grows off the Chalk and there are numerous records of the bee from sites on the sand, both north and south of the North Downs, but rarely far from the Chalk. But it also occurs in various woods on the Weald Clay around Chiddingfold and Ewhurst, where red bartsia grows in the rides.

The males fly very fast from plant to plant, rarely stopping for nectar, in their quest for females. It is almost certainly parasitised by *Nomada flavopicta*, as this cleptoparasitic bee has been seen at many of the localities for *Melitta*.

It was not recorded by Saunders a century ago, partly because it was confused with *M. leporina* at that time, and partly because it did not, and still does not, occur around his favoured haunts of Chobham, Woking and Weybridge; few hymenopterists visited the North Downs where it was no doubt as abundant then as it is today.

Genus *Macropis* Panzer, 1809

Small to medium-sized black solitary bees with strikingly shiny abdomens and characterised by their strong association with yellow loosestrife. The males are distinguished by their yellow face and club-shaped hind tibia and femur. Females nest underground in banks or slopes of wetland sites. The burrow leads to a small number of cells lined with a yellowish wax-like material, derived from the oil collected from yellow loosestrife, which is used to waterproof the cells. The female's sole pollen source is yellow loosestrife in Britain. They fly from mid to late summer.

Nationally only one species, also found in Surrey.

Macropis europaea Warncke, 1973   PLATE 28

National Status: Scarce; Na
Surrey Status: Local
VCH: (as *labiata*) Woking
This is a very local bee of wetland
sites mainly in south-east England
but it can be common where it
occurs. It is unique in Britain for
having females that provision their
nests with fatty floral oils from the
flowers of the sole forage plant
yellow loosestrife, as well as pollen.
The females also line the nests with
an oily substance from the yellow
loosestrife to protect them from the
damp soil in which they nest.

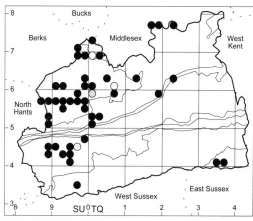

In Surrey it is reasonably widespread and occurs, sometimes in large numbers, wherever
yellow loosestrife grows. It is most common in damp fields, stream-sides and canal banks
west of Woking but also occurs in large numbers along the River Wey as far south and
west as Thundry Meadows, Elstead, and along the Basingstoke Canal at Ash, in Windsor
Great Park and at Runnymede, and even in Kew Gardens. From Kew it must presumably
have spread to the Wetland Centre, Barnes, a distance of 4 km, where it was seen on
29 July 2004 flying over a small patch of yellow loosestrife that had been planted about
five years earlier. It also occurs around Hedgecourt Pond and Wiremill Lake in the extreme
south-east of the county. It has been seen occasionally at flowers of the non-native dotted
loosestrife, *Lysimachia punctata*: two males at Ashtead Common in July 2002, one male
and a probable female at Nonsuch Park in July 1997, and a male at my garden pond at
Milford in July 2005. Nesting has been rarely observed in England but at Bagmoor Common
I have seen a number of females coming in to nest at the base of a small root-plate. I could
not make out whether they were all sharing the same nest entrance as this was hidden by
tall grasses. Others were nesting singly nearby on level ground that was lightly covered
with short grass. The ground itself was dry at the time but is damp all winter. The nest site
was at least 300 metres from the yellow loosestrife which was growing in ditches outside
the reserve. It has been recorded in Surrey visiting flowers of alder buckthorn, creeping
thistle, water mint and water-pepper.

Its status is probably unchanged since 1900.

Genus *Dasypoda* Latreille, 1802

This is a large subterranean-nesting solitary bee, black with white bands on the abdomen. The pollen hairs on the hind tibia and basitarsus are finely plumose and extremely long. It nests in light sandy soils on the coast and inland. The burrow descends at a shallow angle before becoming vertical with lateral burrows, each ending in a cell.

Nationally only one species, also in Surrey.

Dasypoda hirtipes (Fabricius, 1793)   PLATE 29

National Status: Scarce; Nb

Surrey Status: Locally common

VCH: Godalming, Chobham, Woking

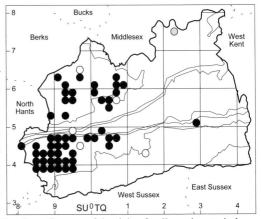

The female of this species is one of the most beautiful and distinctive bees in Britain, having extraordinarily long, golden hairs on the hind tibiae and prominent white hair bands on the abdomen. The male is much duller but is very hairy all over. It occurs mainly around the coasts of southern Britain but is also found more scarcely inland on sandy soils. The female collects pollen from flowers of the daisy family and nests in bare ground.

In Surrey it is found, sometimes abundantly, on most of the sandy areas in the west, but not usually on the heaths, and there is one locality in the east at Holmethorpe sandpit near Redhill (JSD, 2001). It was recorded from Barnes Common in 1968 but has not been seen there since, although it does still occur not far away in Bushy Park, Middlesex. It seems to have become much more common over the last ten years, possibly due to climatic change. The female prefers to nest in compacted bare sand, and many nesting aggregations are found in car parks at the edges of heaths. Some nesting aggregations are enormous and are often shared with the bee-killer wasp *Philanthus triangulum*, which also prefers bare ground. At Frensham Great Pond, the nests of both species cover an area of nearly an acre and there must be about 5,000 nests of the bee and even more of the wasp. The females dig their very long burrows mainly in the afternoon, using their long pollen-hairs as a brush to clear the sand from the burrow entrance, leaving a distinctive fan of loose sand to one side of the entrance. Both females and males are usually found on common ragwort or other yellow composite flowers but they are also often on thistles, and it has been seen on sheep's-bit.

It may have increased and spread since 1900.

SUBFAMILY MEGACHILINAE

This is a large and diverse group of long-tongued solitary bees with a rectangular labrum. Pollen-carrying hairs are in rows beneath the abdomen, except in the cleptoparasitic species.

Nationally 37 species in eight genera, with 30 species in eight genera in Surrey.

Genus *Anthidium* Fabricius, 1804

This large solitary black bee with striking yellow spots on the abdomen nests above ground in dead wood, hollow stems and crevices in mortar; the cell walls and partitions are made from silky plant hairs.

Nationally only one species, also in Surrey.

Anthidium manicatum (Linnaeus, 1758)   PLATE 30

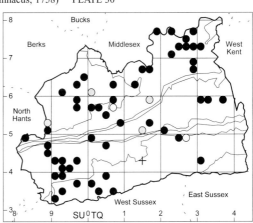

National Status: Widespread

Surrey Status: Local

VCH: Godalming, Wimbledon, Woking, Holmwood

This attractive large bee, with yellow spots at the sides of its abdomen, is widely distributed in Britain but locally common only in the south. It is one of the very few bees to have an English name, 'Wool-carder Bee', from its habit of shaving the hairs off plant leaves for its nest. It was scarce until about 1993 when it started to increase and expand its range. It flies from late May to early August and females forage mainly from labiates.

In Surrey it is widespread and reasonably common, being a frequent visitor to gardens where the female comes to lavender and particularly to lamb's-ear for pollen and for the felt on the leaves, which she strips to make her nest. The famous Gilbert White of Selborne noted this in his Journals, and his entry for August 1773 (White, 1931) reads: "*Apis manicata*. This bee is never observed by me 'til the Stachys germanica blows, on which it feeds all day: tho' doubtless it had other plants to feed on before I introduced that Stachys." In *A Natural History of Selborne* (White, 1788), he described its habits as follows: "There is a sort of wild bee frequenting the Garden Campion for the sake of its tomentum, which probably it turns to some purpose in the business of nidification. It is very pleasant to see with what address it strips off the pubes running from the top to the bottom of a branch and shaving it bare with the dexterity of a hoop shaver; when it has got a vast bundle, almost larger than itself, it flies away, holding it secure between its chin and fore legs". What a wonderful record of his observation! The female forages almost entirely on labiates including selfheal, betony, black horehound, hedge woundwort and garden catmint (*Nepeta*) as well as others already mentioned, but it has also been seen on purple toadflax and *Coronilla*; in Kew Gardens it is abundant on the labiate Order Bed. The males, which are generally larger than the females, are very territorial and interesting to watch. A single male will set up his territory around a clump of black horehound, for instance, so that he can mate with females as they come to forage. Any other male, or even another species of bee, which enters his territory will be driven off by him, sometimes being damaged or even killed by him. However, smaller males may fly round the outside of his territory, hoping to mate with any female trying to reach the forage plant. The uncommon cuckoo bee *Stelis punctulatissima* is a cleptoparasite of this species.

It is probably commoner and more widespread than in 1900.

Genus *Stelis* Panzer, 1806

These small to medium-sized black bees are cleptoparasitic on megachiline bees in the genera *Anthidium, Osmia, Hoplitis* and *Heriades*. Some have pale hair bands or pale markings on the abdomen. After finding the nest of the host the female returns repeatedly to lay an egg in each cell before it is closed. The larva destroys the egg or young larva of the host.

All four British species are rare, unlike most other genera of cleptoparasitic bees.

Nationally four species, all four in Surrey (but one extinct).

Stelis breviuscula (Nylander, 1848)   PLATE 7

National Status: Very rare; RDBK

Surrey Status: Very local

VCH: Unknown

This very small black bee, with narrow white hair bands, is a cleptoparasite of the nationally rare megachiline bee *Heriades truncorum*, which nests in beetle holes in dead wood and pithy stems. Both host and parasite are very similar superficially, although the female *Stelis* does not have the pollen-collecting hairs of the

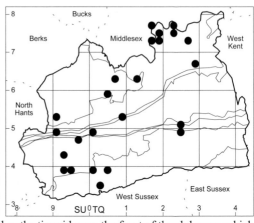

Heriades, and neither sex of *Stelis* has the tiny ridge on the front of the abdomen, which *Heriades* has. This is a newcomer to Britain, being first found in West Sussex in 1984, but

it was soon found in a handful of other sites in that county and also in Middlesex at Bushy Park in 2004 (DWB).

As *Heriades* is locally common in Surrey, it was expected that the parasite would also be found here, and the first specimen was duly found on 19 August 1996 at Wyke Common on Ash Ranges, where it was taken on common ragwort flowers with *Heriades* (DWB). It was found at this heathland site again in 1999 and also in a clay woodland site at Sidney Wood, Dunsfold. From then on it has been found at most nesting sites of *Heriades*, usually wherever ragwort grows near old fence posts. It is often found in large numbers, especially around London, e.g. Kew Gardens, Richmond Park, Barnes Common and the Wetland Centre, Barnes (all DWB). In the last ten years it has been recorded in no fewer than 24 tetrads and in all types of habitat, and is by far the most common of the four *Stelis* species in Surrey.

As a recent newcomer it has increased since 1900.

Stelis ornatula (Klug, 1807) PLATE 7

National Status: Rare; RDB3
Surrey Status: Rare
VCH: (as *octomaculata*)
    Mayford near Woking

This small, black bee has pairs of cream spots on the abdomen in both sexes and is very scarce in southern Britain. It is a cleptoparasite of the megachiline bee *Hoplitis claviventris*, which nests in bramble and other stems, and flies from late May to late August.

In Surrey it has probably always been rare, with only four localities

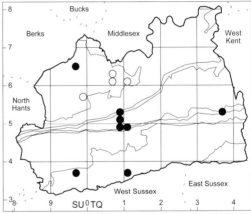

known prior to 1920 and none between then and 1998; from 1998 onwards it has been found in only eight tetrads. The old records were from localities where the recorders lived, the first Surrey record coming from Morice at Mayford, Woking, in 1901. It was found next by Nevinson at Cobham in 1907 and at Byfleet in 1915, and finally by Le Marchant at Weybridge and Mortimer at Byfleet in 1918. It must have been very rare at that time and later, since neither Saunders nor Guichard, the two most prolific Surrey recorders, ever found it.

Most of the modern records come from a small area on the North Downs, where it was first refound at Blatchford Down near Abinger Hammer on 26 July 1998 (ME). A few days later it was found at two places in the Sheepleas, West Horsley, only about two miles to the north (DWB). It was recorded again at Sheepleas on 1 June 1999 (DWB) and later that year at another nearby site, Colekitchen Down above Abinger Hammer (ME). However, the four later records come from localities far from this cluster: Chobham Common at Longcross Halt on 21 June 2001 (DWB), Barrow Green sandpit near Oxted on 22 June

2001 (GAC), Somersbury claypit near Ewhurst on 7 June 2006 (DWB) and Hambledon claypit on 21 May 2007 (JPE), where a female was investigating a hole in a bramble stem in which *Ceratina cyanea* was nesting. At Sheepleas I watched a female follow a female *H. claviventris* which was flying slowly around a root-plate covered in brambles, presumably searching for a nest site.

It may have increased since 1900.

Stelis phaeoptera (Kirby, 1802)

National Status: Very rare; RDB2
Surrey Status: Extinct
VCH: Battersea

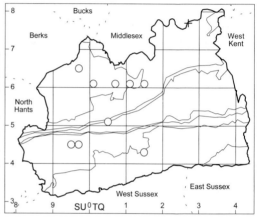

This has always been a rarity of southern Britain but it has declined alarmingly in the last 50 years and is now known from very few sites. It is a cleptoparasite of the fairly common megachiline bees *Osmia leaiana* and *O. aurulenta*, and possibly of other related species. It is a small black bee with no distinctive patterns on the abdomen. In Surrey it was relatively common from 1900 until 1939 but since then it has not been seen and it may be extinct. The earliest record was by F. Smith in about 1860 from Battersea. There were numerous records between 1903 and 1928, from the usual well-worked areas such as Chobham Common, Byfleet, Horsell Common, Oxshott Heath and Cobham. Mortimer recorded it no less than eight times between 1903 and 1930 from Holmwood, where he lived, although his "Holmwood" labels cover a much wider area. There is a specimen taken by Latter, labelled "Godalming 1906", in his collection which was originally at Charterhouse Museum but is now at Haslemere Museum. His pupil Spooner also took it twice on a fence in 1928 at Godalming, when he was at Charterhouse School. Guichard found it on Oxshott Heath as late as 1936 and the final record was made by D.O. Boyd on 30 August 1939 at West Clandon rectory; this specimen is in the NHML, together with most of the earlier ones.

It has declined to extinction since 1900.

Stelis punctulatissima (Kirby, 1802)   PLATE 36

National Status: Scarce; Nb

Surrey Status: Very local

VCH: (as *aterrima*) Holmwood, Weybridge

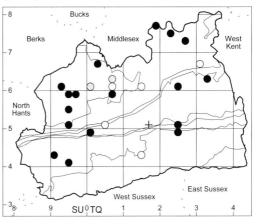

This is the much the largest of the four British *Stelis* species. Both sexes have narrow cream bands on the posterior margins of the last four segments of the abdomen, which are strongly and densely punctate. It is mainly restricted to south-east England and appears to have decreased considerably in recent years; there are many localities where it has not been refound in the last three decades. It is a cleptoparasite of two species of Megachilinae, *Anthidium manicatum* and *Osmia aurulenta*, and flies from mid-June to late August.

In Surrey it is distinctly local, with only 17 modern localities scattered across the county. However there are only a few old localities where it has not been refound and it may well be overlooked. Most records are from localities where *A. manicatum* is frequent, e.g. Kew Gardens where the host is abundant, RHS Wisley and my garden at Milford where both host and parasite are seen regularly each year. Away from gardens, males are mostly seen flying around plants of black horehound, which are also frequented by its host, for instance at Pewley Down, Wandsworth Common, Barnes Common, Thundry Meadows and Banstead Downs. It has never been found near the breeding sites of its other host *O. aurulenta*, which nests only in snail shells on the Chalk.

It was rare or local in 1900 so it may possibly have increased since then.

Genus *Heriades* Spinola, 1808

This small black bee has a raised rim at the front of the first abdominal segment. It nests above ground in old beetle holes in dead wood and occasionally in hollow stems.

Only one species in Britain, also found in Surrey.

Heriades truncorum (Linnaeus, 1758)   PLATE 7

National Status: Scarce; RDB3

Surrey Status: Local

VCH: Weybridge

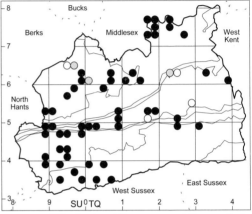

This small black bee is almost hairless, except for weak white hair bands, and the female has a brush of very pale orange pollen-collecting hairs beneath the abdomen. The character which distinguishes it from all other British bees is the keel or carina separating the top of the first abdominal segment from the declivity. The range of this rare bee is restricted to the extreme south-east corner of England and it occurs most frequently in the western Weald of West Sussex, north Hampshire and Surrey. Although it is single-brooded it has a long flight period, from June to September, and nests in old beetle burrows in fence posts or dead wood. Its cleptoparasite is the very rare bee *Stelis breviuscula* which is extremely similar in appearance to *Heriades* except that the female lacks the pollen-collecting hairs.

This bee is one of the Surrey specialities, being probably more common in the county than anywhere else. It was always considered an extreme rarity by the Victorian and Edwardian collectors who immediately wrote a short note in the entomological journals if they found a specimen. Morice (1900a) wrote that he had taken a male at thistles near Weybridge Station on 10 July. He considered this to be the first British record since 1802, being the year of capture of the first two British specimens from Brentford, which were in the Kirby Collection. There had been two other dubious records, in 1846 from Essex and in 1855 from Dulwich, Surrey. Morice (1906) wrote again in the same journal to say that he had taken a second specimen, this time a female nesting in a decayed wooden post, at Valley End, Chobham Common, on 6 July. He thought it "strange that a species, which is so common abroad, should be so extraordinarily successful in eluding observation in this country". But the next year Nevinson (1907) wrote in the same magazine that he had found it in numbers on ragwort and around old posts in various localities about Cobham from July right through to mid-September. He had obviously discovered the art of finding them, i.e. looking for ragwort growing near old fence posts.

After that there are only two specimens in the NHML, from Byfleet in 1912 and from Knaphill in 1936, until Baker started finding it in 1942 at Merstham and thereafter at other sites, including Oxshott Heath where he recorded it nesting in hollow bramble stems, this being the only such record. I.H.H. Yarrow (1954) still considered it a great rarity, when he wrote in *The Entomologist* that a few years earlier he had found it nesting in good numbers in a rotting window frame at Weybridge. In the 1950s P.W.E. Currie (1950,1954) found it at various places and wrote in the same journal that he had seen a large colony at Box Hill, with more than 100 occupied holes in old fence posts, and another smaller colony in his garden at Cheam, with a dozen occupied holes. In the 1970s Guichard recorded it at Chobham Common and Weybridge.

In 1996 I first found it, on ragwort, at Ash Ranges and since then it has been recorded on over 100 occasions, in 52 tetrads and 19 hectads. It is widespread in the county, being particularly common around London, e.g. Wandsworth Common, Richmond Park, Kew Gardens and Barnes Common. It can be very common where it occurs, with hundreds of nest holes in old posts or dead trees. Most nesting aggregations in Surrey have good numbers of the cleptoparasite *Stelis breviuscula* present. About 90% of the foraging records in Surrey are from ragwort but it does also visit other yellow composites, such as hawkweeds, cat's-ear, common fleabane and tansy. When foraging the female has the distinctive habit of wriggling her abdomen up and down very fast on the flower head.

It seems strange that the Victorian and Edwardian collectors failed to find it, except on very few occasions, in places where it is now common. Probably it was genuinely very rare at that time and it has increased in numbers and expanded its range over the last few years. It certainly appears to be expanding its range outside Surrey in the last decade, having been found at a few sites in Essex, Kent and Middlesex. On the other hand it is a very small bee which can be overlooked if its habits are not known.

It has increased and expanded its range since 1900.

Genus *Chelostoma* Latreille, 1809

These are small to medium-sized, black bees with elongate bodies which nest in holes in dead wood and stems. Cells are arranged linearly, separated by partitions of mud and sand grains stuck together by salivary secretions or nectar.

Nationally two species, both being found in Surrey.

Chelostoma campanularum (Kirby, 1802)   PLATE 31

National Status: Widespread
Surrey Status: Fairly common
VCH: Chobham, Woking

This small, long, black bee is widespread in southern Britain but is common only in the south-east corner. Here it is abundant at any species of *Campanula* in gardens and as a nester in small beetle holes in dead trees; it is also found outside gardens at wild *Campanula* species. It flies in one brood from June to August.

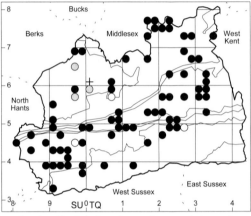

It is also widespread and reasonably common in Surrey and can be abundant locally. It is found most frequently in gardens, coming to all varieties of cultivated *Campanula*, but it also comes to harebell, clustered bellflower and nettle-leaved bellflower, as well as sheep's-bit, outside gardens; at Kew gardens it is abundant on the *Campanula* Order Bed. It can be abundant at nest sites in suitable old dead trees, sometimes swarming round them in hundreds.

It may well have increased since 1900.

Chelostoma florisomne (Linnaeus, 1758)   PLATE 31

National Status: Widespread

Surrey Status: Local

VCH: Holmwood, Wandsworth, Godalming

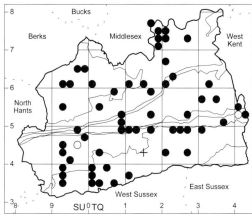

This is a considerably larger bee than the last, and has white hair bands on the abdomen. It is rather more widely distributed in Britain but is generally less common. It flies slightly earlier, from May to July, and the females forage from various species of buttercup, being one of the few bees to do so. It also nests in old beetle holes in dead wood but may use plant stems as well.

It is widespread and reasonably common in Surrey, being found in various types of habitat where buttercups grow, but especially in woodland rides on the Weald Clay, woodland edge and dry acid grasslands with old trees such as at Richmond Park, Kew Gardens and Wandsworth Common. Females have been recorded at bulbous, creeping and meadow buttercups, as well as at germander speedwell (presumably for nectar). It has a habit of sleeping, curled up, in flower heads, which explains its specific name. It is parasitised by the primitive wasp *Monosapyga clavicornis*.

It has probably increased since 1900.

Genus *Osmia* Panzer, 1806

These are medium-sized to large bees with black or metallic brown-green or blue bodies which nest in crevices above ground, such as in posts, mortar walls and old snail shells, except *O. rufa*, which sometimes nests in holes in soil. The female uses chewed leaf pulp or mud for the cell walls and partitions and collects pollen from a variety of plants. They usually have one generation a year and they generally overwinter as adults.

Nationally 11 species, with seven in Surrey.

Osmia aurulenta (Panzer, 1799)   PLATE 32

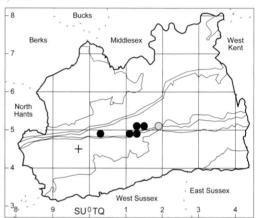

National Status: Widespread
Surrey Status: Very rare
VCH: Godalming
This medium-sized bee nests in snail shells and is locally common on sand dunes, shingle and chalk around the west coasts of much of Britain, but also occurs on calcareous grassland at a few inland sites in southern England. Apparently the male searches for a snail shell, establishes a territory around it and attracts a female to nest in it. The female is covered with short golden-red hairs on the thorax and abdomen whilst the male is considerably smaller and black with red and pale hairs. It collects pollen from bird's-foot trefoil and many other flowers.

In Surrey it is found on a very few sites along the North Downs. Apart from the rather doubtful Godalming record of Latter prior to 1900, cited by Saunders (1902) in the VCH, it was first recorded in the county by Mortimer at Box Hill as late as July 1923, probably because the Victorians and Edwardians rarely visited the North Downs. After a gap of nearly 50 years it was collected at Box Hill in 1976 (GRE). It was next found at Newlands Corner in July 1997 (DWB). But it 1998 it was found at various sites on Westcott Downs above Dorking (DWB and GAC), at nearby White Downs (DWB) and also at Blatchford Down, just to the west (ME). It possibly occurs at other places on the Chalk, and should be looked for.

Probably overlooked by the Victorians, its status may be unchanged since 1900.

Osmia bicolor (Schrank, 1781)   PLATE 33

National Status: Scarce; Nb
Surrey Status: Locally common
VCH: Reigate, Box Hill

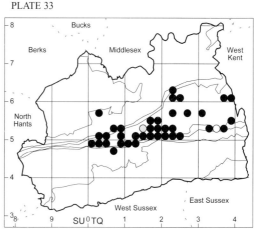

A distinctive, medium-sized, hairy bee, the female having a black head and thorax with an abdomen covered in bright red hairs, whereas the male is small, shiny and entirely black, although the hairs are pale golden when freshly emerged; it is restricted to chalk and limestone areas of southern England, where it is local. It flies from April to July, collects pollen from various flowers and nests in empty snail shells.

In Surrey it is widespread and common along the whole of the North Downs, from Pewley Down, Guildford, in the west to Hutchinsons Bank, Addington, and South Hawke, Oxted, in the east. Here it occurs not only on the open chalk grassland, usually near scrub or trees, but also in open woodland, such as at the Sheepleas. It is an early bee, flying from mid-March to mid-June. At White Downs I once watched a female fly past, carrying a scale of a beech bud. I soon discovered a large nesting aggregation close to beech trees; there were about ten nests per square metre and each snail shell was being covered by a female with a mound of beech scales, presumably to hide it from predators. On Pewley Down females have been seen carrying pieces of grass stem to the snail-shell nest, over which a pile of stems was built (DWB). In May 2008 it was abundant at Netley Park, Shere, where females were foraging from ground-ivy; in a small area of about 10m square about 50 females were nesting in snail shells and covering these with grass stems and beech-bud scales. It is absent from the Hogs Back, possibly due to a lack of the appropriate snail shells.

Its status is probably the same as it was in 1900.

Osmia caerulescens (Linnaeus, 1758)   PLATE 34

National Status: Widespread
Surrey Status: Common
VCH: Generally distributed

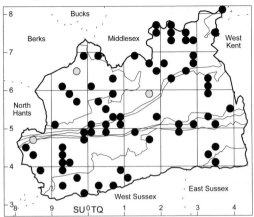

This species is widespread in southern Britain but common only in the south. It is a small species and the whole of the female body is deep metallic blue, with black pollen-collecting hairs under the abdomen. The male has bluish or bronzy reflections on the upper abdomen and is distinguished from other species by its brightly shining front slope to the abdomen, known as the declivity. The female nests in existing cavities such as holes in dead wood and crevices in masonry, the cell walls and closing plug being made of chewed leaves. The adults overwinter in their cocoons. Little is known about its parasites but the wasp *Sapyga quinquepunctata* has been found in its nest. It collects pollen from various different plants and takes nectar from even more. It may have two generations as it flies from mid-April to late July.

It has always been widespread and reasonably common in Surrey, being found regularly in gardens and woodland edges. Being an aerial nester it occurs in a wide variety of habitats. It has been bred from a bramble stem collected at Hambledon Claypit. At Somerset Bridge at Elstead, I watched this bee looking for holes in fence posts, whilst it was followed by the jewel wasp *Chrysura radians*; this may possibly be a cleptoparasite of this bee. Also present on these fence posts was the cleptoparasitic wasp *Sapyga quinquepunctata*.

Its status is probably unchanged since 1900.

Osmia leaiana (Kirby, 1802) PLATE 34

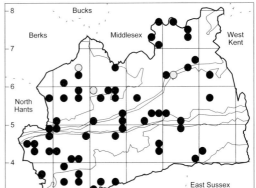

National Status: Widespread
Surrey Status: Common
VCH: (as *fulviventris*) Generally
  distributed

This bee is widespread in southern
Britain but common only in the
south. It is small and found in
gardens and woodland edges, like
O. caerulescens, and the males of
both species are similar, but in this
species, the declivity at the front of
the abdomen is matt, and not
shining. The females are different
because *O. leaiana* is larger and
dark brown with orange pollen-collecting hairs under the abdomen. The females nest in
various cavities in dead wood and walls, and the nest partitions and plug are made of
chewed leaves. The females collect pollen from a variety of plants in the daisy family,
especially the larger yellow ones, but have been seen on bramble flowers and spear thistle.

It is also widespread and reasonably common in Surrey, occurring regularly in gardens
where males are often seen sunning on posts, etc., but is never numerous.

Its status is probably unchanged since 1900.

Osmia pilicornis Smith, 1846

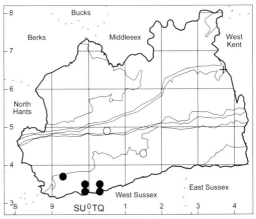

National Status: Very rare; Na
Surrey Status: Very rare
VCH: Shirley, Holmwood

In Britain, this bee is largely
confined to woodland rides in
southern England where it has
become very scarce. It flies from
April to June, collects pollen mainly
from bugle, but also from ground-
ivy, and nests in crevices in dead
wood.

In Surrey it appears to have always
been rare. Some of the few older
records came from the the North
Downs, where it used to occur on the flint and clay woods on the summits of the chalk
downs, such as Newlands Corner in 1917 and 1918. But all the modern records come from
the rides in the Forestry Commission woods on the Weald Clay around Dunsfold and
Brook. It was first refound, after 75 years, in late April 1996 at Oaken Wood, south of

Dunsfold, where it was seen again in 1997 and 2000 (DWB). In early June 1997 it was found in a similar flowery ride in nearby Sidney Wood, where it was seen again in a different area the following year and also in 2000 (DWB). In May 1999 it was discovered flying in some numbers over bugle in a ride in Holmens Grove, Brook, and was seen there again in 2000 (DWB), and in May 2001 it was recorded at Tugley Wood near Chiddingfold (GAC). The silvery males fly extremely fast and are difficult to follow as they dash to and fro, from one clump of bugle to another. However, it has not been seen anywhere since 2001, in spite of numerous searches, and it may now only exist at a very low level, if at all. A similar decline appears to have happened in West Sussex (M. Edwards, pers. comm). It may well have decreased since 1900.

Osmia rufa (Linnaeus, 1758)   PLATES 35, 46

National Status: Universal
Surrey Status: Ubiquitous
VCH: Generally distributed

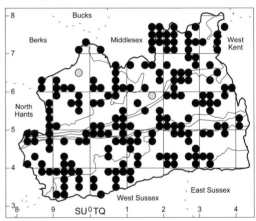

Because of the female's habit of excavating her nesting burrow in the soft mortar joints of houses, this bee has acquired the common name of the Red Mason Bee or Red Mortar Bee. It is almost the only solitary bee to have a common English name. It is widespread and common throughout southern Britain. The female is distinctive because of the pair of black prongs on the front of the face; the head and thorax are metallic bronze-green and the abdomen is more or less covered in red hairs. The male is smaller and less brightly coloured. The females nest in a variety of existing cavities, such as burrows in the soil or in dead wood, and the spaces between roof tiles. The cell walls are constructed of mud, which is brought to the nest site as pellets in the mandibles, and tamped into position with the pair of prongs. As well as collecting pollen from numerous plant species, the females are useful pollinators because they also collect nectar from fruit blossom, such as apple, pear, plum and raspberry. It is usually on the wing from late April to June.

This bee is also widespread and very common in Surrey, being especially noticeable in gardens and town parks in the spring, when there are plenty of flowers and fruit blossom. It is by far the commonest *Osmia* species, occurring in virtually every 10km square, and was equally common in Victorian times. Many people now put up bee boxes in their gardens, consisting of bundles of tubes or bamboo canes, and these are usually almost entirely taken over by this bee. I have reared it from a bramble stem from Knaphill. These nests are frequently parasitised by the wasp *Sapyga quinquepunctata* and the jewel wasp *Chrysis ignita*.

Its status is unchanged since 1900.

Osmia spinulosa (Kirby, 1802) (= *Hoplitis spinulosa*)   PLATE 31

National Status: Restricted

Surrey Status: Locally common

VCH: Reigate, Croydon

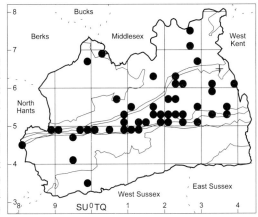

Until very recently this species was included in the genus *Hoplitis,* and briefly in the genus *Hoplosmia.* It is a small but robust black bee and the females have a brush of golden-red, pollen-collecting hairs on the underside of the abdomen. It is widespread in southern Britain but is local, being restricted mainly to open calcareous grassland and coastal dunes. It flies from June to September in a single brood and the females nest in empty snail shells.

In Surrey it is almost restricted to the Chalk of the North Downs from Farnham in the west to South Hawke near Oxted in the east. Here it can be very common and the females are easily found as they forage from the flowers of yellow composites and marjoram in the downland turf. However it has been recorded at a few places off the Chalk: on London Clay at Upper Tooting in 1999, Chessington Zoo in 2001, Beddington Sewage Farm in 1998 and at Wandsworth in 2001; on Weald Clay at Botany Bay near Chiddingfold in 2006; on the sand at Wrecclesham Sandpit near Farnham in 1999 and in some numbers there in 2005, Holmethorpe Sandpit in 2001, Barrow Green Sandpit near Oxted in 2001, Thorpe Park Quarry in 2006, Chertsey Common near Chobham, Wisley Airfield and in my garden at Milford, all in 2008. Saunders (1902) knew of it only from two localities and very surprisingly it was never recorded from any other site between then and 1993, since when it has been found in numerous places. It seems that earlier recorders rarely visited the North Downs.

Its status is probably unchanged since 1900.

Genus *Hoplitis* Klug, 1807

This is a medium-sized, shiny black, solitary bee with inconspicuous white hair bands which nests in crevices above ground and has one generation a year.

Nationally two species (one extinct), one in Surrey.

Hoplitis claviventris (Thomson, 1872) PLATE 7

National Status: Widespread
Surrey Status: Local
VCH: (as *leucomelana*)
  Charlwood, Woking,
  Chobham, Weybridge,
  Ottershaw

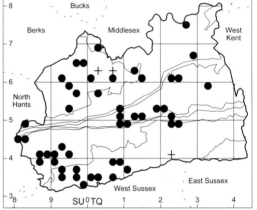

This species is similar in appearance to *Osmia spinulosa* but is fractionally longer and the female differs in having a brush of white pollen-collecting hairs under the abdomen instead of golden-red. It is widespread in Britain in a variety of habitats but is usually uncommon. It flies from late May to late August, visiting various flowers, and nests in stems and cavities. The rare cuckoo bee *Stelis ornatula* attacks the nests of this species.

This bee is widely distributed in Surrey but it is always very local; it is possibly commoner here than in any other county. It is particularly common in the Forestry Commission woods on the Weald Clay around Brook, Chiddingfold and Dunsfold in the south-west, where it frequents rides, clearings and woodland edges and forages from angelica. It occurs fairly commonly in open woodlands on the Chalk at the Sheepleas near West Horsley, where I have watched females searching for nest sites on root-plates of fallen beech trees, and it has been found at various other wooded sites along the North Downs. It has also been recorded at many sites on the sand because it nests above ground and therefore has no preference for special soils. In August 1998 at the Sheepleas I watched a female cuckoo bee *Stelis ornatula* following a female *H. claviventris* as it searched a root-plate for a nest site.

Its status is probably unchanged since 1900.

Genus *Megachile* Latreille, 1802

Medium-sized to large solitary bees with no arolia, or pads, between the two tarsal claws. Females are polylectic and mainly nest in crevices above ground such as decaying wood and old walls, but also in crevices in the soil. Cells are constructed from cut pieces of leaves or petals, rectangular pieces for side walls and circular pieces for end walls of the cell. The cells are provisioned with a semi-liquid mixture of pollen and nectar and the bees overwinter as diapausing prepupae within cocoons. Only one generation a year. The species are difficult to identify, even under a microscope. They are commonly known as leaf-cutter bees and are parasitised by various species of cuckoo bees in the genus *Coelioxys*.

Nationally nine species (two extinct), all having been found in Surrey.

Megachile centuncularis (Linnaeus, 1758)   PLATE 37

National Status: Universal
Surrey Status: Common
VCH: Generally distributed

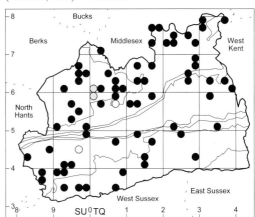

The female of this species, which is common throughout Britain, has long red pollen hairs under the abdomen and is one of the smaller members of the genus. Nests are built in crevices in holes in wood, in cavities in old walls and even in the ground. Various leaves are used for the cells, but mainly rose. It is parasitised by the cuckoo bee *Coelioxys inermis*.

In Surrey it is widespread and reasonably common, being frequently found in gardens where the females can cause unsightly damage to roses, by cutting circular holes around the leaves for building their nests. In 2004 about 50 specimens emerged from each of two trap nests that had been placed in small trees on Chobham and Esher Commons the previous year (DWB) and it has been bred from a bramble stem. In the Order Beds at Kew Gardens it was seen in large numbers, foraging from various peaflowers in the family Fabaceae in 2002 (DWB); it has also been recorded visiting lesser burdock.

Its status is unchanged since 1900.

Megachile circumcincta (Kirby, 1802)

National Status: Scarce
Surrey Status: Extinct
VCH: Chobham, Woking

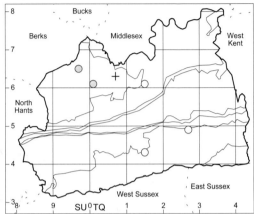

Although still widespread in Britain, but rare and very local, this bee is now largely restricted to coastal dunes. Nest burrows are mainly excavated in sandy soil.

It has always been a rare bee of the heaths in Surrey but it has not been recorded since 1973. It was first found by Saunders in 1876 at Chobham Common, and between then and 1926 it was recorded by the usual hymenopterists at most of the well-worked heathland sites, e.g. Horsell Common, Oxshott Heath, Weybridge and Holmwood. G.E. Frisby (1907) wrote that he had found it sparingly on Redhill Common in 1906 and there is a specimen of his in the NHML. There was then a gap of over 40 years before Guichard refound it at the famous sandpit on Horsell Common in 1970. In the same year he also refound it on Chobham Common, where he took it again the next year. However, the last specimen in Surrey was recorded by him at that locality on 22 June 1973. It is probably now extinct but it might possibly be refound in an overlooked sandy site, as was *M. dorsalis*, especially if climate warming continues.

It has declined since 1900, probably to extinction.

Megachile dorsalis Pérez, 1879   PLATE 8

National Status: Restricted; Nb
Surrey Status: Very rare
VCH: (as *argentata*) Weybridge

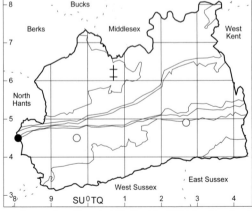

This is a local bee of southern Britain, now entirely restricted to sandy coasts, apart from Surrey, the Brecks and a few other inland sites, where it excavates nests in the sand. It is small, the female having white pollen hairs and the male having a distinctive white hair-patch near the tip of the abdomen.

Until 2005 it had been recorded in Surrey on very few occasions and had not been seen for nearly 100 years. It was first found at Byfleet in 1844 by Shuckard and then at nearby Weybridge by F. Smith and Shuckard in 1866. There is a specimen in the NHML which was taken in 1906 at Redhill Common by G.E. Frisby who noted (1907) that there was a small colony there. There are two specimens, one dated 1906 and another 1913, and both labelled 'Godalming', in the O.H. Latter Collection in Haslemere Museum. These probably came from Thursley or Hankley Common, where he often collected. This coastal species may have established itself for a few years at these localities and then died out again. However, on 13 June 2005 I came across a large colony at Wrecclesham sandpit near Farnham where freshly emerged males were abundant along 200m of south-facing sand cliff. There were no females present at that date but a few were seen a week later and by 21 June both sexes were abundant and females were nesting all along the top of the cliff. I estimated there were about 1,000 pairs. There were still some females around on 11 July but they disappeared shortly afterwards, presumably due to the prolonged heatwave at that time.

This bee is probably the host for the small black cleptoparasitic bee *Coelioxys mandibularis* on the south coast of Kent. I could find no small *Coelioxys* at the aggregation but there were large numbers of *Coelioxys rufescens*, presumably parasitising the abundant *Anthophora bimaculata*, and quite a few of the larger *C. conoidea* parasitising the *Megachile maritima*. The size of this population suggests that it has been established there for some years and it is likely that there will by now be other aggregations in similar sandpits in the area. These old sandpits are being filled ever more rapidly and the bee may not survive for more than a few years unless it spreads to the dry sandy heaths.

Its status is probably unchanged since 1900.

Megachile ericetorum (Lepeletier, 1841)

National Status: Extinct
Surrey Status: Extinct
VCH: Weybridge

This is a large black bee with pale hairs and yellowish-white hair bands on the abdomen; until very recently it was included in a separate genus *Chalicodoma*. It nests in holes in dead wood or hollow plant stems. It is a summer species which prefers to forage on flowers of Fabaceae.

The only authenticated records for Britain are the two specimens taken by F. Smith at Weybridge, Surrey, on separate dates in 1844. Saunders (1896) says that he examined these specimens but they were very faded. There are one or two other unlabelled and dubious specimens.

Megachile lapponica Thomson, 1872

National Status: Extinct
Surrey Status: Extinct
VCH: No records

This is a medium-sized golden-haired black bee with pale hair bands and a red pollen brush. The only British record is of a single, freshly emerged, female taken at Weybridge, Surrey, in July 1847 by F. Smith. It was possibly never native and this specimen may have been accidentally imported in dead wood; females nest in dead wood on the continent.

Megachile ligniseca (Kirby, 1802)

National Status: Widespread
Surrey Status: Common
VCH: Chobham, Woking, Surbiton

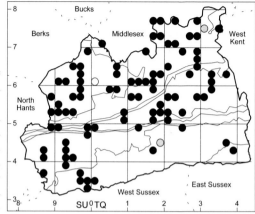

A large and robust species, this bee is widely distributed in southern Britain but is generally uncommon. The female has pale golden pollen hairs underneath the abdomen, with black ones on the last two segments, and the male has normal front tarsi, unlike the males of the other two large species. It nests in holes in dead trees and fence posts. It flies from June to August and forages from many plants including thistles.

In Surrey it is widespread and reasonably common, except on the clay where it appears to be scarce. Being a crevice-nester it is not restricted to any specific habitat and it has been found as far into inner London as Battersea Park, Wandsworth and Tooting Bec Commons, Dulwich and Brixton. Females have been recorded at flowers of creeping and spear thistle, as well as lesser burdock and broad-leaved everlasting-pea.

Its status is probably unchanged since 1900.

Megachile maritima (Kirby, 1802)

National Status: Widespread
Surrey Status: Very local
VCH: Chobham, Woking

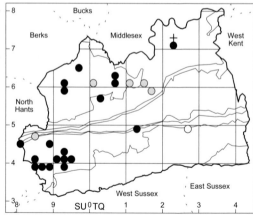

This large, handsome bee is mainly coastal in southern Britain but also occurs in a few hot sandy places inland. The male has strongly flattened and expanded tarsi on the front legs, which are creamy white, with long hairs, and are very distinctive; the male *M. willughbiella* has similar tarsi but mainly orange femora, rather than black. The female is very similar to *M. willughbiella* but has longer hairs on the fore tarsi. It excavates its nest burrows in sandy soils and, unlike the other species, it sometimes nests in small aggregations. It flies from early June to mid-August. It is parasitised by the cuckoo bee *Coelioxys conoidea*.

In Surrey it is found only on the hottest of dry sandy heaths, but occasionally on dry acid grassland, e.g. twice at Brooklands near Weybridge in 2004 (DWB), and once on chalk grassland at Westcott Downs in 1999 (GAC). The first county records were both made by Saunders in 1890 at Chobham and Wimbledon Commons but there were very few other reports until Baker found it at Oxshott Heath (where he saw one carrying a birch leaf to its nest) and nearby Fairmile Common in 1962 and 1963, followed by Guichard in 1972, who took it at Oxshott Heath and Horsell Common sandpit. From the 1990s it has been found much more frequently and at more localities, especially on the south-western heaths, e.g. Thursley, Hankley and Witley Commons. According to the EMM it was seen abundantly by G.E. Frisby at Redhill Common in 1906 and by the Champion brothers at Horsell Common in 1914. In a very hot dry sandy area, similar to coastal dunes, at Frensham Great Pond, it has been seen twice recently in good numbers, in company with its parasite (DWB). It is a common visitor to my garden where it comes to broad-leaved everlasting-pea. It may have increased since the 1990s, but this is difficult to prove because the earlier recorders did not visit the heaths of the south-west. Being a heat-loving bee, any increase would probably be due to recent climate change.

It may have increased since 1900.

Megachile versicolor Smith, 1844   PLATES 37, 46

National Status: Universal

Surrey Status: Common

VCH: Woking, Weybridge

This is a small leaf-cutter and is difficult to distinguish from the common *M. centuncularis*. It is similarly common and widespread in Britain, nesting in crevices in dead wood, dead bramble stems and possibly in sandy soils. It has a long flight period, from June to September, and is parasitised by the cuckoo bee *Coelioxys inermis*.

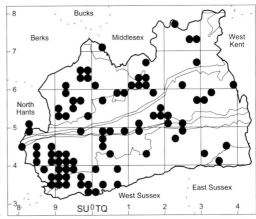

It is widespread and common in Surrey, being particularly frequent on the dry western heaths. Females have been recorded visiting flowers of common knapweed and angelica, as well as broad-leaved everlasting-pea in my garden.

It may have increased since 1900.

Megachile willughbiella (Kirby, 1802) PLATE 37

National Status: Universal
Surrey Status: Common
VCH: Generally distributed

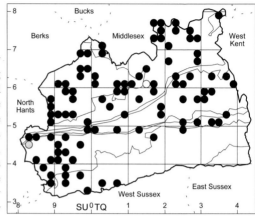

This is a common and very widely distributed bee in Britain, being often seen in gardens. It is large, and the male has distinctive white flattened front tarsi, similar to those in *M. maritima*. It nests in crevices in dead wood and in the ground, often using the soil in flower pots as a nest site. It flies from June to August. It is parasitised by *Coelioxys elongata, C. rufescens* and *C. quadridentata*.

It is also common and widespread in Surrey although it appears to be very scarce on the clay. The female forages for pollen at a variety of plants and favours bellflowers; one was seen on harebell at Bagmoor Common in 2002 (RDH) and another on sheep's-bit at Elstead cemetery (DWB); it comes in numbers to broad-leaved everlasting-pea in my garden. A female was also seen collecting pollen from rosebay willowherb at Reigate (RDH) and from bird's-foot trefoil at Ham House (DWB).

Its status is unchanged since 1900.

Genus *Coelioxys* Latreille, 1809

These are medium-sized black bees with prominent white hair-bands on the abdomen. The male abdomen has a rounded end, bearing a number of short stout prongs, while that of the female is distinctively pointed. They are cuckoo bees (cleptoparasites) on species of *Megachile* and *Anthophora*. The female uses her pointed abdomen to cut a slit in the host bee's cell, through which an egg is laid. The very long curved jaws of the second-instar larva are used to destroy the egg or young larva of the host bee. Later instars have normal jaws and feed on the host bee's provisions. These bees are infrequently seen and rarely in numbers. The females can be separated under a microscope by the varied shapes of the pointed apex of the abdomen but the males are more difficult.

Nationally seven species with five in Surrey, the other two being coastal.

Coelioxys conoidea (Illiger, 1806)

National Status: Scarce
Surrey Status: Very local
VCH: (as *vectis*) Shirley,
   Wimbledon

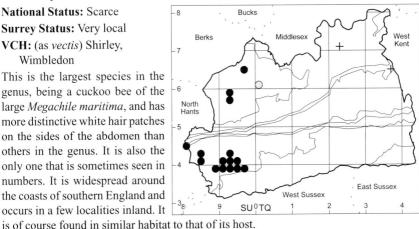

This is the largest species in the genus, being a cuckoo bee of the large *Megachile maritima*, and has more distinctive white hair patches on the sides of the abdomen than others in the genus. It is also the only one that is sometimes seen in numbers. It is widespread around the coasts of southern England and occurs in a few localities inland. It is of course found in similar habitat to that of its host.

In Surrey it used to be extremely rare but in the last ten years it has become frequent on the south-western heaths and has also been found at three localities in the north-west. It was first recorded by F. Smith in about 1860 at Wimbledon Common and at Shirley near Croydon, but it was then not seen for over 100 years until Guichard took it at Horsell Common in 1965. There was then another gap of 30 years before it was found in 1997 in dune-like habitat at Frensham Common, where it occurred in some numbers around a nesting aggregation of its host (DWB). Since then three or four have been recorded annually at various sites on the south-western dry heaths, such as Hankley, Thursley, Witley, Mare Hill and Hambledon Commons, as well as at three sites on the north-western heaths, Chobham Common in 2001, Pirbright Ranges in 2004, and nearby Bisley Ranges in 2007. In 2005 it was seen in some numbers at Wrecclesham Sandpit near Farnham (all DWB). This recent increase is presumably related to the similar increase of its host.

It has probably increased since 1900.

Coelioxys elongata Lepeletier, 1841   PLATE 36

National Status: Universal
Surrey Status: Very local
VCH: Woking, Chobham,
   Oxshott, Ripley

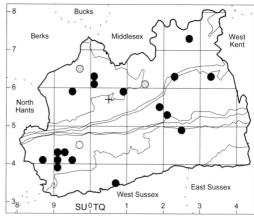

This cuckoo bee is widespread in Britain but like all the species it is never common. The female attacks the nests of the common *Megachile willughbiella* and possibly those of the mainly coastal *M. circumcincta*, flying from June to August.

In Surrey it is widespread but distinctly local, having been recorded in only about 15 sites since 1984, in spite of the fact that its main host is widespread and common. Saunders (1902) cites four localities: his own records from Chobham Common and Horsell Common in about 1890 and Morice's records from Ripley and Oxshott Heath at about the same time. There were only about ten records between then and 1993 but since then there have been about 20. As usual with this species, all records have been of singletons. Bees of this genus are rarely seen at flowers but a female was seen on common fleabane at Nonsuch Park on the very late date of 1 September 2004, and another on greater bird's-foot trefoil at Ottershaw on 4 August 2004 (RDH).

Its status is probably unchanged since 1900.

Coelioxys inermis (Kirby, 1802)   PLATE 36

National Status: Widespread
Surrey Status: Rare
VCH: (as *acuminata*) Chobham

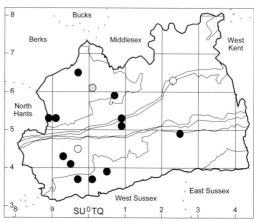

Another widespread but uncommon cuckoo bee which flies from June to July and attacks the nests of *Megachile centuncularis, M. versicolor* and possibly *M. ligniseca.*

Although this is considered to be one of the commonest species in the genus nationally, it is certainly not so in Surrey, where it is very local and scarce, but is possibly overlooked. It has only been recorded at 12 localities since 1984 and almost all of these are in the west of the county; most records are from heathland but it has been taken twice at Sheepleas on the Chalk and also from clay woodland and gardens. At Bagmoor Common a female was seen at cross-leaved heath in 2002 (RDH). The known hosts are common so it is odd that it is so rarely found; however it is always seen singly and this may mean that it is overlooked.

It was clearly scarce in 1900 and its present status is probably unchanged.

Coelioxys quadridentata

(Linnaeus, 1758)

National Status: Very rare; RDB3
Surrey Status: Possibly extinct
VCH: Woking, Chobham, Oxshott

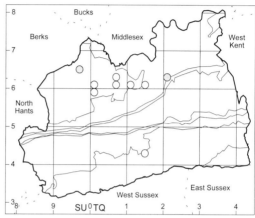

This cuckoo bee attacks the nests of *Anthophora furcata*, and probably also those of *A. quadrimaculata* and *Megachile circumcincta*, and is widespread but rare in southern Britain.

It was always uncommon in Surrey but it has not been recorded for over 25 years and may now be extinct. This decline may be due to the similar decline to extinction of its possible host *Megachile circumcincta*. It was first found in the county by Morice at Oxshott Heath in 1890, followed by Saunders who took it at Chobham Common in 1892, and again in 1896 at Horsell Common. From 1904 to 1928 it was recorded almost annually in Surrey, at these three sites and at other well-worked ones such as Byfleet, Weybridge, Holmwood and Cobham, by all the well-known hymenopterists including Richards, Nevinson, Nixon, Mortimer and the Champion brothers. There was then a gap of ten years until that prolific collector Guichard took it at Horsell Common again and then found it on various occasions until 1973, both there and at Byfleet and Chobham Common, the last record being on 24 June 1973. Finally, Baker recorded one near his home in a nesting aggregation of *A. quadrimaculata* in an old stone wall at Ewell East railway station in August 1982.

It has declined to extinction since 1900.

Coelioxys rufescens Lepeletier & Serville, 1825

National Status: Widespread
Surrey Status: Very local
VCH: Chobham, Holmwood

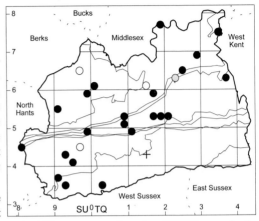

Very similar to other smaller species, this cuckoo bee is widespread but never common in southern Britain, flying from June to August. Its main hosts are *Anthophora bimaculata* and the coastal *Megachile circumcincta*, but it also attacks nests of *A. furcata* and *M. centuncularis*.

In Surrey it is widespread and the commonest species in the genus but it is very local. It was clearly a rare species 100 years ago as Saunders (1902) knew of only three records: his own from Horsell Common in 1890 and from Chobham Common in 1896 and Morice's record from Holmwood in 1890. There were very few reports between then and 1987 but in the last 20 years it has been found at over 20 sites. It is hard to say whether this apparent increase is real or whether it is due to increased recording coverage.

Its main host is assumed to be *Anthophora bimaculata* because *M. circumcincta* is now probably extinct in the county. *A. bimaculata* is widespread and common on the heaths and on dry acid grassland and almost all records of this cuckoo bee coincide with its range. However, it has been found at a few places, on chalk and clay, where its assumed host does not occur so it may be using another host, presumably a different species of *Anthophora* or *Megachile*. On the other hand these odd records may be of wanderers. Like most of the species in the genus it is normally seen singly but in 2005 it was seen flying in large numbers, possibly as many as 50, in a very large nesting aggregation of *A. bimaculata* and the small *Megachile dorsalis* on a south-facing cliff at Wrecclesham sandpit near Farnham. Females were seen only entering the burrows of *A. bimaculata* (DWB).

It may have increased since 1900.

SUBFAMILY APINAE

This large subfamily of diverse genera was until recently divided into two: the Anthophorinae, and the Apinae consisting of the bumblebees and the honey bees.They are long-tongued solitary and social bees, many being robust and large, such as the bumblebees, large carpenter bees (*Xylocopa*) and some *Anthophora*. They nest in the ground, in plant stems and in burrows in wood. A notably large number of species are cuckoo bees, having no pollen-collecting hairs.

Nationally 64 species in nine genera, with 61 species in all nine genera in Surrey (12 probably now extinct).

Genus *Nomada* Scopoli, 1763

This is a large genus of small to medium-sized cleptoparasitic bees with almost hairless bodies, coloured with yellow, red and black bands and spots, and having a close resemblance to wasps. Females, which are cleptoparasites mainly on various species of *Andrena*, enter the open cell of the host bee and insert their eggs into the wall of the cell. The first-instar larva kills the egg or young larva of the host bee with its large sickle-shaped jaws, afterwards eating the host bee's provisions. The pupae are not enclosed within a cocoon. Some species have two generations a year.

Nationally 28 species, with 27 in Surrey (three extinct, one doubtful).

Nomada argentata Herrich-Schäffer, 1839   PLATE 25

National Status: Rare; RDB3
Surrey Status: Rare
VCH: (as *atrata*) Clandon, Woking

This small dark and very distinctive *Nomada* is rare and very local in southern England, where it is a cleptoparasite of the scarce mining bee *Andrena marginata*. Both sexes are almost entirely black, except for varying amounts of red on the abdomen, mandibles and legs, the males tending to be darker than the females. Some

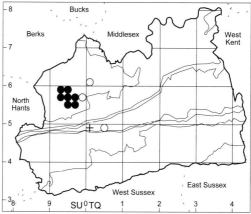

populations of its host forage from small scabious, mainly on chalk downland, in July and August, but others forage from devil's-bit scabious, often on acid grassland, in August and September; there may possibly be two distinct ecological races involved here, although current genetic studies tend to disprove the theory that they may represent separate species. *N. argentata* parasitises both these types of host, and likewise flies at two separate times. It was first found in Britain when Saunders (1900) collected a male on field scabious at Newlands Corner near West Clandon on 4 August 1900. On 13 August 1900 his friend and neighbour Morice (1900b) collected another male there and on the following day took a male and four females on devil's-bit scabious on the road from Woking to Chobham. In August 1901 Saunders found it on Horsell Common and Morice at Mayford near Woking, presumably on devil's-bit scabious because of the locations. There are two specimens collected by Nevinson in Oxford University Museum which he collected in August 1908 and 1909 at Newlands Corner. It was not recorded again until 1984, when Guichard took it on 18 August at Brookwood Cemetery near Woking, where devil's-bit scabious is abundant over many acres. He told me about this locality in 1997 and I duly went there in mid-August that year and found it commonly over a wide area, with its host equally common. Since then it has been seen there in most years. In mid-September 2003 it was found on the nearby Bisley Ranges, where devil's-bit scabious is also abundant, when it is not cut by the range wardens (DWB, GAC). Here it is not as common, possibly due to the regular cutting of the scabious, but it was seen there again in August 2005; however, its host is abundant there. These two sites are almost the only ones in the country where this *Nomada* is found on devil's-bit scabious. *A. marginata* is still at Newlands Corner, and in some years is common on small scabious, but in spite of numerous searches I have failed to refind the *Nomada* there. At Brookwood Cemetery the males usually emerge in early August, about a week before the females and often before the scabious is in flower; they can then be found clustering round flowers of thistles. Females have been seen following the host females to their nest-sites at the edges of paths. Both males and females are normally found on the scabious flowers but many were on thistles at Brookwood Cemetery in August 2005 when they emerged before the scabious was in flower.

Its status today is much the same as it was in 1900.

[*Nomada armata* Herrich-Schäffer, 1839

National Status: Very rare; RDB1

Surrey Status: Extinct

VCH: No records

This large red species is now apparently confined in Britain to Salisbury Plain, Wiltshire, although it used to be rather more widespread in southern England. It is a cleptoparasite of the large and rare *Andrena hattorfiana*, a scabious specialist, which still occurs in a few places in Surrey.

Guichard (1977) includes this species in his list for Horsell Common on the strength of a 19th century specimen, possibly one of F. Smith's, but Saunders does not mention this in his Synopsis, nor in his 1896 book, nor in the VCH. This specimen is not in the NHML and until it is located and confirmed this record must be treated as doubtful.]

Nomada baccata Smith, 1844   PLATE 15

National Status: Rare; Na

Surrey Status: Locally common

VCH: (as *alboguttata*) Chobham, Ripley, Frensham

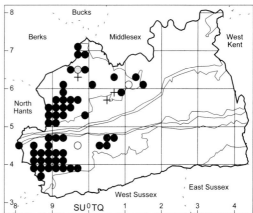

This small *Nomada* is virtually confined to the lowland heaths of central southern England where it can be an abundant cleptoparasite of the heather specialist, *Andrena argentata*. It flies from late July to late August.

In Surrey it is usually abundant on all the western heaths. The very attractive females are mainly reddish brown on the head, thorax and abdomen, with creamy markings on the very short, rounded abdomen, and appear to be pink in flight. The rather darker males, which emerge a few days before the females, can be seen flying fast and low over the bare sand, waiting for a virgin female to emerge and immediately pouncing on and mating with her; often two or three males will pounce on the same female, rolling around with her in a frenzied melee. Later the females can be seen patrolling the same area, searching for nests of its host in the soft sand, sometimes following a female host to its nest site. At times the host and parasite can be so numerous that they swarm over the bare sand in clouds of 50 or more per square metre. On a few hundred metres of soft, sandy tracks on Hankley Common I once estimated that there were about 50,000 *N. baccata* and a similar number of *A. argentata*. However, its host is not entirely confined to heather and at Wrecclesham Sandpit near Farnham it occurs some miles from any heather; here *N. baccata* also occurs commonly. It can often be found visiting flowers of common ragwort. This is a scarce *Nomada* in Britain, the best sites being in Surrey.

It may well be commoner now than in 1900, as Saunders mentioned only a few localities.

Nomada conjungens Herrich-Schäffer, 1839

National Status: Very rare; RDB2
Surrey Status: Very rare
VCH: Unknown

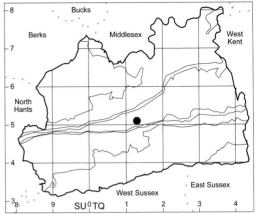

This small reddish *Nomada* is very rare and confined to southern England. It is a cleptoparasite of the rare mining bee *Andrena proxima* and flies from mid-May to early June. It is always much scarcer than its host. It was added to the British List only in 1916.

It was unknown in Surrey until G.A. Collins took a female on the south-west slopes of Westcott Downs on 5 June 2007. Its host appears to have become much commoner and expanded its range in the last decade and this *Nomada* has presumably followed this expansion. Its host was found at a white umbellifer on the eastern slopes of Westcott Downs in May 1999, near to the site where the *Nomada* was found. It has not been recorded there since 1999 but it is easily overlooked, being small and black.

Being a very recent newcomer it has increased since 1900.

Nomada fabriciana (Linnaeus, 1767)   PLATE 38

National Status: Widespread
Surrey Status: Common
VCH: Generally distributed

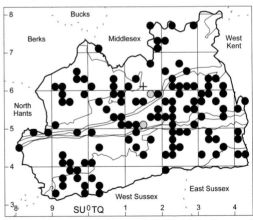

This red-bodied *Nomada* is widespread and locally common throughout the British Isles, being a cleptoparasite of the equally widespread and common, double-brooded *Andrena bicolor*; it may also attack the nests of various other *Andrena* species, such as *A. nigroaenea, A. angustior, A, flavipes, A. varians* and *A. chrysosceles,* but none of these have been confirmed as hosts. It is also double-brooded, flying from March to June and again from June to August.

In Surrey it is widespread and common wherever its host *A. bicolor* flourishes. It is common on the Chalk and in the Weald Clay woodlands but remarkably scarce on the western heaths. The females vary much in size, some large specimens being almost twice the size of the smallest; these large ones may have developed in nests of larger hosts, such as *A. nigroaenea*. It has been seen visiting primrose, dandelion and buttercup for nectar. Its status is probably unchanged since 1900.

Nomada ferruginata (Linnaeus, 1767)

National Status: Rare; RDB1
Surrey Status: Very rare
VCH: Unknown

This early spring species used to be rarely, but widely, distributed in southern Britain but it then declined, almost to the point of extinction, until 1987, when it started a remarkable resurgence. It flies very early in April and May and is a cleptoparasite of the widespread *Andrena praecox* which is found on sallow blossom, and possibly of *A. varians*.

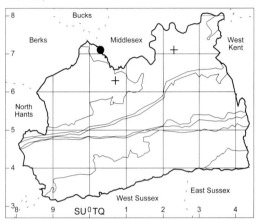

Saunders does not mention the species in his book nor in the VCH but Guichard (1977) gives a record (as *N. xanthosticta*) of F. Smith from Weybridge in 1851; this record requires confirmation. There is also a specimen in Oxford University Museum from Wimbledon Common dated April 1900 from the R.C.L. Perkins collection. However, on 26 April 1996 G.A. Collins took one at Thorpe Hay Meadow and this is the only confirmed record for Surrey. Now that it has become less rare it should be searched for wherever there is a flourishing population of its host.

Because it is a recent newcomer it has increased since 1900.

Nomada flava Panzer, 1798   PLATES 1, 38

National Status: Widespread
Surrey Status: Ubiquitous
VCH: (as *ruficornis*) Generally distributed

This close relative of *Nomada panzeri* and *N. signata*, with yellow and brown bands on the abdomen, is widespread in southern Britain and is one of the commonest species in the genus. It flies in a single brood from April to June and its main host is the common and widespread *Andrena carantonica*, but it may also attack *A. nigroaenea*.

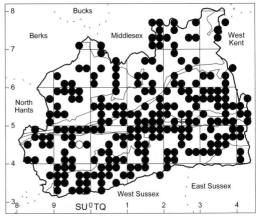

It is certainly the commonest *Nomada* throughout Surrey, being abundant in places. The females are usually seen, sometimes in numbers, flying low over grass at the base of hedges or on banks, searching for the nests of its host, whilst the males are seen flying around small shrubs waiting for females. It is not possible to separate the males from those of *N. panzeri* using morphological characters. It has been seen visiting a very wide range of flowers for nectar and in Surrey it has been recorded from such diverse plants as forget-me-not, dandelion, sanicle, alder buckthorn, germander speedwell, buttercup, green alkanet and bluebell.

It is no doubt as common now as it was in 1900.

Nomada flavoguttata (Kirby, 1802)   PLATE 38

National Status: Universal
Surrey Status: Ubiquitous
VCH: Guildford, Cobham, Ottershaw, Woking

This small species is found commonly in most of the British Isles. It is a dark bee with a red and black abdomen on which are two pairs of small yellow spots; the female has red markings on the head and thorax but the male has none. It is double-brooded, flying in the spring and summer and is a cleptoparasite of various small

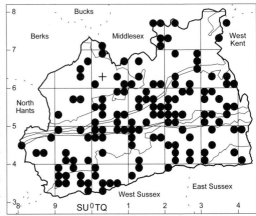

species of mining bee, including *Andrena minutula*, *A. semilaevis* and *A. subopaca*.

It is widespread and common in Surrey, as are the three hosts, although it is scarce on the western heaths. It is particularly common on the Chalk and on the Weald Clay. It is most often seen flying and crawling around the host's nesting sites but it occasionally comes to flowers for nectar such as dandelion, field pepperwort, sheep's-bit and *Cotoneaster*. It may be commoner now than in 1900.

Nomada flavopicta (Kirby, 1802)

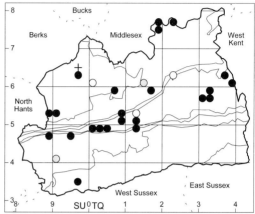

National Status: Scarce; Nb
Surrey Status: Very local
VCH: (as *jacobaeae*) Clandon, Woking, Chobham

This medium-sized *Nomada* is restricted to southern Britain where it is a very local species of open flower-rich grassland. Superficially it resembles a large *N. rufipes* but it has two yellow spots at the back of the thorax, whereas *N. rufipes* has only one large yellow marking. It flies in late summer from the end of June to September and in the past was thought to parasitise various species of *Andrena*; it has now been shown to be a cleptoparasite of certain species of *Melitta*.

It is widespread but rather local in Surrey where it is most common on the Chalk; here it is probably a parasite of *M. tricincta*, which is usually abundant on red bartsia on the downs, but also of *M. haemorrhoidalis*, which forages from various species of *Campanula* growing on the Chalk. Where it occurs on the sand in the west it is probably attacking nests of *M. leporina*. I was rather puzzled to find the *Nomada* in the Order Beds in Kew Gardens until I noticed that it was close to the bed containing the Campanulaceae, the flowers of which were alive with foraging female *M. haemorrhoidalis*. It has been found visiting the flowers of small scabious and common ragwort.

Its status is probably unchanged since 1900.

Nomada fucata Panzer, 1798   PLATE 14

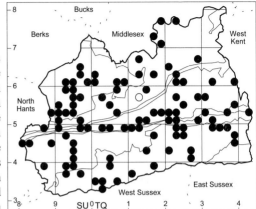

National Status: Restricted; Na
Surrey Status: Common
VCH: Godalming

This medium-sized *Nomada* was rare in Saunders' time but it became common and widespread in southern England in the 1930s, then retreated to the south coast in the 1970s and has recently spread again to become a common cleptoparasite of *Andrena flavipes* wherever this nests in southern Britain. It flies in two broods from April to June and again in July and August. It visits a variety of flowers.

Saunders (1896) does not mention any Surrey record in his book, although Billups (1891b) had recorded it in *The Entomologist* in 1891 from Oxshott Heath. He did, however, mention a record of Latter from Godalming in the VCH. After that there are very few records until 1990 by which time it had clearly become very common and widespread. It is sometimes seen in enormous numbers at large nesting aggregations of its host, e.g. at Hambledon Claypit, Papercourt Gravelpits and Wrecclesham Sandpit. It is also seen at flowers such as thistle, buttercup, forget-me-not, knapweed and dandelion.

It has clearly increased dramatically since 1900.

Nomada fulvicornis Fabricius, 1793   PLATE 11

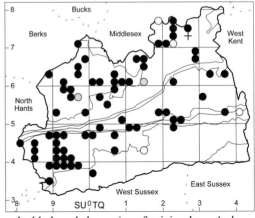

National Status: Scarce; RDB3
Surrey Status: Common
VCH: (as *lineola*) Wandsworth, Woking

This large *Nomada* is widespread but rare in southern England. It has black and yellow bands on the abdomen and both sexes are difficult to separate from the common and very similar looking *N. marshamella*. It is double-brooded, flying in the spring from late March to early June and in the summer from late June to late August, and parasitises four scarce, double-brooded, species of mining bee: *Andrena bimaculata, A. pilipes, A. tibialis* and *A. nigrospina*.

It is surprisingly widespread and common in Surrey, although it is absent from the Weald Clay where its presumed hosts in the county, *A. bimaculata* and *A. tibialis*, are also absent. Saunders considered it to be widespread and common nationally, but he mentioned only two localities for Surrey in the VCH: Wandsworth Common where he collected it in about 1890, which is the earliest record for the county, and Horsell Common in 1896. It was recorded by the usual later collectors, Mortimer, Richards, etc., but the vast majority of records are from the last 20 years.

It is commoner now than in 1900.

Nomada goodeniana (Kirby, 1802)   PLATE 38

National Status: Universal

Surrey Status: Ubiquitous

VCH: (as *succincta*) Generally distributed

This is a large, very common and widespread species in the British Isles, having a distinctive black and yellow banded abdomen, similar to *Nomada marshamella*. It flies from April to August in two broods, but the second brood is usually very scarce. It apparently parasitises various species of large mining bees, such as *Andrena nigroaenea* (its main host)*, A. thoracica, A. nitida* and *A. carantonica.*

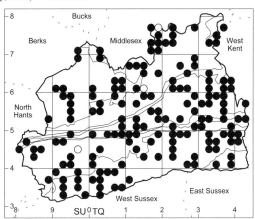

In Surrey it is widespread and very common in the spring but it has never been recorded from the summer brood. It is not known which *Andrena* is the main host in the county. It is usually found searching for nests of its host and it has been seen on forget-me-not and creeping buttercup.

It is probably as common now as in 1900.

Nomada guttulata Schenck, 1861

National Status: Very rare; RDB1
Surrey Status: Very rare
VCH: No records

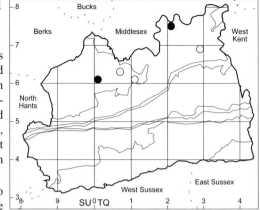

This small black and red species has always been extremely rare and confined to a few counties in southern England. It is a cleptoparasite of the scarce black and red mining bee *Andrena labiata* and, like its host, is normally found at flowers of germander speedwell in May and June.

There are only three old and two modern records for Surrey, in spite of the fact that its host is now widespread in the county. It was first recorded on 7 May 1915 at Cobham by Nevinson (five specimens in Oxford University Museum). It was next collected on 23 May 1927 at Mitcham Common by Nixon (specimen in NHML) and was then found in 1940 at Weybridge by Baker (specimen in NHML). More recently a female was found in Richmond Park, with its host, at a large patch of germander speedwell on 21 May 2003 (DWB) and a male was collected just north of Horsell Common on 15 May 2004 (AJH). It could turn up again in almost any place where its host occurs in numbers, but the edges of the western commons are probably the best areas to search for it.

It appears to have increased since 1900.

Nomada hirtipes Pérez, 1884

National Status: Scarce; RDB3
Surrey Status: Rare
VCH: (as *lateralis*) Box Hill

This cuckoo bee is confined to southern Britain where it is very local. The female has a red abdomen with pairs of lateral yellow spots and attacks the nests of the scarce mining bee *Andrena bucephala*. It flies in one brood from late April to mid-June.

In Surrey it is decidedly rare, being found mainly on the Chalk at nesting aggregations of its host which is also a rarity in the county. The earliest record is from Box Hill, cited by Saunders (1896), but this record is not mentioned by him in the VCH. There is also a record of this bee from Box Hill by Billups (1891a) in *The Entomologist*, and it still occurs there today. After 1900 there were just four records, all from the Chalk at White Hill, Mickleham, which is near Box Hill, by Baker and Guichard in the 1960s, until 1991 when it started to be found more frequently. Since then it has been found mainly on the North Downs: at Headley Heath in 1991 (RKAM); Riddlesdown Quarry in 1997 (RDH, GAC); Blatchford Down near Dorking in 1998 (ME); Box Hill and Westcott Downs in 2000 (GAC); Westcott Downs again in 2004, in good numbers at the host's nests (DWB). Away from the Chalk it has been found on the Weald Clay in large numbers at a nesting aggregation of its host on the bank of the canal in Sidney Wood, Dunsfold, in 1997 and 1998, a single male at Coldharbour Common, below Leith Hill, in 2000 and six males at flowers of wild strawberry and a female at cypress spurge in Hambledon Claypit in 2005 (all DWB).

It may be commoner now than in 1900.

Nomada integra Brullé, 1832   PLATE 17

National Status: Rare; Na

Surrey Status: Rare

VCH: (as *ferruginata*) Chobham, Woking, Redhill

This small, red-bodied species is distributed sporadically over southern Britain but is everywere uncommon and local. It flies from mid-May to early July and is a cleptoparasite of the scarce mining bee *Andrena humilis*.

In Surrey it is rare, having been found at only seven localities since 1985, all of them on sandy soils

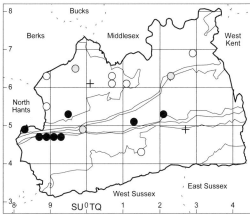

where its host nests. There are numerous older records, nearly all from the north of the county, of which the earliest is that of Saunders who took it at Woking (probably on Horsell Common) in 1894. For the next 100 years it was taken regularly by all the usual collectors, with many specimens deposited in the NHML. The seven modern sites are: Sandy Hill, Upper Hale above Farnham, 1991 (SRM); Headley Heath, 1996 (ME); Puttenham Common, 1996 and subsequently (ME et al); Runfold, 2000 (ASD); Ranmore Common near Dorking, on acid sand on top of chalk, 2002; Cobbett Hill near Ash Ranges, in a Malaise trap, 2003; Seale, at old sandpit, 2005 (all DWB). At the Puttenham Common site it is very numerous in most years at a large nesting aggregation of *A. humilis*.

Its status is probably much the same as in 1900.

Nomada lathburiana (Kirby, 1802)   PLATE 18

National Status: Widespread; RDB3

Surrey Status: Local

VCH: No records

This bee has increased greatly in recent years and is expanding its range, being now widespread in England and Wales. It flies from April to June and attacks the nests of the attractive mining bee *Andrena cineraria*.

It was unknown in Surrey to Saunders, who admitted in his 1896 book that he had never taken it. The

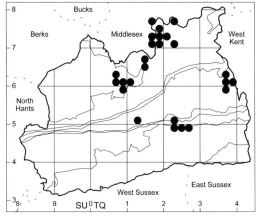

earliest record is mentioned in the diary of Morice, which is at Oxford University Museum. He collected it on 4 May 1906 at Wimbledon Common, where it was later taken again by Richards in 1937. After that there was a long gap until it was recorded at Ham Common in 1997 (RDH); it has been found there regularly in enormous numbers, probably about 5,000+ pairs, in a vast aggregation of 10,000+ pairs of *A. cineraria*. Since 1997 it has apparently spread rapidly southwards, being found as follows: Richmond Park, 1999; Barnes Common, 2000; Selsdon, 2000; Chelsham, 2000; Kew Gardens, 2001; Reigate Heath, 2001; Earlswood Common, 2001; Ditton Common, 2002; Featherbed Lane, Addington, 2005; Priory Park, Reigate, 2005; Ockham Common, Wisley, 2006. Its host has also expanded its range rapidly southwards in the same period and has been found at almost all these sites. It has been recorded taking nectar from germander speedwell.

It has increased and expanded its range enormously since 1900.

Nomada leucophthalma (Kirby, 1802)   PLATE 13

National Status: Universal

Surrey Status: Local

VCH: (as *borealis*) Generally distributed

This rather dark and fairly large *Nomada* is widespread and locally common in the British Isles, occurring on heaths, moors and in open woodland. It is one of the earliest *Nomada* to appear in the spring, flying from early March to mid-May. It is a cleptoparasite of the locally common *Andrena clarkella* and the rare *A. apicata*.

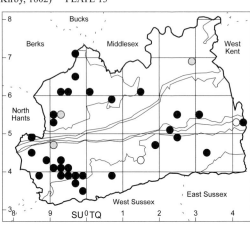

It is widespread in Surrey but very local, being commonest on the western heaths. The earliest record seems to be of a specimen in the NHML collected by Saunders from Horsell Common in 1896. Away from the heaths it has been found in a few places on the Weald Clay. It has also been taken at two localities on the North Downs but both of these were in sandy areas, Alderstead Heath in 1998 and Banstead Heath in 1999 (GAC). In the east it occurred at two sites on Lower Greensand, Moorhouse Sandpit, Limpsfield, in 1999 and Reigate Heath in 2000 (both GAC). It is usually found at nesting sites of its hosts but has also been seen at flowers of forget-me-not.

Its status has probably not changed since 1900.

Nomada marshamella (Kirby, 1802)   PLATE 38

National Status: Universal
Surrey Status: Local
VCH: (as *alternata*) Generally
   distributed

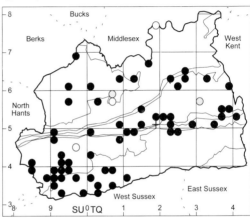

This large and striking *Nomada*, with strongly-marked black and yellow bands on the abdomen, is very common and widespread throughout much of the British Isles. It is double-brooded, flying from March to September, but the second brood is never numerous. It is a cleptoparasite of the common mining bee *Andrena carantonica*, which is single-brooded, and possibly of the scarce *A. trimmerana*, which is double-brooded.

It is fairly common and widespread in Surrey, but is scarce on the western heaths and apparently absent from the dry acid grasslands around London, where both its hosts occur. It is usually seen flying low over grassy banks, or over litter in open woodland, searching for nests of its hosts.

Its status is probably unchanged since 1900.

Nomada obtusifrons Nylander, 1848

National Status: Rare

Surrey Status: Extinct

VCH: No records

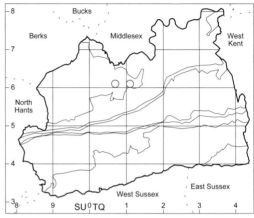

This small species is distinguished in both sexes from all other *Nomada* by its flat-topped raised area between the antennae instead of a sharp ridge as in all the other species. In Britain it is widespread but very scarce and extremely local, being a cleptoparasite of the very local *Andrena coitana*.

There are only two records for Surrey; the first record was from Cobham on 28 July 1912 by Nevinson and the specimen is in Oxford University Museum. Mortimer took a single specimen at nearby Byfleet in July 1913 and this is in the NHML. These records may both be from the same site because both collectors were notoriously imprecise with their locality data. It is said to be attracted to the flowers of sheep's-bit, which is still frequent at Brooklands, near Byfleet, so it is worth searching this area although its host, an extremely rare bee in Surrey, has never been recorded there.

Nomada panzeri Lepeletier, 1841   PLATE 38

National Status: Universal

Surrey Status: Local

VCH: Confused with *flava*

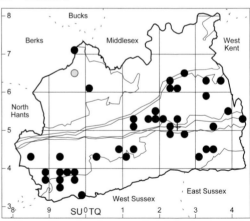

This is a locally common species over most of the British Isles. With its brown and yellow banded abdomen it is so similar in appearance to the very common *N. flava* that the males cannot easily be separated, even under a microscope. It has a very long flight period, in one brood, from mid-April to late June, probably because it parasitises several species of mining bees which emerge at different times. There has been much debate about exactly which species it attacks but it seems probable that they include *Andrena fulva, A. lapponica, A. fucata, A. helvola* and *A. synadelpha.*

It appears to be a rather local species in Surrey, being apparently absent from large areas in the north of the county, but it may be overlooked there on account of its close similarity to

N. flava. On the high, bilberry-clad Lower Greensand ridges, where it has been found at Hindhead Common, Friday Street and Holmbury Hill, its host may well be *A. lapponica*. It is difficult to say what its hosts are at other sites, but from a look at the distribution maps of the possible hosts, it may be *A. helvola*, which also avoids the north of the county. Flowers of wood spurge have been recorded as a nectar source.

It is difficult to decide whether or not it has declined since 1900.

Nomada roberjeotiana Panzer, 1799

National Status: Rare; RDB3
Surrey Status: Extinct
VCH: Chobham, Woking

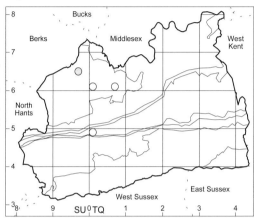

This small species is a cleptoparasite of the mining bee *Andrena tarsata* and formerly occurred throughout England wherever its host was frequent. It was, however, always liable to extreme fluctuations in its abundance and range and has recently become so rare that it has hardly been recorded for some years. It flies from the end of June to late August and is found on moors and heaths, visiting tormentil, the forage plant of its host.

It has been found at only three localities in Surrey since 1900 and there have been no records at all since 1972, due to the decline of its host. The earliest record is of a specimen from Chobham Common in 1878, collected by Saunders, who also took it there in 1892 and at Horsell Common in 1891. It was still present at Horsell Common in 1906 when Le Marchant took one there on 26 July and was still at Chobham Common as late as 1972 when Guichard collected it on 15 July. Mortimer collected it in 1912 and 1913 at Byfleet, where it was also taken by Guichard in 1939. All these records are supported by specimens in the NHML. Its host has become very scarce and is now only known at Bagmoor and Chobham Commons, Brookwood Cemetery and Folly Bog, but these sites are still worth searching for this very elusive *Nomada*.

It has declined since 1900.

Nomada ruficornis (Linnaeus, 1758) PLATE 38

National Status: Universal

Surrey Status: Common

VCH: (as *bifida*) Generally distributed

This is a common and widespread spring *Nomada* throughout the British Isles. It is a rather dark, medium-sized bee with yellow and black bands on a reddish abdomen and extensive red markings on the head and thorax of the female. It flies in one brood from April to June and is a cleptoparasite of the very common spring mining bee *Andrena haemorrhoa*.

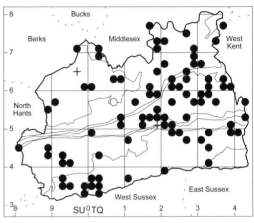

It is equally widespread and common in Surrey wherever its host occurs. The females are often seen flying low over grass searching for the nests of the host. It is common in open woodland and woodland edge on the Weald Clay and is frequently seen at flowers of wood spurge there; it has also been recorded on forget-me-not, hogweed, hawthorn and dandelion. Its status is the same as in 1900.

Nomada rufipes Fabricius, 1793 PLATE 12

National Status: Widespread

Surrey Status: Common

VCH: (as *solidaginis*) Generally distributed

This smallish *Nomada* is common and widespread over much of the British Isles. It has a black and yellow banded abdomen (sometimes also with orange), a very distinctive single oblong yellow mark on the back of the thorax, and red legs. It is one of the few late summer species, flying in a single brood from July to September, and

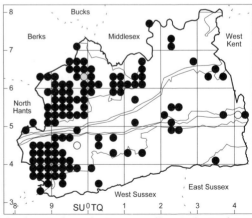

parasitises the heather specialist mining bee *Andrena fuscipes* as well as *A. denticulata*.

In Surrey it is abundant on all the western heaths, but only sporadic on the Lower Greensand ridge around Leith Hill and Hurtwood; on these heaths its host is clearly *A. fuscipes*. However, at a few localities away from heather, e.g. on clay woodland in the west, the host may be *A. denticulata*. It has been recorded coming for nectar to ragwort, angelica and *Eryngium*.

Its status has not changed since 1900.

Nomada sexfasciata Panzer, 1799

National Status: Very rare; RDB1
Surrey Status: Extinct
VCH: Chobham, Woking

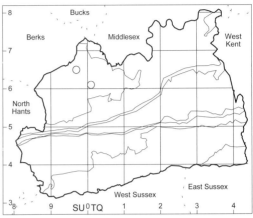

This large species, a cleptoparasite of the scarce *Eucera longicornis*, is now restricted to one site in Devon although it was formerly sporadically distributed in southern England.

Saunders (1896) described it as not rare where its host bee occurred and knew it in Surrey from Chobham Common and Woking. It was collected frequently from Chobham Common between 1900 and 1910, with many specimens in the NHML and Oxford University Museum collected by Saunders, Nevinson, Le Marchant, etc. There are also specimens in both museums collected from Horsell Common in 1914 by H.G. and R.J. Champion. It has not been recorded since that year and must now be assumed to be extinct in Surrey. Its host bee has also declined dramatically since 1900 although it still occurs frequently in the south-western clay woods.

It has declined to extinction since 1900.

Nomada sheppardana (Kirby, 1802)   PLATE 38

National Status: Restricted
Surrey Status: Very local
VCH: (as *furva*) Generally
    distributed

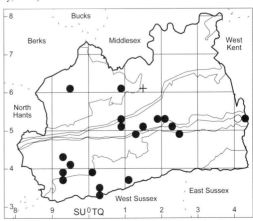

This is the smallest of all the *Nomada*, being mainly black with, in the females, a reddish-orange band on the abdomen and, in the males, pale cream, interrupted bands on the abdomen. It is confined to southern Britain where it is local but sometimes common at nest sites of its hosts. It flies in one brood from May to July and is unusual for a *Nomada* because it is a cleptoparasite of species of *Lasioglossum* rather than *Andrena*.

It is widespread in Surrey but very local; however, it is easily overlooked on account of its diminutive size. Here it is known from a few sites on the Chalk where it has been seen flying around nesting aggregations of *Lasioglossum morio* (DWB) and it also occurs in woodland rides on the Weald Clay, where it may also attack nests of *L. parvulum*. It has also been found at a few sites on the sand, including a male in my garden at Milford.

If it really was common and widespread in 1900 it may have declined since then, unless it is under-recorded because of its size.

Nomada signata Jurine, 1807   PLATE 19

National Status: Very rare; RDB2
Surrey Status: Rare
VCH: No records

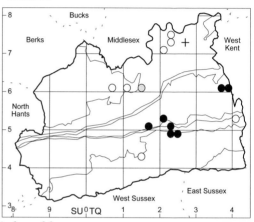

This bee is now very rare in southern Britain, having declined considerably during the last few decades. The female can readily be distinguished from *N. flava* by its pair of irregular yellow spots on the rear of the thorax and its clear, uninterrupted yellow bands on the abdomen; the male is more difficult. It flies from early April to late May and is a cleptoparasite of the common and beautiful mining bee *Andrena fulva*.

Surrey still has six sites where it has been found since 1991, all of them in the east of the county, but it was more widespread in the past. Saunders treated it, together with *N. flava* and *N. panzeri*, as a variety of *N. ruficornis* and he did not therefore include it in the VCH list, nor in his 1896 book, although he did state in the book that he had taken "var. *signata*", without giving the locality. However, there is a specimen in the NHML, taken by Saunders in April 1876 from Wandsworth Common, which may be the specimen he was referring to. Since then there are numerous old records, all from the eastern side of the county where its host is much commoner, and all supported by specimens in the NHML, as follows: Holmwood area, 1921 (Mortimer); Oxshott Heath, 1925; Byfleet, 1925 and 1926 (Richards); Wimbledon Common, 1932 (J.F. Perkins); Limpsfield Common, 1939 (Guichard); Richmond Park, 1946 (Richards); Putney Heath, 1949 (A.W. Jones); Oxshott Heath, 1952 (Guichard); Box Hill, 1970 (Z. Boucek). There is a specimen in Oxford University Museum from Cobham of about 1910 (Nevinson).

Since 1991 there has also been a considerable number of records for such a rarity: Headley Heath, sandy area, 1991, 1995 and 1996 (ME); Reigate Heath, 2001 (RDH); Hutchinsons Bank, Addington, 2005, 2008 (GAC, VVP); garden adjoining Priory Park, Reigate, 2005, 2006, 2007 (JPE); Reigate Heath, 2006, 2007 (DWB, GAC, GRE, JPE); Box Hill, 2007 (VVP). On 19 May 2007 it was common all over Reigate Heath, at some spots in good numbers. It should be searched for wherever its host is nesting as it could easily be overlooked for *N. flava,* and it may still be present in some of its former localities.

It is difficult to say whether it has changed its status since 1900.

Nomada striata Fabricius, 1793

National Status: Widespread

Surrey Status: Local

VCH: (as *ochrostoma*) Chobham, Woking

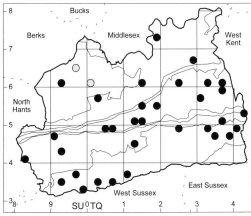

Although widely distributed over most of the British Isles, it is never common. It is a medium-sized *Nomada*, having a mainly red abdomen with distinctive pairs of large yellow spots, and with various red markings on the black head and thorax. It flies, in a single brood, from May to July, being one of the few *Nomada* species around in midsummer. It almost certainly parasitises the mining bee *Andrena wilkella* and possibly also *A. fucata.*

Although widespread in Surrey it is distinctly local and never found in numbers. Comparison of the distribution map of this *Nomada* with that of *A. wilkella* does show a fairly close correlation. The host is commonest on the chalk and in Weald Clay woodlands and the *Nomada* is also commoner here than elsewhere. In the clay woodlands it often comes to flowers of wood spurge and has been recorded at bulbous buttercup.

Its status is no doubt the same as in 1900.

Genus *Epeolus* Latreille, 1802

These are medium-sized black and reddish solitary bees with conspicuous white or cream patches of dense short hairs on the thorax and abdomen. Females, which are cleptoparasites on species of *Colletes*, enter an open cell of the host bee and insert an egg on the cell wall. The first-instar larva destroys the host's egg with its long, curved jaws and then eats the host's provisions. There is only one generation a year.

Nationally two species, both found in Surrey.

Epeolus cruciger (Panzer, 1799)   PLATE 10

National Status: Widespread
Surrey Status: Locally common
VCH: (as *rufipes*) Woking, Chobham

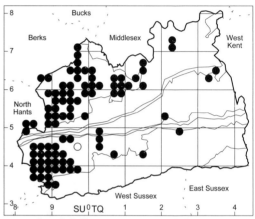

This bee is so similar to the only other Surrey species in the genus it needs to be examined micro-scopically for identification. However, in the female of this species the hind femur is usually all red, whereas in *E. variegatus* it is usually mainly black; the male usually has a mainly red pygidium whereas the male *E. variegatus* usually has a black one. It is a cleptoparasite of *Colletes succinctus* and *C. marginatus*, and possibly also of *C. fodiens*. It is widespread in southern Britain being especially common on coastal dunes, and heaths and moors.

In Surrey it is common, and sometimes abundant, on all the heaths and even small areas of heather, wherever its host, the heather specialist *C. succinctus,* occurs. The maps of the two species are almost identical, both having isolated localities in the east, e.g. Wimbledon Common, Croham Hurst and Headley Heath. It has not yet been found at Reigate Heath or Limpsfield Chart although *C. succinctus* is at both sites. The females are usually to be seen around nest sites of the host bee, flying slowly and low, and crawling from hole to hole and going in and out of the holes in their search for an uncompleted nest in which to lay an egg; it has also been seen on sheep's-bit. It emerges at the end of June, about two weeks later than *E. variegatus*, and continues to the end of September.

It is no doubt as common on the heaths as it was in 1900.

Epeolus variegatus (Linnaeus, 1758)   PLATE 9

National Status: Widespread
Surrey Status: Locally common
VCH: No records

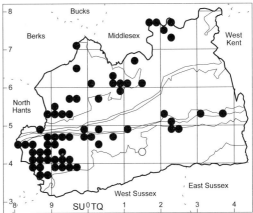

Very similar to *E. cruciger* but reference should be made to that species for differences. It is also widespread in southern Britain, being most common in the southeast. It parasitises several different species of *Colletes*.

In Surrey it is widespread and especially common on the sand in the south-west; it is absent from the clay and chalk. It is also common on the Thames Gravel Terraces at Kew, Richmond Park, Barnes Common and Wimbledon Common. In Surrey it is parasitic on *Colletes daviesanus*, which is virtually restricted to the sands and gravels, and *C. fodiens*, which is entirely restricted to the sands and gravels. It may also parasitise *C. succinctus*, which is only on sand and gravel. It is usually seen wherever its hosts are nesting. Being a parasite, the female does not collect pollen but it is often seen taking nectar at ragwort. It is on the wing about a fortnight earlier than *C. succinctus,* to coincide with the rather earlier flight time of its two main hosts. Saunders (1902) does not mention it, because at that time it was still confused with *E. cruciger*, although in his 1896 book he gives Woking and Weybridge as localities where it had been found.

Its status is probably unchanged since 1900.

Genus *Eucera* Scopoli, 1770

This is a large black solitary bee with brown hairs on the thorax, the males having exceptionally long antennae and a yellow-marked face. Females nest, sometimes in aggregations, below ground, lining the cells with a secretion that prevents the semi-liquid provisions from being absorbed into the soil. They have only one generation a year and pupate in cocoons, overwintering as prepupae or possibly as adults. Nationally two species, with only one in Surrey.

Eucera longicornis (Linnaeus, 1758)   PLATE 8

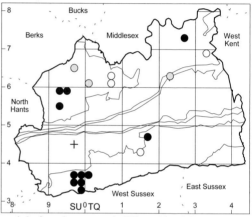

National Status: Restricted; Na
Surrey Status: Rare
VCH: Godalming, Woking, Chobham

The male is unmistakable because of its extraordinarily long antennae, coupled with a yellow clypeus; the female is less striking but can be told in the field by having a white hair band, followed by a pale golden hair band, on the tail. It has always been restricted to southern Britain but there has been a dramatic decline over the last 30 years and it is now found only rarely inland. It is mainly found on coastal cliffs and landslips, where it nests gregariously. It is one of the few solitary bees to have an English common name, 'the long-horned bee'.

In Surrey it has also declined, but it still hangs on at a handful of sites, especially in the clay woods. The map shows the numerous localities where it was recorded in the past, even quite recently, e.g. Horsell and Chobham Commons as late as 1972 (both KMG). One of the best sites is the disused claypit at Hambledon, where the males can be seen in good numbers every year flying fast and low over the south-facing clay cliff where the females nest, or coming to flowers of ground-ivy for nectar. In May 2007 some of these males were observed 'bombing' female *Nomada marshamella*. In June 2006 there were about 50 females nesting in a small stretch of bare clay on this cliff. The females fly around foraging for pollen at the flowers of meadow vetchling, its favoured pollen source. This site was discovered only in 1997 and is unfortunately due for development so it may well be lost soon. Another nesting site was found in a ride at nearby Oaken Wood, Chiddingfold, in 1996 (DWB). A male was seen in 1999, and a pair in May 2000, in a clay woodland ride just north of Dunsfold airfield but no nest site was found (DWB). In June 2006 it was seen frequently along the main ride in Botany Bay, Chiddingfold, where both sexes were coming to meadow vetchling. A single male was seen in another disused claypit at North Holmwood in 1998 (GAC); it was refound there in May 2008 by the ranger, S. Glasspool, who saw and photographed about 15 males flying around a south-facing clay bank.

Away from the wealden woods there is a strong population at Bisley Ranges; on Short Siberia Range an enormous aggregation of about 100 nests was found in the butts as recently as June 2008 (JSD, DWB) and a male was found on Stickledown Range. A singleton was also found at Stoney Castle, Ash Ranges, in May 1998 (JSD) so there may well be another breeding population there. A single male, possibly a straggler, was taken on Wandsworth Common on the late date of 13 July 1997 (DWB). It flies from May to July.

This is one of only two solitary bees mentioned by Gilbert White of Selborne in his Journals (White, reissued 1931) and even then it had the common name of 'long-horned bee'. His entry for 21 July 1770 reads: "*Apis longicornis* carries wax on it's thighs into it's hole in the walks: in this wax it deposits it's eggs." And that for 9 June 1772 reads: "*Apis longicornis* the long-horned bees bore their nests in the ground where it is trodden the hardest." And his entry for 4 June 1774 reads: "*Apis longicornis* works at it's nest in the ground only in a morning while the sun shines." If only modern recorders would make such useful observations!

It has probably declined considerably since 1900.

(There is one other British species of *Eucera*, *E. nigrescens*, which was always extremely rare in southern England and has not been seen for over 30 years. It has never been recorded in Surrey but, because it is so similar in appearance to *E. longicornis*, all *Eucera* specimens should be examined microscopically to ensure the correct identification.)

Genus *Anthophora* Latreille, 1803

These are large black solitary bees with brownish or black hairs, the males (and females of *A. bimaculata*) having yellow-marked faces. They have a distinctively square labrum. They nest below ground or in crevices in dead wood or masonry. There is only one generation a year and in at least one species the adults emerge from the pupae in late summer but remain in their cells until the following spring. They are parasitised by various species of cleptoparasitic bees in the genera *Coelioxys* and *Melecta*.

Nationally five species with all five in Surrey, but one now extinct.

Anthophora bimaculata (Panzer, 1798)   PLATE 39

National Status: Restricted

Surrey Status: Locally common

VCH: Chobham, Woking, Weybridge, Godalming, Coombe Wood

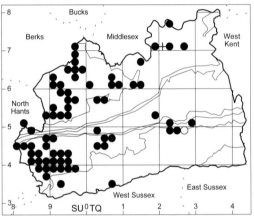

This is the smallest species of the genus in Britain and can be identified by both sexes having yellow-marked faces; it has a diagnostic shrill hum as it flies and has conspicuous pale green eyes when alive. It is restricted to the very south of England, where it can be abundant on dry sandy soils, such as inland heaths and coastal sand dunes. It excavates its nests in bare soil, sometimes in large aggregations, where it is parasitised by the bee *Coelioxys rufescens*. It flies from late June to mid-September and forages from numerous different plants including ragwort, sheep's-bit, thistles, lavender and garden catmint.

In Surrey it is common, and sometimes abundant, on all the dry heaths and also locally on dry acid grassland, such as Brooklands at Weybridge, and Ditton, Barnes and Wimbledon Commons. Although it may nest on level sand, it prefers to nest in sloping banks or even in small vertical cliffs, such as the south-facing side of the old sandpit on Horsell Common where there are hundreds of densely packed burrows. It has occasionally been seen in May, for example 6 May 2004 at Ham Common and 18 May 2008 at Wandle Park, and is now regularly seen in early to mid-June.

Its status is probably unchanged since 1900.

Anthophora furcata (Panzer, 1798)   PLATE 39

National Status: Widespread
Surrey Status: Local
VCH: Chobham, Woking

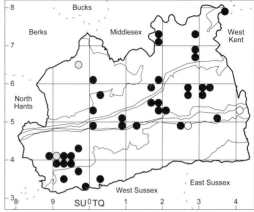

A medium-sized dark grey bee, with a red tail in the female, that can be recognised under the microscope by its three-toothed mandibles. It is widespread in southern Britain and can be found in almost any habitat. It excavates its nests in rotting wood and forages from different plants in the labiate family, flying from late May to August.

In Surrey it is widespread but rather local and uncommon, and is possibly overlooked because it is so drab. It can be found almost anywhere, from heaths to grassland and woods, but especially in gardens and usually flying around labiate flowers including hedge woundwort, but it has also been seen at bramble. The map appears to show an association with the Chalk, as well as with the Weald Clay woods in the south-west. Many females were seen flying into the base of an upturned root-plate of an oak in a wood in my garden one summer. I assumed they were nesting in the soil of the rootplate, but stupidly failed to investigate; they were presumably nesting in the decaying tree roots.

It status is probably unchanged since 1900.

Anthophora plumipes (Pallas, 1772)   PLATE 20

National Status: Widespread
Surrey Status: Locally common
VCH: (as *pilipes*) Generally
   distributed

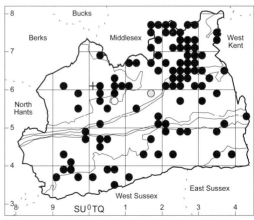

This is the largest and most attractive species in the genus, the female being robust, hairy and entirely black, except for orange hairs on the hind tibia, so that it can easily be mistaken for a bumblebee. The males have brown hairs and are extremely territorial, driving any intruders away from their patch. It is fairly common over southern Britain and flies from March to late May.

In Surrey it is fairly widespread and locally common, especially in and around London, probably because it prefers to nest in walls. It is one of the earliest bees on the wing in early spring, from early March, when it flies very fast from flower to flower. It is usually seen in gardens where it it is very fond of lungwort and, in my garden, the introduced honeywort (*Cerinthe*) species, but it will also visit labiates such as ground-ivy and red dead-nettle. The females collect pollen from a variety of flowers. The beautiful cuckoo bee *Melecta albifrons* is the cleptoparasite of this species. A small aggregation of nests was found in the rootplate of a fallen beech at Nonsuch Park in May 2004 (RDH). I discovered a large aggregation of 20 to 30 nests in a mound at the base of a large cedar in Edolphs Copse near Charlwood in April 2001. The site was infested with many female *Melecta albifrons*, which were going in and out of the burrows, but some of the female *A. plumipes* were hauling these out of their burrows with their mandibles.

Its status is probably unchanged since 1900.

Anthophora quadrimaculata (Panzer, 1798)

National Status: Scarce; Nb
Surrey Status: Very local
VCH: No records

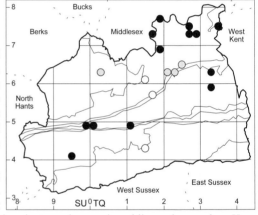

This is another medium-sized robust black bee which is restricted to southern England and is commonest around London where it tends to frequent gardens. It flies from early June to mid-August and nests in small aggregations in banks or walls.

It is very local in Surrey and most records are from around London. Here it can usually be found at catmint, lavender or other labiates in private gardens, or in public gardens such as Ham House and Kew Gardens, where it can be reasonably common. Presumably it is found in built-up areas because it nests in walls of buildings. It was never recorded by Saunders, possibly because it did not occur where the Victorian and Edwardian collectors were active. The earliest record appears to be of a specimen in the NHML taken by Mortimer in July 1922 at Holmwood. There were very few records between then and 1996, although Baker recorded it a few times around Ewell in 1956 and in the 1980s. Since 1996 it has been recorded on 24 occasions so it may be increasing its range. Baker collected the very rare cleptoparasitic bee *Coelioxys quadridentata* from a nesting aggregation of this *Anthophora* in an old stone wall at Ewell East Station in 1982.

It has probably increased since 1900, being overlooked before then.

Anthophora retusa (Linnaeus, 1758)

National Status: Very rare; RDB1
Surrey Status: Extinct
VCH: Chobham, Woking, Godalming

This extremely rare large bee is very similar, in both sexes, to the common *A. plumipes* and it is necessary to inspect them both under a microscope for identification. Both females are all black but this species has yellow spurs on the hind tibiae whereas *A. plumipes* has black spurs; with the males one has to compare hair lengths on the

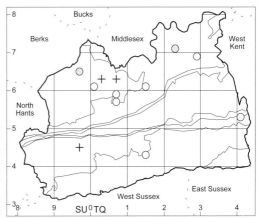

mid tibiae. From being a rather local bee of the south-east corner of England, it has declined alarmingly in the last 30 years and is now known from only five sites, all on the coast. It flies from early April to mid-June, slightly later than *A. plumipes*. The now extinct cuckoo bee *Melecta luctuosa* attacked its nest.

In Surrey this was a reasonably common bee on the heaths and sandy areas until the 1950s when it suddenly disappeared and has not been seen for over 50 years. Morice, 1901 reported that it was almost as common as *A. plumipes* around Woking at that time. Climate change might help it to recover and a female was recorded in 1999 just over the county border at Farnborough in North Hampshire. The earliest record was made in 1891 at Chobham Common by Saunders and from then on it was recorded at all the usual sites by most of the well-known hymenopterists of the the time, e.g. Horsell Common (Saunders, Champion brothers, R.C.L. Perkins), Wisley (G. Fox Wilson in 1921), Wimbledon Common (J.A.J. Boyer from 1952 to 1953), Holmwood (Mortimer), Mitcham Common (G.E.J. Nixon), Oxshott Heath (Richards), Weybridge (Morice), Limpsfield and Ottershaw (Morice). Guichard took it on five occasions at various sites, the last being in 1949 at Limpsfield Common. Finally, A.E. Stubbs recorded the very last specimen in Surrey at Staple Hill on Chobham Common in 1954.

It has declined dramatically to extinction since 1900.

Genus *Melecta* Latreille, 1802

These are large black bees with distinctive white hair patches on the sides of the abdomen. Females, which are cleptoparasites of species of *Anthophora*, dig into the nest of their host bee, make a small hole in the cell wall and lay an egg on the cell wall. The hole in the cell is repaired with mud and the burrow entrance is replugged with soil. The first-instar larva destroys the host's egg with its specially adapted long sickle-shaped jaws and then eats the host's provisions. Pupation occurs within cocoons and there is one generation a year.

Nationally two species, with both in Surrey, but one now extinct.

Melecta albifrons (Forster, 1771)   PLATE 20

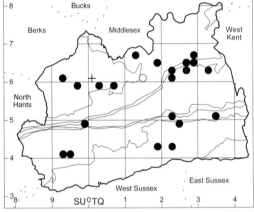

National Status: Widespread
Surrey Status: Very local
VCH: (as *armata*) Woking, Chobham, Godalming

A beautiful and unmistakable spring bee, with the head and body black except for pairs of snow-white hair patches on the abdomen, and with white on the tibiae; both sexes are similar. It is widely distributed in southern England but is scarce and local. It is a cleptoparasite of *Anthophora plumipes*.

It is also widely distributed in Surrey, but is also scarce and local. It is usually found in the same sites as its host, typically in gardens. It comes to a variety of flowers for nectar and I have seen it at honesty in my garden. At Edolphs Copse near Charlwood in May 2001 I watched a large nesting aggregation of *A. plumipes* at the base of an old cedar tree. The females were busy going in and out of their burrows and there were five female *M. albifrons* mingling with them and also entering their hosts' burrows. On two occasions a female *A. plumipes*, using her mandibles, dragged an *M. albifrons* out of her burrow.

Its status is probably unchanged since 1900.

Melecta luctuosa (Scopoli, 1770)

National Status: RDB1 (Extinct)
Surrey Status: Extinct
VCH: Chobham

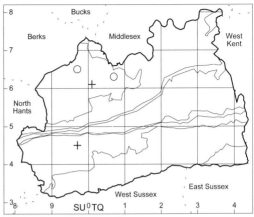

This bee is similar to *M. albifrons* in appearance and was formerly widely distributed in south-east England, but it has not been seen for nearly 100 years and is assumed to be nationally extinct. It is a cleptoparasite of *Anthophora retusa*, which has declined dramatically and is now known from only five sites on the south coast. It has only ever been recorded from four sites in Surrey, and was last seen in 1901, so must be presumed extinct. Saunders recorded it first at Chobham Common in 1878 and also recorded the last one there in 1901; he found it at Horsell Common in 1890, although he does not mention this record in the VCH. Nevinson took it at Weybridge in 1901 and Latter recorded it at Godalming in 1890, although this record is not mentioned by Saunders in VCH either. Morice (1901) said that, although *M. albifrons* swarmed in nests of *A. retusa* and *A. plumipes* around Woking, *M. luctuosa* had only been found once, by Saunders at Chobham Common.

It had declined to extinction as early as 1901.

Genus *Ceratina* Latreille, 1802

This is a small, shining, metallic blue, solitary bee that excavates holes
in wood or stems, and is the only British representative of the small
carpenter bees.

Nationally only one species, also in Surrey.

Ceratina cyanea (Kirby, 1802)   PLATES 5, 43, 46

National Status: Rare; RDB3
Surrey Status: Locally common
VCH: Weybridge

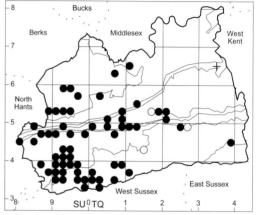

This small, shining, blue carpenter
bee, the male with a white-marked
face, has always been a rare species
of southern England. It is found
mainly in the extreme south-eastern
counties of Hampshire, Sussex,
Kent and Surrey. Within this area it
can be locally common on chalk
downland, heaths and open woodlands. Females nest in broken dead
bramble stems, or occasionally
stems of herbaceous plants, by excavating the pith. Both sexes hibernate as adults in these
disused nests.

In Victorian and Edwardian times it was considered a great rarity in Surrey and every
capture was worthy of a note in the EMM. The first record came from Weybridge in 1876,
followed by Croydon in 1882, Holmwood in 1906, Redhill in 1907 and Cobham in 1911,
all places from which it has not been recorded since. However, since 1986, and especially
since 1996, it has been found to be common and widespread in the south-west of the
county, extending as far north as Walton-on-Thames and as far east as Reigate, with an
outlier in the south-east at Lingfield. It frequents all types of habitat from open sunny
woodland rides in Forestry Commission woods on the Weald Clay at Botany Bay, Sidney
Wood and Holmens Grove, to edges of dry sandy heathland in the south-west, old sandpits
such as Wrecclesham, as well as south-facing chalk slopes on the North Downs. It has so
far been found in about 60 sites since 1996 and may be as common here as anywhere in
England.

As it was never recorded in the south of the county in the past it is possible that it has
increased and spread recently, but it could equally well have been overlooked formerly,
because it is not easily seen when flying low over small herbaceous plants in a rather slow
and distinctive flight. It has been seen visiting germander speedwell, red campion, forget-
me-not, tormentil, dandelion, chickweed, bugle, sheep's-bit, wood spurge, ragwort, Oxford
ragwort, goldenrod and devil's-bit scabious as well as garden plants such as *Hebe*, *Oxalis*
and *Potentilla*. It is found much more easily by looking for its very characteristic nest sites
in broken bramble stems, either lying on the ground or on the bramble bushes. The hole at

the end is very large because the female excavates virtually all the pith from the stem, and it is possible to collect about 30 stem nests in an hour at good sites such as Witley Common or my own garden. When these stem nests are opened in the winter they can contain up to six adult hibernating bees of this species. It is thought that some individuals can live up to 18 months. It is the only solitary bee that can be found as an adult throughout the year. Although only single-brooded, it has a very long flight period, from April (or even late March) to mid-September. Because both sexes hibernate they tend to go on flying until the warm autumn weather comes to an end.

It has increased and expanded its range dramatically since 1900.

Genus *Xylocopa* Latreille, 1809

This is a very large carpenter bee which nests in holes made in wood and in other cavities.

Nationally one breeding species, also in Surrey but only as a vagrant.

Xylocopa violacea (Linnaeus, 1758)   PLATE 43

National Status: Very rare
Surrey Status: Vagrant
VCH: No records

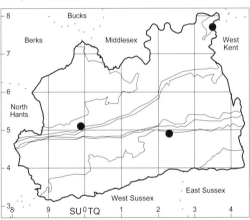

This very large and striking violet-black carpenter bee, with electric-blue wings, is well-known and common in mainland Europe, where it nests in crevices in walls and other holes, and also makes holes in dead wood with its powerful mandibles. Both males and females hibernate as adults in burrows. Up to 1974 it was a rare vagrant to southern England, with only a few records, one of these being from timber on a ship, so that it was considered to be accidentally introduced. A female actually nested unsuccessfully in a post in Hertfordshire in 1920. But in the last few years up to four or five have been reported each year and on one occasion a female attempted to nest in the wooden supporting post of a bird table. As almost all of these have been in the south-east or on the south coast it seems that these are genuine vagrants that may have flown across the Channel unaided, rather than being accidental introductions with imported timber or other produce. It nested and then hibernated in a dead apple tree near Leicester in 2006 and 2007, and also nested in another dead apple tree at Tonbridge, Kent, in 2006, and could well become resident in England in the near future.

The only three Surrey records are all very recent. The first came from Guildford on 14 July 2003, when D. Powell saw a male flying round flowers in his garden, realised that it was like the large blue bees he had seen on holiday in the Mediterranean, and rushed for his digital camera. He managed to take three good photos before it flew off and sent these to me to identify; the two red segments towards the end of the antennae indicated that it was a male. This occurred during an extremely hot period when there was a mass immigration of other orders of insects. The second was from Reigate Heath in June 2004 where B. Martin watched a female for three weeks frequenting flowers in a polytunnel and going into a very large bamboo cane every evening. Unfortunately it never nested but he took many photographs of it, one of which was published in *British Wildlife* magazine. The third was seen by J. Riley, an experienced naturalist, on 9 September 2006 in his garden at Nunhead, Peckham, where it was visiting runner bean flowers.

It has increased since 1900 but only as a vagrant.

Genus *Bombus* Latreille, 1802

These are large to very large, hairy bumblebees which are social, except for the subgenus *Psithyrus* which are social parasites on other bumblebees. Hairs on the thorax and abdomen are mostly black with various combinations of yellow, tawny, red or white bands. Pollen is carried in the corbicula (pollen baskets) on the hind legs. Normally one generation a year but a few species have two. Colonies vary from 30-50 workers to 200 or more workers. Males appear in mid to late summer and the fertilised queens overwinter. Some species are parasitised by the velvet ant *Mutilla europaea*.

Bumblebees have an annual life cycle very similar to that of social wasps. Queens overwinter in underground burrows, in leaf litter or under bark. In the spring the queen starts a nest either underground, usually in an abandoned small mammal burrow, or at the surface of the ground, under dry leaf litter. The queen makes a space in the nesting material and then builds a honey pot from wax secreted from below her abdomen. She fills her honey pot with regurgitated nectar and some eggs are then laid on a mass of pollen which is surrounded by a wax cell. The queen incubates the cell by lying across it. The larvae are progressively fed on a pollen-nectar mixture, the wax cell being gradually enlarged to accommodate the growing larvae. The first adults are workers which build further cells and forage for food. Some species, called 'pocket-makers', build wax pockets near the base of the cell, into which the foragers deposit their loads of pollen to feed the larvae. This diet is supplemented by a pollen-nectar mixture regurgitated to the larvae through a small hole in the cell. In other species, called 'pollen-storers', the foraged pollen is stored in empty pupal cocoons or specially built wax cylinders. A pollen-nectar mixture is squirted into the larval cell through a hole in the wax covering. Further wax cells make an irregular-shaped nest. At pupation the larva spins a silken cocoon. The wax from the cell is then removed and used to build further cells.

Nationally 24 species, with 20 in Surrey, but six of these are probably now extinct.

Nationally, as well as in Surrey, there are now only six common species: *B. hortorum, B. lapidarius, B. lucorum, B. pascuorum, B. pratorum* and *B. terrestris.* These are all generalist foragers and are easily seen in gardens. The others are more specialist species which seem to require large ranges of flower-rich grassland; it is these species which have almost all declined dramatically, especially over the last 20 years, and in one case to extinction. This decline is due to a decrease in suitable habitat caused by modern forms of agriculture, such as ploughing up of old meadowland, use of herbicides, etc. This decline may at last be halted by various agri-environment schemes. Surrey has never supported many of the rarer species due to lack of suitable large-scale habitat.

Bombus distinguendus Morawitz, 1869

National Status: Very rare; Nb
Surrey Status: Extinct
VCH: Shirley, Norwood

Formerly a scarce but widespread species in Britain with a northern bias, it has declined so seriously in the last 50 years that it is now confined to the Inner and Outer Hebrides and the north coast of Scotland.

The only records for Surrey are those of F. Smith from Shirley and Norwood, probably in about 1850, and of R.C. Bradley from Chobham Common in 1918 (det. GRE).

Bombus hortorum (Linnaeus, 1761)

National Status: Universal
Surrey Status: Ubiquitous
VCH: Generally distributed

This large black, yellow and white-banded species is widespread in Britain but it is now found less often than any of the other five common bumblebees, although still frequent in gardens. It is never common at a site, possibly because the nests are small, only having 30-80 workers. The females have a very long tongue and specialise in visiting flowers with a long tubular corolla,

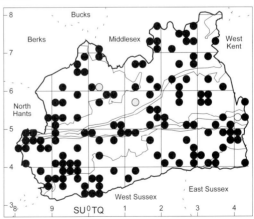

such as honeysuckle, labiates such as hedge woundwort, and particularly foxglove. The queens emerge in early May, rather later than other species.

In Surrey it is widespread but never common and it appears to be declining.

It appears to have declined since 1900.

Bombus humilis Illiger, 1806

National Status: Scarce
Surrey Status: Very rare
VCH: (as *venustus*) Woking

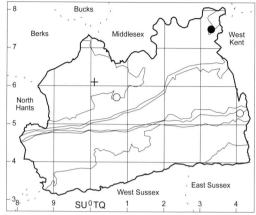

Formerly frequent in southern England, this brown bumblebee has declined seriously in the last 50 years and is now almost confined to coastal sites and extensive calcareous grassland inland.

For Surrey, Saunders (1902) cites only the Woking record of Morice (probably about 1890). In the Fox Wilson Collection at RHS Wisley there are six specimens collected by G. Fox Wilson at Wisley on the following dates: June 1919, 30 July, 12 August and September 1920, July 1921 and July 1923. It was recorded in Surrey by Guichard in 1937 and 1938 at Limpsfield Common, and was then considered to have become extinct. However, a dead worker was found in a house in East Dulwich on 1 May 2003 and was identified by Peter Harvey, one of the country's experts on this bumblebee. Its main stronghold in Britain is now on both sides of the Thames Estuary, reaching as far west as the Isle of Dogs, across the Thames from the Surrey Docks. The East Dulwich specimen was presumably a straggler from these Essex or Kent colonies but there is the intriguing possibility that it came from a colony in Surrey, possibly breeding on a post-industrial site nearby.

It has declined since 1900.

Bombus hypnorum (Linnaeus, 1758)   PLATE 3

National status: Rare
Surrey Status: Rare
VCH: Unknown

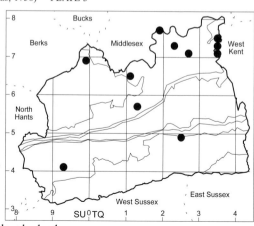

This common European bumble-bee has a ginger-brown thorax and a black abdomen with a distinctive white tail. It was first discovered in Britain at Landford, Wiltshire as recently as July 2001. In the following years it was found quite commonly on the campus of Southampton University and nearby, and has since spread over much of southern England, and in 2007 it reached as far north as Northumberland.

The first Surrey record was of a male seen on 28 May 2004, first by N. Ward and shortly afterwards by T. Ings in the grounds of CABI Bioscience UK Centre, Egham. The second sighting was of a male in a garden at Upper Sydenham, near Dulwich, just within the county boundary, on 5 June 2005 by S. Connop. A worker was collected at nearby Crystal Palace Park in July 2006 (R.A. Jones) and another was found dead at Peckham, just further north, also in 2006. It seems from this cluster of records that it must be breeding in that area. On 20 May 2007 a female was photographed on the flowers of *Heucera cylindrica* 'Goldfinch' near the main entrance to Kew Gardens by David Element, on 2 June 2007 a male was found at Bookham by G.A. Collins and a week later another female was photographed at a sandpit in Reigate by J.P. Early. In late April 2008 a queen and worker were found at bilberry on Mare Hill Common (GRE) and others were seen there subsequently; in May another was photographed at Wandle Meadow LNR, South Wimbledon (DE). The only breeding record is from Walton-on-Thames, where a nest was found in a bird box in a residential garden by G. Cooper in May 2008.

As a very recent colonist it has increased since 1900.

Bombus jonellus (Kirby, 1802)   PLATE 40

National Status: Universal
Surrey Status: Locally common
VCH: Woking, Chobham, Coombe Wood, Shirley, Purley Downs

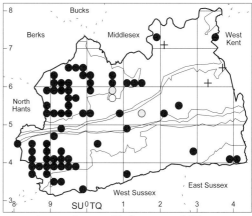

This yellow, black and white-banded bumblebee is very similar to the fairly common *Bombus hortorum*, but it is usually rather smaller. It is widespread in Britain but common only on heaths, moors and the coast. It often has two broods in the south, flying from March through to September. It collects pollen from a variety of flowers and nests above and below ground. The nests are attacked by the cuckoo bumblebee *Bombus sylvestris*.

In Surrey it is fairly common and widespread on the heaths but it also occurs infrequently in the east on the Chalk and Weald Clay. It used to be considered as a species associated with heathland but it may be spreading into other habitats such as chalk grassland, dry acid grassland and gardens. On the other hand it may have been overlooked in these habitats previously, due to its similarity to *B. hortorum*, although Saunders cited records from Purley Downs and Shirley, which could have been chalk habitats. On the heaths it forages from heather during the summer, but I have seen workers in numbers foraging from tree heather in my garden in late spring; it has also been recorded on forget-me-not, cat's-ear, dwarf gorse and germander speedwell.

Its status is probably unchanged since 1900.

Bombus lapidarius (Linnaeus, 1758)   PLATE 41

National Status: Universal
Surrey Status: Ubiquitous
VCH: Generally distributed
This is one of the commonest bumblebees and the most easily recognised. The females are black, with no yellow bands, but with a very distinctive red end to the abdomen. The males are similar except that they usually, but not always, have a yellow band on the thorax and yellow markings on the face. It is widespread in Britain, flies from March to October and has large underground nests.

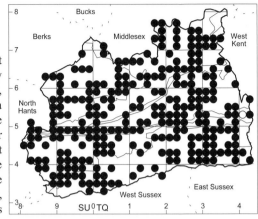

In Surrey it is also common and widespread and is found in almost any habitat and is regularly found in gardens. It visits a wide range of flowers for pollen and nectar without any specific preferences. The nests are attacked by the similarly coloured cuckoo bumblebee *Bombus rupestris*. The only other species in Surrey with which it could be confused is the very rare *Bombus ruderarius*, and the different characters need to be examined under a microscope; *B. ruderarius* females have red hairs on the corbicula, whereas those of *B. lapidarius* have black hairs.

Its status is unchanged since 1900.

Bombus lucorum (Linnaeus, 1761)   PLATE 42

National Status: Universal
Surrey Status: Ubiquitous
VCH: Generally distributed
This and *B. terrestris* are the two very common white-tailed bumblebees; they both have black and yellow bands and the workers are virtually indistinguishable. However the queens of this species have pure white tails, whereas those of *B. terrestris* generally have buff tails.

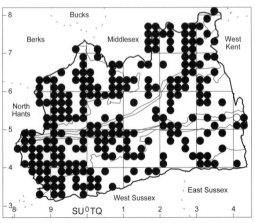

It is very common and widespread in Surrey and often seen in gardens, visiting a wide range of flowers.

Its status is unchanged since 1900.

[*Bombus monticola* Smith, 1849

A large red-tailed bumblebee which is restricted to upland areas in Britain and is therefore absent from south-east England.

The National Trust organised an aculeate survey of Hindhead Common in 1951, using volunteers. The survey report showed about five records of this species being seen. There is also one specimen in the Haslemere Museum labelled 'Devils Punchbowl, Hindhead, Surrey. 1951. G.J.F. Bensley. *Bombus lapponicus*'. On examination I found it was in fact a male of the similar-looking red-tailed *B. lapidarius*. A search of Hindhead Common was carried out in 1997 and 1998 for this species but there was no sign of it, although there were many *B. lapidarius* at bilberry flowers in the spring (DWB). It seems clear that *B. monticola* (at that time known as *B. lapponicus*) had been misidentified and that it has never been recorded in Surrey.]

Bombus muscorum (Linnaeus, 1758)

National Status: Universal
Surrey Status: Extinct
VCH: Unknown

Although still widespread in Britain it has declined severely since 1970 and is now found mainly in scattered coastal localities in the south, but is commoner in the north.

This brown bumblebee has always been rare inland and the only confirmed Surrey record is of a recently discovered queen in the O.H. Latter Collection at Charterhouse, taken by Latter on 11 June 1914 at Godalming (which could mean anywhere within ten miles of Godalming). It must be presumed to be extinct in Surrey.

Its status is unchanged since 1900.

Bombus pascuorum (Scopoli, 1763)   PLATE 40

National Status: Universal
Surrey Status: Ubiquitous
VCH: (as *agrorum*) Generally
distributed

This is one of the three orangey-brown bumblebees in Britain, and the only one now found in Surrey. It is very common and widespread throughout Britain, flying from March to October, collecting pollen from various flowers, especially white dead-nettle in the spring, and nesting above ground in tall open grassland and under plant litter. The

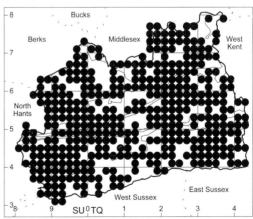

nests are attacked by the cuckoo bumblebee *Bombus campestris*.

In Surrey it is still one of the commonest bumblebees and is also very widespread. It tends to visit flowers with fairly long corollae such as vetches and clovers and the labiates. It is found in a wide range of habitats and is a common garden bumblebee, often coming to lavender in large numbers.

Its status is unchanged since 1900.

Bombus pratorum (Linnaeus, 1761)   PLATE 40

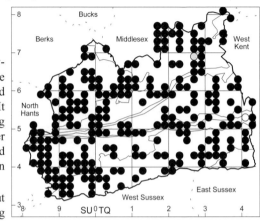

National Status: Universal

Surrey Status: Ubiquitous

VCH: Generally distributed

This smallish black and yellow-banded bumblebee has a distinctive orange tail and is common and widespread throughout Britain. It has two broods each year, flying from early spring till late summer and nesting underground in old mouse nests or above ground in holes in trees.

In Surrey it is very widespread but only reasonably common, being associated especially with gardens and woodland edges and clearings. The workers collect pollen from many flowers but particularly from blackthorn and rosemary in the early spring and later from raspberry and bramble. It is usually scarce on heaths, except on bilberry in the spring. The workers vary greatly in size and can be so small that they do not appear to be bumblebees at all. The nests are attacked by the cuckoo bumblebee *Bombus sylvestris*. Its status is probably unchanged since 1900.

Bombus ruderarius (Müller, 1776)

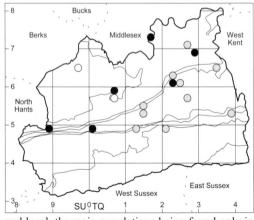

National Status: Widespread

Surrey Status: Very rare

VCH: (as *derhamellus*)
    Generally distributed

Similar to the common red-tailed bumblebee *B. lapidarius* but with a shorter body, this species nests on the ground, often using old mouse nests, and requires a large area of undisturbed grassland with plenty of flowers throughout the flight period. From being a common species in southern England it has declined sharply during the last thirty years and is now very scarce and local, the main populations being found only in extensive unimproved grassland.

It is now on the verge of extinction in Surrey. It seems to have been very local from 1900 onwards, with only a few published records. It was found at Wisley in 1920 and 1930 by G. Fox Wilson and again there, more recently, in 1974 and 2000 (AJH). In 1961 and 1963 it was found at various places on the North Downs, i.e. Norbury Park, Fetcham Downs, White Downs, Banstead Downs and Oxted (A.W. Jones). The International Bee Research Association files show three records in 1970 from the south London area, at Merton, Croydon and Brockham, and in 1990 it occurred at Mitcham Common (RKAM). There is a batch of records in the 1950s from the Ewell area, with three males in 1956 from the north edge of Priest Hill and one from nearby Cheam in 1951 (all DBB). The most recent records are of a male, also at Priest Hill, Ewell, in July 2001, another male on the Chalk at Pewley Down, Guildford, in July 1998, a male at bird's-foot trefoil on a dry gravelly riverside meadow at Ham House in June 2006 and a male at field scabious on the Hogs Back above Sands in July 2007 (all DWB). These recent records, from widely scattered localities, give hope that this declining species may just be hanging on south of London around Ewell and Banstead and may even be recovering and spreading along the Chalk of the North Downs. On the other hand it may have been overlooked previously, due to its close similarity to the common *B. lapidarius*.

It has declined since 1900.

Bombus ruderatus (Fabricius, 1775)

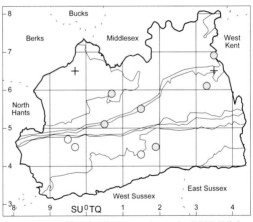

National Status: Scarce; Nb

Surrey Status: Extinct

VCH: (as *harrisellus*) Generally distributed

This extremely scarce and local bumblebee is very similar in appearance to, and difficult to separate from, *Bombus hortorum*.

Although it was reported as widespread in Surrey by Saunders (1902) there have only been 11 fully authenticated records since then, as follows: a female collected by O.H. Latter in the Godalming area on 28 May 1914, a specimen in Haslemere Museum (det. ME); a specimen in RHS Wisley Collection collected by G. Fox Wilson in July 1920 (det. ME); two specimens collected by Mortimer at Holmwood in June 1921 and 1922, both in NHML (det. GRE); one collected by C. Diver at Compton in 1929 (det. G.M. Spooner); a specimen collected by Baker at Clandon on 30 July 1958; a series collected by A.W. Jones (det. J.C. Felton) from Riddlesdown on 7 August 1961, Holmwood on 30 June 1963, South Norwood on 6 June 1964 and Fetcham Downs on 9 August 1964; the last record was from RHS Wisley on 27 July 1972 (AJH). This bee is now presumed to be extinct in Surrey.

It has declined to extinction since 1900.

Bombus soroeensis (Fabricius, 1777)

National Status: Scarce
Surrey Status: Extinct
VCH: Croydon

This species is rather small, very variable in colour and liable to confusion with other species. It is now scarce and very local in Britain, being mainly found in northern Scotland and western Britain. It frequents mainly heaths and moors but in southern England it is still common on chalk grassland on Salisbury Plain.

The only record for Surrey is that of G.A.J. Rothney in about 1880 from Croydon, probably referring to the heathland at nearby Addington Hills.

It has been extinct since before 1900.

Bombus subterraneus (Linnaeus, 1758)

National Status: Extinct
Surrey Status: Extinct
VCH: (as *latreillellus*) Generally distributed

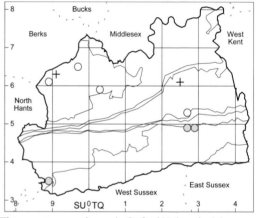

Formerly widespread and locally common in south-eastern England, it has declined so dramatically in the last 50 years that it is now extinct nationally.

Saunders, who collected a specimen at Bagshot in July 1890, and another at Banstead Downs in September 1890, considered it to be widespread in 1900, but there are only very few reliable records since then. There are two specimens in Oxford University Museum from Chobham Common and Pyrford in 1914 (det. C. O'Toole), and another collected by R. Jermyn in 1922 from Camberley, specimen in NHML (det. GRE). There are also unconfirmed records from Reigate Hill in 1906, Redhill Common in 1971, and Redstone Cemetery, Redhill, in 1972. The last fully authenticated record was from Hindhead Common on 12 September 1951 by Baker.

It has declined to extinction since 1900.

Bombus sylvarum (Linnaeus, 1761)

National Status: Scarce; Nb
Surrey Status: Extinct
VCH: Generally distributed

A rather greyish species with two dull yellow bands on the thorax and a dull red tip to the abdomen, which nests in a hollow on the ground or just below. In Britain this species was formerly frequent in southern England but it has declined so seriously in the last 15 years that populations are now known from only a few areas.

This bee has been extinct in Surrey for nearly 100 years, although it was probably reasonably common and widespread in Saunders' time, when it was associated with heathland and chalk downland habitats. Since 1900 there has been only a handful of Surrey records. There are old reports from Chobham Common and Reigate Hill in 1900 and from Horsell Common and Pyrford in 1914 but these may not be reliable. There are two specimens from Wisley Common in 1920 in the G. Fox Wilson Collection at RHS Wisley, and one in NHML from Holmwood area in 1922 (Mortimer). The last confirmed record for Surrey is of a specimen taken at Compton in 1929 by C. Diver, the specimen in his collection having been determined by Spooner. It has declined to extinction since 1900.

Bombus terrestris (Linnaeus, 1758)   PLATE 42

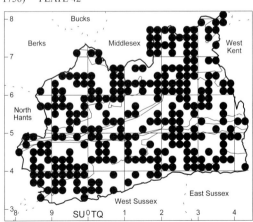

National Status: Universal
Surrey Status: Ubiquitous
VCH: Generally distributed

This is the other common white-tailed bumblebee and it is also widespread in Britain.

In Surrey it is also very common in most habitats and is frequently seen in gardens where the females take nectar mainly from short open flowers because they have short tongues. The gigantic buff-tailed queens are one of the earliest bumbleebees to emerge in early spring and they can be seen flying low over the ground as they prospect for nest sites, which are usually old rodent holes. In recent years queens and workers have been observed foraging for nectar and pollen right through the winter and some of these winter nests have been successful in rearing males and queens. In my own garden, from 2003 to 2007, I have watched queens and workers on warm days in December, January and February on south-facing walls collecting nectar from yellow jasmine by piercing the base of the corolla, and a worker with a full pollen basket on flowers of japonica (*Chaenomeles*).

Its status is unchanged since 1900.

Subgenus *Psithyrus* Lepeletier, 1832

Until recently *Psithyrus* had full generic status, but it has now been reduced to a subgenus within *Bombus*.

All species are cuckoo bumblebees and are social parasites of other *Bombus* species. In spring the overwintered and fertilised female searches out a small nest of a suitable host bumblebee. It enters the nest and hides while it acquires the nest scent, then dominates and kills the host queen. The cuckoo female then lays eggs which develop into males or females, while all the foraging and nest duties are carried out by the host workers. No cuckoo workers are reared.

Bombus barbutellus (Kirby, 1802)

National Status: Widespread
Surrey Status: Very rare
VCH: Generally distributed

This cuckoo bumblebee is a social parasite of *Bombus hortorum* and is very similar to its host, except that it has an almost round face instead of the very elongate face of its host. It is widely distributed in Britain but is rarely common. The overwintered females appear from late April and the males and new females are found from July to September.

In Surrey it was apparently common and widespread in Victorian times but, as can be seen from the map, it had become very local by the 1960s and 1970s and was last reported at that time in July 1974 at RHS Wisley (AJH). However, after an absence of 29 years I found a queen on bugle in a flowery woodland clearing at Whitebeech, Chiddingfold, on 23 May 2002. The alarming decline of this species is presumably related to the less dramatic, recent decline of its host.

It has declined seriously since 1900.

Bombus bohemicus (Seidl, 1837)

National Status: Widespread
Surrey Status: Rare
VCH: Unknown

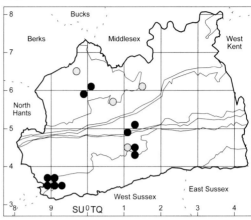

This cuckoo bumblebee is a social parasite of the abundant *Bombus lucorum* and is very similar to another cuckoo bumblebee, *B. vestalis*, both having a pair of narrow yellow patches at the base of the white tail. Although it was distributed throughout Britain, it has been disappearing from many sites in the south in recent years and is now far more frequent in the north, possibly due to climate change.

It has always been very local in Surrey, being found mainly on the higher ground such as Leith Hill, Gibbet Hill and on the North Downs. There was a batch of records in the 1970s and a few in recent years. Five were recorded around Gibbet Hill, Hindhead, two in the spring at bilberry (*Vaccinium myrtillus*) in 1998 and three at common ragwort in July 1996 and August 1998 (all DWB). Other recent records are Horsell Birch in April 1989 (RKAM), two at White Downs in August 1993 (AJH), Leith Hill in April 1997 (DWB), Friday Street on the earliest date of 12 April 1997 (GAC), White Downs in August 2000 (H.J. Berman) and Horsell Common in June 2007 (AJH). It was not known to Saunders, presumably being confused with *B. vestalis*.

It is not possible to say whether its status has changed since 1900.

Bombus campestris (Panzer, 1801)

National Status: Universal
Surrey Status: Local
VCH: Chobham, Godalming

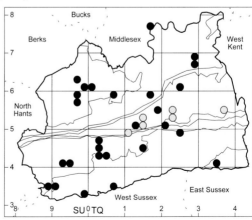

This bee is a social parasite of the very common *Bombus pascuorum* and possibly other bumblebees, and is widespread in Britain. It is a very variable species, usually having two yellow stripes on the thorax and an orangey-yellow tail, but it is often all black or nearly black. The over-wintered females are found from late April onwards, and males and new females in July to September.

In Surrey it is widespread but local and never common, and it occurs in a wide variety of habitats. As its host is still abundant, it should be commoner but it may be overlooked due to its similarity to other bumblebees. An entirely black form is seen not infrequently in some years; in 2001 I collected three all-black males.

Its status is probably the same as in 1900.

Bombus rupestris (Fabricius, 1793)   PLATE 41

National Status: Scarce; Nb
Surrey Status: Local
VCH: Generally distributed

This large cuckoo bumblebee is a social parasite of the common and widespread *Bombus lapidarius*; both of them are very similar, being black with red tails, but the female of *rupestris* has very dark wings. It is widespread in England, being much commoner in the south. It declined considerably from the 1940s onwards and became very scarce, but it has started to increase recently.

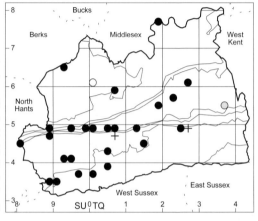

In Surrey it was widespread in Saunders' time but after the 1920s it was not recorded again, apart from a single record in 1963, until it was found at three different sites in 1998: St. Catherines Hill and Pewley Down, Guildford, and two at Hindhead Common (all DWB). In 1999 it was recorded at four different sites, most in July and one in August; in 2000 there was only a single record but in 2001 there were again four; there was then a gap until 2005 when it was found at five sites, with four again in 2006 and four also in 2007.

It has clearly made a dramatic comeback and it may now be almost as common and widespread as it was in 1900.

Bombus sylvestris (Lepeletier, 1832)   PLATE 42

National Status: Universal

Surrey Status: Common

VCH: (as *quadricolor*) Generally distributed

This bee is a social parasite of the common and widespread *Bombus pratorum*, and possibly of the less common *B. jonellus*. It is widespread and common in Britain, and rather similar to the very common *B. vestalis*, except that it has no yellow patches at the base of the white tail.

In Surrey it is widespread but never common.

Its status is probably unchanged since 1900.

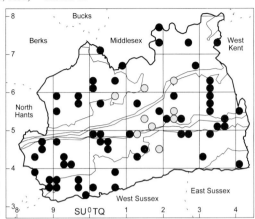

Bombus vestalis (Geoffroy, 1785)   PLATE 42

National Status: Widespread

Surrey Status: Ubiquitous

VCH: Generally distributed

This cuckoo bumblebee is a social parasite of the very common *Bombus terrestris*. It is very similar to *B. bohemicus* but it has large and distinctive, intense yellow patches at the base of the white tail.

This bee is widespread and common in Surrey, as it is elsewhere in Britain.

Its status is unchanged since 1900.

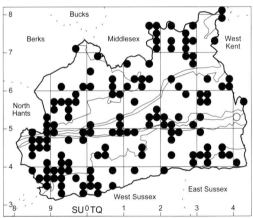

Genus *Apis* Linnaeus, 1758

This is the honey bee which has been cultivated for many centuries. There are five, or more, species in the world. They are distinguished by having hairy eyes, a very long marginal cell on the forewing and a pollen basket, or corbiculum, on the flattened tibia of the hind leg. They have the most complex structure of the British social bees, having perennial nests. New colonies are formed by a swarm, consisting of a queen and workers, splitting off from a pre-existing colony.

Apis mellifera Linnaeus 1758   PLATE 43

National Status: Universal
Surrey Status: Ubiquitous
VCH: Generally distributed

The wild honey bee became almost extinct in this country about 100 years ago and it is now an entirely cultivated insect, although nests of escaped bees can sometimes be found in the wild and these may survive for some years, especially those in wall cavities of houses or outbuildings. In 2004 M. Adler found two nests in adjoining gardens at Brentmoor Heath, both of them in disused green woodpecker nests, one in a cherry and the other in an oak. Very occasionally nests are found hanging in the open from tree branches, e.g. Royal Common in 2000 (JSD); such nests are unlikely to survive the winter.

Honey bees are found at almost every site and therefore no distribution map is given. They have become a lot less common in recent years, due to the virus caused by the *Varroa* mite and possibly to the enormous increase in numbers of *Philanthus triangulum,* the females of which may each take hundreds of bees as prey for their young; many beekeepers have been forced to give up apiculture in recent years. They are among the very few insects which have a commercial value, not only for their honey but also because they are such efficient pollinators, especially of fruit crops.

APPENDIX 1 – Gazetteer of sites

Abinger	TQ0947	Buckland Hills	TQ2252
Addington	TQ3764	Burrowhill Green	SU972629
Albury Heath	TQ0646	Byfleet	TQ0661
Alderstead Heath	TQ3055	Camberley	SU8861
Ash	SU8950	Capel Claypit	TQ1738
Ash Common	SU9053	Carshalton	TQ2864
Ash Ranges	SU9153	Charlwood	TQ2441
Ashtead Common	TQ1759	Cheam	TQ2463
Bagmoor Common	SU9242	Chelsham	TQ3759
Bagshot Heath	SU9161	Chertsey	TQ0466
Banstead Downs	TQ2561	Chessington Zoo	TQ1762
Barnes Common	TQ2276	Chiddingfold	SU9635
Barrow Green Sandpit	TQ3752	Chiddingfold Forest	SU93
Battersea Park	TQ2877	Chobham Common	
Beddington Sewage Farm			SU9666-9963
	TQ2866	Churt Common	SU8640
Betchworth	TQ2149	Clandon Downs	TQ0549
Bisley Ranges	SU9358	Clapham Common	TQ285745
Blackheath Common	TQ0346	Claygate	TQ1563
Black Pond, Esher Common		Cobbett Hill	SU9453
	TQ128622	Cobham	TQ1060
Blatchford Down	TQ103488	Coldharbour	TQ1443
Bletchingley	TQ3250	Colekitchen Down	TQ0848
Blindley Heath	TQ3645	Colliers Wood	TQ2670
Bookham Common	TQ1256	Colony Bog, Pirbright Common	
Botany Bay	SU9734		SU9259
Bourne Wood, Tilford	SU8544	Compton	SU9547
Box Hill	TQ1751-1852	Coulsdon	TQ3058
Bransland Wood	TQ327484	Cranleigh	TQ0639
Brentmoor Heath	SU9361	Cranleigh Brickworks	TQ0635
Bricksbury Hill	SU8349	Croham Hurst	TQ3363
Brixton	TQ3175	Crooksbury Common	SU8845
Brockham Hills	TQ2051	Croydon	TQ3265
Brook	SU9337	Crystal Palace	TQ339710
Brooklands	TQ0662	Dawcombe	TQ2152
Brookwood Cemetery	SU9556	Denbies Hillside	TQ1349-1550
Boundless Copse	SU899369	Ditton Common	TQ149659

APPENDIX 1 – Gazetteer of sites (continued)

Dorking	TQ1649	Hankley Common	SU8840
Dormansland	TQ4042	Happy Valley, Coulsdon	TQ3056
Dulwich	TQ3372	Haslemere	SU9032
Dunsfold	TQ0036	Headley	TQ2054
Earlswood Common	TQ2748	Headley Heath	TQ2053
East Dulwich	TQ3474	Headley Warren	TQ1954
Edolphs Copse	TQ2342	Hedgecourt Pond	TQ3540
Effingham Common	TQ1055	Henley Park Ranges	SU932537
Egham	TQ0171	Hindhead Common	SU9036
Elstead	SU9043	Hogs Back	SU8948-9748
Epsom Common	TQ1860	Holmbury Hill	TQ1043
Epsom Downs	TQ2158	Holmens Grove	SU9236
Esher Common	TQ1262	Holmethorpe	TQ2951
Ewell	TQ2262	Holmwood	TQ1442
Ewhurst	TQ0940	Horley	TQ2843
Fairmile Common	TQ1261	Horsell Birch	SU9859
Farnham	SU8446	Horsell Common	TQ0060
Farthing Downs	TQ3057	Howell Hill	TQ2361
Featherbed Lane, Addington		Hurtwood	TQ0843
	TQ375623	Hutchinsons Bank	TQ3861
Fetcham Downs	TQ1554	Kenley	TQ3258
Fisherlane Wood	SU9832	Kew Gardens	TQ1877
Folly Bog	SU9261	Knaphill	SU9658
Frensham Common	SU8540	Lakeside Park, Ash	SU8851
Frensham Great Pond	SU8440	Leatherhead	TQ1656
Friday Street	TQ1245	Leigh	TQ2246
Glovers Wood	TQ2240	Leith Hill	TQ1343
Godalming	SU9744	Limpsfield Chart	TQ4352
Godstone	TQ3551	Limpsfield Common	TQ4052
Gomshall	TQ0847	Lingfield	TQ3844
Guildford	SU9949	Lyne near Chertsey	TQ0166
Hackhurst Downs	TQ0948	Mare Hill Common	SU9340
Hagthorne Bog	SU9260	Mayford near Woking	SU9956
Ham Common	TQ1871	Merstham	TQ2953
Ham House	TQ172729	Merton	TQ2569
Hambledon Claypit	SU9737	Mickleham	TQ1753
Hambledon Common	SU9638	Milford	SU9441

APPENDIX 1 – Gazetteer of sites (continued)

Mitcham Common	TQ2967	Reigate	TQ2550
Molesey	TQ1368	Reigate Heath	TQ2350
Moorhouse Sandpit, Limpsfield		Reigate Hill	TQ2552
	TQ4253	Richmond Park	TQ2073
Mountain Wood	TQ090509	Riddlesdown	TQ3260
Netley	TQ0748	Riddlesdown Quarry	TQ3359
Newchapel	TQ3642	Ripley	TQ0556
Newdigate	TQ1942	Rowhill LNR, Farnham	SU8549
Newlands Corner	TQ0449	Royal Common, Elstead	SU9242
Nonsuch Park	TQ2363	Runfold Wood	SU8646
Norbury Park	TQ1653	Runnymede	TQ0072
North Holmwood Claypit		Sands	SU8846
	TQ173472	Sayers Land, Dunsfold	TQ0136
Nower Wood	TQ1954	Seale	SU8947
Nunhead Cemetery	TQ3575	Selsdon	TQ3562
Oaken Wood	SU9933	Send	TQ0255
Ockham Common	TQ0858	Send Marsh	TQ0355
Old Common, Cobham	TQ1161	Shackleford	SU9345
Ottershaw	TQ0163	Sheepleas	TQ0851
Outwood	TQ3245	Shere	TQ0747
Oxshott Heath	TQ1461	Shirley	TQ3564
Oxted Downs	TQ3854	Sidney Wood	TQ0234
Papercourt Gravelpits	TQ0356	Somersbury Claypit, Ewhurst	
Peckham	TQ3477		TQ1037
Pewley Down	TQ0049	Somerset Bridge, Elstead	
Pirbright	SU9456		SU9243
Pirbright Ranges	SU9258	South Croydon	TQ3363
Priest Hill	TQ232615	South Hawke	TQ3753
Priory Park, Reigate	TQ2549	South Norwood	TQ3568
Purley Downs	TQ3261	St Martha's Hill	TQ0248
Putney Heath	TQ2373	Stoke d'Abernon	TQ1258
Puttenham Common	SU9146	Stroud Wood, Grayswood	
Puttenham Heath	SU9447		SU9235
Pyrford	TQ0358	Surbiton	TQ1867
Ranmore Common	TQ1250	Tandridge	TQ3750
Redhill	TQ2750	Thorpe Hay Meadow	TQ029702
Redhill Common	TQ273495		

APPENDIX 1 – Gazetteer of sites (continued)

Thundry Meadows, Elstead		Wetland Centre, Barnes	
	SU8943		TQ225766
Thursley Common	SU9040	Weybridge	TQ0763
Tilford Woods	SU8543	Whitebeech	SU9835
Tooting Bec Common	TQ2972	White Downs	TQ1048-1149
Tugley Wood	SU9833	White Hill, Mickleham	SU1853
Upper Hale	TQ8349	Wimbledon Common	TQ2372
Walton Heath	TQ2253	Windsor Great Park	SU9770
Walton-on-Thames	TQ1066	Winterfold	TQ0642
Wandle Meadow LNR		Wire Mill Lake	TQ3641
	TQ264709	Wisley Common	TQ0758
Wandle Park	TQ266704	Wisley RHS Garden	TQ0658
Wandsworth Common	TQ2774	Witley Common	SU9240
Wandsworth Park	TQ2475	Woking	TQ0058
West Clandon	TQ0452	Woodham, near Woking	TQ0362
Westcott	TQ1348	Woolmer Hill	SU8733
Westcott Downs	TQ1349-1550	Worms Heath	TQ3757
West End Common, Esher		Worplesdon	SU9753
	TQ1263	Wrecclesham Sandpit	SU8144
West Ewell	TQ2163	Wyke Common	SU915525
West Horsley	TQ0753		

APPENDIX 2 – References

Allen, G.W. 2001.
Aculeate Hymenoptera in Watsonian Kent. Provisional distribution maps to December 2000. Privately circulated.

Amiet, F. 1996.
Allgemeiner Teil, Gattungsschlüssel, die Gattungen *Apis, Bombus* und *Psithyrus. Insecta. Fauna Helvetica. 12. Hymenoptera. Apidae*, **1**: 1-98.

Amiet, F., Hermann, M, Müller, A. & Neumeyer, R. 2001.
Halictus, Lasioglossum. Fauna Helvetica. 6. Apidae, **3**: 1-208.

Amiet, F., Hermann, M, Müller, A. & Neumeyer, R. 2004.
Anthidium, Chelostoma, Coelioxys, Dioxys, Heriades, Lithurgus, Megachile, Osmia, Stelis. Fauna Helvetica. 9. Apidae, **4**: 1-273.

Amiet, F., Hermann, M, Müller, A. & Neumeyer, R. 2007.
Ammobates, Ammobatoides, Anthophora, Biastes, Ceratina, Dasypoda, Epeoloides, Epeolus, Eucera, Macropis, Melecta, Melitta, Nomada, Pasites, Tetralonia, Thyreus, Xylocopa. Fauna Helvetica. 9. Apidae, **5**: 1-356.

Amiet, F., Müller, A. & Neumeyer, R. 1999.
Colletes, Dufourea, Hylaeus, Nomia, Nomioides, Rhophitoides, Rophites, Sphecodes, Systropha. Fauna Helvetica. 4. Apidae, **2**: 1-219.

Archer, M.E. 1990.
The aculeate solitary wasps and bees (Hymenoptera: Aculeata) of Leicestershire. *Transactions of the Leicester Literary and Philosophical Society*, **84**: 9-25.

Archer, M.E. 2002.
The Wasps, Ants and Bees of Watsonian Yorkshire. Yorkshire Naturalists' Union.

Archer, M.E. 2007.
Archer's status values for the Solitary Wasps and Bees. *BWARS Newsletter*, Autumn 2007: 29-38.

Baker, D.B. 1994.
On the nomenclature of two sibling species of the *Andrena tibialis* (Kirby, 1802) group (Hymenoptera, Apoidea). *Entomologist's Gazette*, **45**: 281-290. [*A. nigrospina* and *A. pilipes*]

Baldock, D.W. & Collins, G.A. 1999, 2000, 2003, 2006, 2008.
Aculeate Hymenoptera in Surrey. Provisional distribution maps. Privately circulated.

APPENDIX 2 – References (continued)

Banaszak, J. & Romasenko, L. 1998.
Megachilid Bees of Europe (Hymenoptera, Apoidea, Megachilidae). Bydgoszsz. (Also 2nd edition 2001.)

Benton, T. 2006.
Bumblebees. New Naturalist Library. Collins.

Betts, C. & Laffoley, D.D'A., eds. 1986.
The Hymenopterist's Handbook. 2nd edition. Amateur Entomologists' Society. [This includes a separate supplement, Aculeate Flight Table, which is very useful]

Billups, T.R. 1881.
Dufourea vulgaris, Schk., at Woking. *Entomologist's Monthly Magazine,* **18**: 161.

Billups, T.R. 1891a.
Nomada lateralis, Panz., at Box Hill. *The Entomologist,* **24**: 174.

Billups, T.R. 1891b.
Two and a half hours' investigation of the entomology of Oxshott Heath. *The Entomologist,* **24**: 201-204.

Celary, W. 2005.
Melittidae of Poland. Polish Academy of Sciences. Krakow.

Chinery, M. 1973.
A field guide to the insects of Britain and Western Europe. London: Collins.

Chinery, M. 1986. *Collins guide to the insects of Britain and Western Europe.* London: Harper Collins. [Reprinted, 1991 and 1993]

Currie, P.W.E. 1950.
(*Heriades truncorum* taken at Burford Bridge, Surrey). *Entomologist's Monthly Magazine,* **86**: xxxvi.

Currie, P.W.E. 1954.
Heriades truncorum (Linn.) (Hym.) in Surrey. *The Entomologist,* **87**: 229.

Edwards, E. & Jenner, M. 2004.
Field Guide to the Bumblebees of Great Britain and Ireland. Ocelli Ltd.

Edwards, R., ed. 1997.
Provisional atlas of the aculeate Hymenoptera of Britain and Ireland. Part 1. Huntingdon: Biological Records Centre.

APPENDIX 2 – References (continued)

Edwards, R., ed. 1998.
Provisional atlas of the aculeate Hymenoptera of Britain and Ireland. Part 2. Huntingdon: Biological Records Centre.

Edwards, R., & Telfer, M.G. eds. 2001.
Provisional atlas of the aculeate Hymenoptera of Britain and Ireland. Part 3. Huntingdon: Biological Records Centre.

Edwards, R., & Telfer, M.G. eds. 2002.
Provisional atlas of the aculeate Hymenoptera of Britain and Ireland. Part 4. Huntingdon: Biological Records Centre.

Edwards, R., & Broad, G. eds. 2005.
Provisional atlas of the aculeate Hymenoptera of Britain and Ireland. Part 5. Huntingdon: Biological Records Centre.

Edwards, R., & Broad, G. eds. 2006. *Provisional atlas of the aculeate Hymenoptera of Britain and Ireland. Part 6.* Huntingdon: Biological Records Centre.

Else, G.R. 1995.
The distribution and habits of the small carpenter bee *Ceratina cyanea* (Kirby, 1802) in Britain (Hymenoptera, Apidae). *British Journal of Entomology and Natural History*, **8**: 1-6.

Else, G.R. 1995.
The distribution and habits of the bee *Hylaeus pectoralis* Förster, 1871 (Hymenoptera, Apidae) in Britain. *British Journal of Entomology and Natural History*, **8**: 43-47.

Else, G.R. 1995.
Nomada guttulata Schenck (Hym., Apidae) in Hampshire in 1993. *Entomologist's Monthly Magazine*, **131**: 46.

Else, G.R. 1998.
The status of *Stelis breviuscula* (Nylander) (Hymenoptera: Apidae) in Britain, with a key to the British species of *Stelis*. *British Journal of Entomology and Natural History*, **10**: 214-216.

Else, G.R. 1999.
Identification. Leaf-cutter bees. *British Wildlife*, **1999**: 388-392.

Falk, S. 1991.
A review of the scarce and threatened bees, wasps and ants of Great Britain. Research and Survey in Nature Conservation, no. 35. Peterborough: Nature Conservancy Council.

APPENDIX 2 – References (continued)

Falk, S. 2005.
A provisional species list of the bees and aculeate wasps of Vice-county Warwickshire. Privately circulated.

Frisby, G.E. 1907.
Hymenoptera at Redhill in 1906. *Entomologist's Monthly Magazine,* **43**: 15.

Garland, S. & Appleton, T. 1997.
Checklist of the aculeate Hymenoptera of Lancashire and Cheshire. *Lancashire and Cheshire Entomological Society,* **116-120**: 112-114.

Gauld, I. & Bolton, B. eds. 1988.
The Hymenoptera. British Museum (Natural History) & Oxford University Press.

Guichard, K.M. 1974.
Colletes halophila Verhoeff (Hym., Apidae) and its *Epeolus* parasite at Swanscombe in Kent, with a key to the British species of *Colletes* Latreille. *Entomologist's Gazette,* **25**: 195-199.

Guichard, K.M. 1977.
The Hymenoptera Aculeata of Chobham Common, the Woking area and Oxshott Heath, Surrey. *Entomologist's Gazette* **28**: 245-259.

Harvey, P.R. 2000.
Aculeate Hymenoptera in Essex and the East Thames Corridor, Provisional Distribution Maps 1999 Update. Grays.

Harvey, P.R. 2007.
Aculeate Hymenoptera of Essex. 2006 maps of species with modern records. Essex Field Club.

Harvey, P.R. & Plant, C.W. 1996.
A provisional list of the bees, wasps and ants (Hymenoptera: Aculeata) of Essex. *Essex Naturalist,* **13**: 43-115.

Koster, A. 1986.
Het genus *Hylaeus* in Nederland (Hymenoptera, Colletidae). *Zoologische Bijdragen.* No. **36**.

Latter, O.H. 1913.
Bees and Wasps. London

Lousley, J.E. 1976.
Flora of Surrey. Newton Abbot: David & Charles.

APPENDIX 2 – References (continued)

Michener, C.D. 2000.
The Bees of the World. Baltimore: John Hopkins University Press.

Morice, F.D. 1900a.
Re-occurrence of *Heriades truncorum*, L., in England.
Entomologist's Monthly Magazine, **36**: 203-204.

Morice, F.D. 1900b.
Rare Hymenoptera near Chobham (Surrey). *Entomologist's Monthly Magazine*, **35**: 273.

Morice, F.D. 1901.
Hymenopterological Notes. *Entomologist's Monthly Magazine*, **37**: 96-98.

Morice, F.D. 1906.
Heriades truncorum Linn., near Chobham. *Entomologist's Monthly Magazine*, **42**: 214.

Morice, F.D. 1902.
Sphecodes rubicundus, v. Hag., near Ripley and Chobham. *Entomologist's Monthly Magazine*, **38**:184

Morice, F.D. 1912.
Prosopis genalis Thoms., at Woking. *Entomologist's Monthly Magazine*, **48**: 240-241.

Morris, R.K.A. 1997.
The Hymenoptera of Mitcham Common: the fauna of a small London grass heath, with comments on the use of site quality scores for site evaluation. *London Naturalist,* **76**: 105-127.

Mortimer, C.H. 1913.
Dufourea halictula (Nyl.) at Byfleet, Surrey. *Entomologist's Monthly Magazine*, **49**: 214-215.

Müller, A., Krebs, A. & Amiet, F. 1997.
Bienen. Mitteleuropäische Gattungen, Lebensweise, Beobachtung. München: Naturbuch-Verlag.

Nevinson, E.G.B. 1907
Heriades truncorum, Linn., near Chobham, Surrey. *Entomologist's Monthly Magazine*, **43**: 276-277.

Ornosa, C. & Ortiz-Sanchez, F.J. 2004.
Hymenoptera, Apoidea 1. [*Colletidae, Melittidae* and *Apidae*] *Fauna Iberica*, vol. 23.

APPENDIX 2 – References (continued)

O'Toole, C. & Raw, A. 1991.
Bees of the World. London: Blandford.

Perkins, R.C.L. 1919.
The British species of *Andrena* and *Nomada*. *Transactions of the Entomological Society of London* (1919): 218-319.

Perkins, R.C.L. 1922.
The British species of *Halictus* and *Sphecodes*. *Entomologist's Monthly Magazine*, **58**: 46-52, 94-101, 167-174.

Perkins, R.C.L. 1925.
The British species of *Megachile*, with descriptions of some new varieties from Ireland, and of a species new to Britain in F. Smith's collection. *Entomologist's Monthly Magazine*, **61**: 95-101.

Pesenko, Y.A., Banaszak, J., Radchenko, V.G. & Cierzniak, T. 2000.
Bees of the family Halictidae (excluding Sphecodes*) of Poland: taxonomy, ecology, bionomics.* Bydgoszcz.

Prys-Jones, O. & Corbet, S.A. 1991.
Bumblebees. (Naturalists Handbooks, 6) Second edition, revised. Slough: The Richmond Publishing Co. Ltd.

Roberts, S.P.M. 1993.
Bees, wasps and ants. *Endangered Wildlife in Dorset. The County Red Data Book.* Dorset Environmental Records Centre.

Robinson, N.A. 2005.
A list of the bees, wasps and ants of Cumbria. *BWARS Newsletter*, Autumn 2005: 25-56.

Robinson, N.A. 2007.
The bees, wasps and ants of north-east England. *BWARS Newsletter*, Autumn 2007: 40-70.

Saunders, E. 1880.
Synopsis of the British Heterogyna and Fossorial Hymenoptera. *Transactions of the Entomological Society*, **1880**: 201-304

Saunders, E. 1882.
Synopsis of British Hymenoptera, Diploptera and Anthophila; part I to end of Andrenidae. *Transactions of the Entomological Society*, **1882**: 165-290.

Saunders, E. 1884.
Synopsis of British Hymenoptera, Anthophila: part II, Apidae. *Transactions of the Entomological Society*, **1884** 159-250

APPENDIX 2 – References (continued)

Saunders, E. 1891.
Dufourea vulgaris, Schk., at Chobham, Surrey. *Entomologist's Monthly Magazine*, **27**: 249-250.

Saunders, E. 1896.
The Hymenoptera Aculeata of the British Isles. London: Reeve & Co. Ltd.

Saunders, E. 1897.
Hints on collecting aculeate Hymenoptera. *Entomologist's Monthly Magazine*, **33**: 31-35, 80-84, 136-140, 177-180, 246-251.

Saunders, E. 1900.
Nomada atrata [= *argentata*], Smith, = *brevicornis*, Schmied., re-admitted into the British list. *Entomologist's Monthly Magazine*, **36**: 204-206.

Saunders, E. 1902.
Hymenoptera Aculeata. *A history of the County of Surrey*, **3** Zoology. Constable, London.

Saunders, E. No date [about 1908].
Wild Bees, Wasps and Ants and other stinging insects, (with four coloured plates by Constance Saunders). Geo. Routledge & Sons, London.

Saunders, E. 1910.
On four additions to the list of British Hymenoptera. *Entomologist's Monthly Magazine*, **46**: 10-12. [Includes *Dufourea halictula*.]

Scheuchl, E. 1996.
Illustrierte Bestimmungstabellen der Wildbienen Deutschlands und Österreichs. Band II: Megachilidae – Melittidae.

Scheuchl, E. 2000.
Illustrierte Bestimmungstabellen der Wildbienen Deutschlands und Österreichs. Band I: Anthophoridae.

Schmid-Egger, C. & Scheuchl, E. 1997.
Illustrierte Bestimmungstabellen der Wildbienen Deutschlands und Österreichs unter Berücksichtigung der Arten der Schweiz. Band III: Schlüssel der Arten der Familie Andrenidae.

Shirt, D. [Ed.] 1987.
Insects. British Red Data Books, 2. Peterborough: Nature Conservancy Council.

APPENDIX 2 – References (continued)

Smith, F. 1876 (reprinted 1891).
Catalogue of the British Bees in the collection of the British Museum. British Museum, London.

Step, E. 1932.
Bees, wasps, ants and allied insects of the British Isles. London: F. Warne & Co., Ltd.

Stubbs, A.E. & Falk, S.J. 2002.
British Hoverflies. British Entomological and Natural History Society.

Trevis, G. 2006.
A review of Worcestershire Hymenoptera. Worcestershire Record.

Webb, J., Bloxham, M. & Slawson, C. 2002.
A provisional checklist of the aculeate Hymenoptera of Staffordshire. Staffordshire Ecological Record.

Westrich, P. 1989.
Die Wildbienen Baden-Württembergs. 2. Ulmer, Stuttgart.

White, G. 1788.
The Natural History and Antiquities of Selborne in the County of Southampton. London.

White, G. 1931.
Gilbert White's Journals, edited by W. Johnson. London

Williams, R. 2007 (seventh edition).
British Hymenoptera. Glossary – for use with identification keys. Vanellus Photofiles, Wedmore.

Willmer, P. 1985.
Bees, Ants and Wasps. A key to genera of the British Aculeates. [Obtainable from the Field Studies Council, Publications, The Annexe, Preston Montford Lane, Shrewsbury SY4 1DU.]

Yarrow, I.H.H. 1954.
Heriades truncorum (Linnaeus) at Weybridge, Surrey. *The Entomologist*, **87**: 121.

APPENDIX 3 – Glossary and acronyms

abdomen   The last part of a bee, with 6 (female) or 7 (male) visible segments

antenna (ae)   The 2 long sense organs on the front of the head, with 12 (female) or 13 (male) segments

arolium (a)   The lobed pad between claws of tarsus

BENHS   British Entomological and Natural History Society

BWARS   Bees Wasps and Ants Recording Society

cleptoparasite   A nest stealer. The female parasite lays her egg on the stored pollen of the bee host and the larva eats the pollen

clypeus   The central plate of the face

corbiculum (a)   The hind tibia fringed by long hairs to form the pollen basket

coxa   First segment of leg, nearest to body

cuticle   The hard outer skin of bee

declivity   The downward-sloping front of abdomen

diapause   The period of suspension of development during the life of a bee

dimorphism   Two distinct forms of bee, with different body structure or colour e.g. difference between sexes

EMM   Entomologist's Monthly Magazine

facial fovea   The area on face next to eyes which is depressed and densely pubescent

femur (femora)   The first long section of the leg, next to the tibia

gena   The cheek of the head

hectad   A square of 10km x 10km

labrum   The plate at the base of tongue, just below the clypeus

LNR   Local Nature Reserve

Malaise trap   A tent-like insect trap which collects insects in alcohol

mandibles   The biting mouth parts, hinged at the bottom corners of clypeus

monolectic   Foraging for pollen from only one species of flower

NHML   The Natural History Museum, London

NNR   National Nature Reserve

ocellus (i)   One of the 3 simple eyes on top of the head

oligolectic   Foraging for pollen from a small and closely-related group of flowers

OUM   Oxford University Museum

ovipositor   The egg-laying tube of insects, etc. In bees this has become modified for use as a sting

APPENDIX 3 – Glossary and acronyms (continued)

parasite	An organism living in or on the host bee and obtaining its food from the host
parasitoid	An organism which lives as a parasite during some or all of its larval stage but having a free-living adult stage
polylectic	Foraging for pollen from a wide variety of flowers
prepupa	The final stage of larva before turning into pupa
pronotum	The front part of thorax
propodeum	The first segment of the abdomen, fused to the thorax
pubescence	Very short, fine hairs on body
punctate	In microsculpture of the cuticle, having pits separated from each other
pygidium	A modified, usually triangular, area on the last tergite of the abdomen (mainly in females)
RDB	Red Data Book
RHS	Royal Horticultural Society
scape	The lowest segment of antenna nearest to head
scutellum	A rounded plate behind the main part of thorax
spur	Spine at end of tibia
SSSI	Site of Special Scientific Interest
sternite	One of the 6 (female) or 7 (male) segments of the bottom section of the abdomen
striation	Microsculpture of cuticle consisting of almost parallel lines and furrows
tarsus (i)	The last part of the leg, divided into 5 segments and a claw, and attached to the tibia
tergite	One of the 6 (female) or 7 (male) segments of the top section of the abdomen
tetrad	A square of 2km x 2km
thorax	The middle part of the bee, between the head and abdomen
tibia (ae)	The second long section of the leg, between femur and tarsus
trochanter	The second short segment of leg, between coxa and femur
VCH	Victoria County History
WHS	World Heritage Site

APPENDIX 4 – Index of plants

Listed by common name

alder buckthorn, *Frangula alnus*
angelica, *Angelica sylvestris*
apple, *Malus* spp.
autumn hawkbit, *Leontodon autumnalis*

beaked hawk's-beard, *Crepis vesicaria*
beech, *Fagus sylvatica*
bell heather, *Erica cinerea*
betony, *Stachys officinalis*
bilberry, *Vaccinium myrtillus*
birch, *Betula pendula/pubescens*
bird's-foot trefoil, *Lotus corniculatus*
black horehound, *Ballota nigra*
blackthorn, *Prunus spinosa*
bluebell, *Hyacinthoides non-scripta*
bramble, *Rubus fruticosus* agg.
brassica, *Brassica* spp.
broad-leaved everlasting-pea, *Lathyrus latifolius*
bugle, *Ajuga reptans*
bulbous buttercup, *Ranunculus bulbosus*
buttercup spp., *Ranunculus* spp.

cabbage, *Brassica oleracea*
Canadian goldenrod, *Solidago canadensis*
catmint, *Nepeta* spp.
cat's-ear, *Hypochaeris radicata*
cedar, *Cedrus* spp.
charlock, *Sinapis arvensis*
cherry laurel, *Prunus laurocerasus*
chickweed, *Stellaria media*
clover, *Trifolium* spp.
clustered bellflower, *Campanula glomerata*
common fleabane, *Pulicaria dysenterica*
common knapweed, *Centaurea nigra*
common ragwort, *Senecio jacobaea*
common reed, *Phragmites australis*
common vetch, *Vicia sativa*
cow parsley, *Anthriscus sylvestris*
creeping buttercup, *Ranunculus repens*
creeping cinquefoil, *Potentilla reptans*

creeping thistle, *Cirsium arvense*
cross-leaved heath, *Erica tetralix*
cypress spurge, *Euphorbia cyparissias*

dandelion, *Taraxacum* spp.
devil's-bit scabious, *Succisa pratensis*
dock, *Rumex* spp.
dog rose, *Rosa canina*
dotted loosestrife, *Lysimachia punctata*
dwarf gorse, *Ulex minor*
dyer's greenweed, *Genista tinctoria*

field maple, *Acer campestre*
field pepperwort, *Lepidium campestre*
field scabious, *Knautia arvensis*
figwort, *Scrophularia* spp.
fool's water-cress, *Apium nodiflorum*
forget-me-not, *Myosotis* spp.
foxglove, *Digitalis purpurea*

germander speedwell, *Veronica chamaedrys*
goldenrod, *Solidago virgaurea*
gorse, *Ulex europaeus*
greater bird's-foot trefoil, *Lotus pedunculatus*
greater knapweed, *Centaurea scabiosa*
greater stitchwort, *Stellaria holostea*
green alkanet, *Pentaglottis sempervirens*
gromwell, *Lithospermum officinale*
ground-elder, *Aegopodium podagraria*
ground-ivy, *Glechoma hederacea*

harebell, *Campanula rotundifolia*
hawk's-beard, *Crepis* spp.
hawkweed spp., *Hieracium* spp.
hawthorn, *Crataegus* spp.
heather, *Calluna vulgaris*
hedge bindweed, *Calystegia sepium*
hedge woundwort, *Stachys sylvatica*
hemlock water-dropwort, *Oenanthe crocata*
hoary mustard, *Hirschfeldia incana*
hogweed, *Heracleum sphondylium*

APPENDIX 4 – Index of plants (continued)
Listed by common name

honesty, *Lunaria annua*
honeysuckle, *Lonicera periclymenum*

ivy, *Hedera helix*

knapweed, *Centaurea* spp.

lamb's-ear, *Stachys byzantina* (= *lanata*)
lavender, *Lavandula* spp.
lesser burdock, *Arctium minus*
lesser hawkbit, *Leontodon saxatilis*
lesser stitchwort, *Stellaria graminea*
lungwort, *Pulmonaria* spp.

marjoram, *Origanum vulgare*
marsh thistle, *Cirsium palustre*
meadow buttercup, *Ranunculus acris*
meadow vetchling, *Lathyrus pratensis*
mint, *Mentha* spp.
musk mallow, *Malva moschata*

nettle-leaved bellflower, *Campanula trachelium*
Norway maple, *Acer platanoides*

oak, *Quercus* spp.
oxeye daisy, *Leucanthemum vulgare*
Oxford ragwort, *Senecio squalidus*

pear, *Pyrus* spp.
pignut, *Conopodium majus*
pine, *Pinus* spp.
plantain, *Plantago* spp.
plum, *Prunus domestica*
prickly sow-thistle, *Sonchus asper*
primrose, *Primula vulgaris*
purple toadflax, *Linaria purpurea*

ragged robin, *Lychnis flos-cuculi*
ragwort spp., *Senecio* spp.
rape, *Brassica napus*
raspberry, *Rubus idaeus*
red bartsia, *Odontites vernus*
red campion, *Silene dioica*
red clover, *Trifolium pratense*

red dead-nettle, *Lamium purpureum*
rose, *Rosa* spp.
rosebay willowherb, *Chamerion angustifolium*
rosemary, *Rosmarinus officinalis*
rough hawkbit, *Leontodon hispidus*
runner bean, *Phaseolus coccineus*

sallow, *Salix caprea/cinerea*
sanicle, *Sanicula europaea*
scentless mayweed, *Tripleurospermum inodorum*
sea-holly, *Eryngium* spp.
selfheal, *Prunella vulgaris*
Shasta daisy, *Leucanthemum x superbum* (= *maximum*)
sheep's-bit, *Jasione montana*
shepherd's-purse, *Capsella bursa-pastoris*
shrubby cinquefoil, *Potentilla fruticosa*
small-flowered crane's-bill, *Geranium pusillum*
small scabious, *Scabiosa columbaria*
smooth hawk's-beard, *Crepis capillaris*
smooth tare, *Vicia tetrasperma*
spear thistle, *Cirsium vulgare*
speedwell, *Veronica* spp.
spurge, *Euphorbia* spp.
star-of-Bethlehem, *Ornithogalum* spp.
stemless thistle, *Cirsium acaule*

tansy, *Tanacetum vulgare*
thistle spp., *Cirsium/Carduus* spp.
tor grass, *Brachypodium pinnatum*
tormentil, *Potentilla erecta*
trailing tormentil, *Potentilla anglica*
tree heather, *Erica arborea*
Turkey oak, *Quercus cerris*

upright hedge-parsley, *Torilis japonica*

vetch, *Vicia* spp.

APPENDIX 4 – Index of plants (continued)
Listed by common name

water mint, *Mentha aquatica*
water-pepper, *Persicaria hydropiper*
weld, *Reseda luteola*
white bryony, *Bryonia dioica*
white dead-nettle, *Lamium album*
white mignonette, *Reseda alba*
wild carrot, *Daucus carota*
wild mignonette, *Reseda lutea*
wild parsnip, *Pastinaca sativa*
wild strawberry, *Fragaria vesca*
willow, *Salix* spp. other than *S. caprea/cinerea*

willowherb, *Epilobium* spp.
wood avens, *Geum urbanum*
wood spurge, *Euphorbia amygdaloides*

yarrow, *Achillea millefolium*
yellow iris, *Iris pseudacorus*
yellow jasmine, *Jasminum nudiflorum*
yellow loosestrife, *Lysimachia vulgaris*

APPENDIX 5 – Useful addresses

Bees Wasps and Ants Recording Society (BWARS). Membership Secretary D.W. Baldock, Nightingales, Haslemere Road, Milford, Surrey GU8 5BN. Email: david@tiphia.eu

The society is dedicated to recording the distribution of all aculeates. It has over 400 members, including members in almost every country in Europe. It has so far produced, with Biological Records Centre, seven parts out of ten of the *Provisional atlas of the aculeate Hymenoptera of Britain and Ireland.* It is hoped that this atlas will be completed in another four years. The Society publishes a newsletter twice a year and also has a large Members' Handbook, with many useful articles. It holds occasional workshops on identification of groups of aculeates. There is an excellent website at www.bwars.com with images of many bees and wasps, the latest news and interactive national distribution maps for all species of bees and wasps.

Bumblebee Conservation Trust, School of Biological and Environmental Sciences, University of Stirling, Stirling FK9 4LA. Scotland. www.bumblebeeconservationtrust.co.uk

British Entomological and Natural History Society (BENHS). HQ at Dinton Pastures near Reading, with library and collections. It holds regular workshops, field and indoor meetings. Journal is published quarterly. www.benhs.org.uk

British Wildlife, The Old Dairy, Milton on Stour, Dorset SP8 5PX. www.britishwildlife.com Bi-monthly magazine on all aspects of British natural history, with a regular report on bees and wasps.

Pemberley Books, 18 Bathurst Walk, Richings Park, IVER, Bucks SL0 9YJ. www.pemberleybooks.com Best for books.

Jeremy Early. www.natureconservationimaging.com Images and life histories of British flora and fauna including numerous aculeates.

David Element. www.david.element.ukgateway.net Photographs of British and northern European fauna including many entomological subjects. Links to Hymenoptera websites and useful book references may be found on his page 1 of Hymenoptera.

Watkins and Doncaster, PO Box 5, Cranbrook, Kent TN18 5EZ. Tel: 01580 753133. www.watdon.com Entomological equipment suppliers of pins, boxes, lenses etc.

Hillside Books, Little Linden, Linden Grove, Lindfield, Haywards Heath, West Sussex RH16 2EE. www.insects.demon.co.uk Entomological books

APPENDIX 5 – Useful addresses (continued)

and equipment suppliers.

David Henshaw, 34 Rounton Road, Waltham Abbey, Essex. Entomological equipment suppliers, especially good for glass tubes and microscopy accessories.

Brian Nelson (replaces Marris House Nets). www.entomology.org.uk Best for nets and Malaise traps.

Kim Taylor of **Warren Photographic,** Albury, Surrey for bee boxes. He has ceased selling these but he still has a few finished boxes and a supply of wooden parts and glass tubes for making bee boxes. Readers should contact him on info@warrenphotographic.co.uk

Surrey Wildlife Trust, School Lane, Pirbright, Woking, Surrey GU24 0JN. www.surreywildlifetrust.org

Surrey Heathland Project, Artington House, 42 Portsmouth Road, Guildford, Surrey GU2 4DZ. www.surreyheathlandproject.org.uk This organisation encourages the management and restoration of heathland in Surrey and promotes its appreciation.

Surrey Biodiversity Information Centre, c/o Surrey Wildlife Trust, School Lane, Pirbright, Woking, Surrey GU24 0JN. Tel. 01483 795448. Email: surrey.brc@surreywt.org.uk It seeks to hold a comprehensive record of the wildlife of Surrey and provides a professional information service relating to the county's biodiversity.

Greenspace Information for Greater London, c/o London Wildlife Trust, Skyline House, 200 Union Street, London SE1 0LX.

www.gigl.org.uk The capital's open space and biodiversity records centre.

INDEX
Figures in bold indicate plate numbers

INDEX (continued)
Figures in bold indicate plate numbers

INDEX (continued)

Figures in bold indicate plate numbers

INDEX (continued)
Figures in bold indicate plate numbers